C000133993

SIR PATRICK
MOORE
THE SKY
AT NIGHT

FRONT MATTER IMAGES
Below right: The Ant Nebula (Mz 3), as imaged by the
Hubble Space Telescope.
Pages 4–5: Centre of the Omega Nebula (M17),
also known as the Swan Nebula, taken by the Advanced
Camera for Surveys (ACS) aboard the HST in 2002.
Page 7: Mars, as viewed by the HST Wide Field Planetary
Camera-2 in 1997.
Page 8: The Hubble Space Telescope in the Space Shuttle
Discovery's cargo bay, during a service mission in 1997.
Page 11: The Tadpole Galaxy (UGC 10214), in the
constellation of Draco, as imaged in 2002 by the ACS
aboard NASA's Hubble Space Telescope.

Published in Great Britain in 2002
by Philip's, a division of Octopus Publishing Group Ltd,
2–4 Heron Quays, London E14 4JP

ISBN 0–540–07959-6

A CIP catalogue record for this book is available from
the British Library.

Printed in Slovenia by DELO tiskarna by arrangement
with Prešernova družba

Details of other Philip's titles and services can be found
on our website at: **www.philips-maps.co.uk**

SIR PATRICK
MOORE
THE SKY
AT NIGHT

Contents

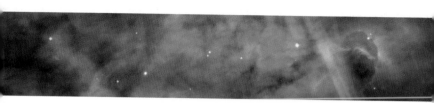

Acknowledgements

My grateful thanks are due to all those who have joined me on the programme during the period covered in this book:

The late D. A. Allen	R. Ellis	D. Macchetto	The Earl of Rosse
P. Angel	W. Everitt	A. Macdonald	The late C. A. Ronan
H. J. P. Arnold	E. Erickson	D. Malin	J. Scott
A. Aveni	H. Ford	J. Mason	J. Spyromilio
M. Barrett	D. Fuller	B. May	D. Sramek
T. Bastian	M. Grady	L. Miller	H. Stobie
J. Bell Burnell	F. Graham-Smith	P. Morgan	J. Tate
A. Boksenberg	M. Gill	J. Mould	C. Taylor
E. Brooks	G. Gilmore	C. Murray	C. Pillinger
C. Burrows	R. Griffiths	M. Mobberley	S. Unger
M. Bode	R. Guernsey	I. Morison	F. van Leeuwen
R. Cannon	P. Hewett	M. Mountain	H. Walker
R. Catchpole	R. Hill	P. Murdin	J. Wall
P. Cattermole	D. Hogg	G. Nelson	F. Watson
P. Charles	S. Hughes	I. Nicolson	D. Westphal
A. Chapman	G. Hunt	L. Öpik	P. Williams
C. Corbally	R. Jastrow	F. Owen	R. West
C. Cunningham	J. James	S. Patterson	G. White
F. Chaffee	P. Jewel	C. Panarios	W. Whiting
J. Davies	G. Keene	J. Peacock	F. Witteborn
P. Diamond	P. Lawson	T. Pedas	A. Wright
C. Doherty	C. Kitchin	R. Perley	J. Zarnecki
E. Dunham	D. Lynden-Bell	A. Rodgers	J. Zhao
	C. Lintott	J. Rothernberg	

And, of course, to my producers: Pieter Morpurgo (until 1998) and now Ian Russell, plus the invaluable assistance of Laura Vine.

PICTURE ACKNOWLEDGEMENTS
Front/Back Cover NASA/H. Ford (JHU)/G. Illingworth (USCS/LO)/M. Clampin & G. Hartig (STScl)/ACS Science Team/ESA 2–3 NASA/ESA/The Hubble Heritage Team (STScl/AURA) 4–5 NASA/H. Ford (JHU)/G. Illingworth (USCS/LO)/M. Clampin & G. Hartig (STScl)/ACS Science Team/ESA 7 D. Crisp & the WFPC2 Science Team (JPL/Calif. Institute of Technology)/NASA 8 NASA/JPL 11 NASA/H. Ford (JHU)/G. Illingworth (USCS/LO)/M. Clampin & G. Hartig (STScl)/ACS Science Team/ESA 12 Original portrait by Justus Sustermans (1636) 13 PM collection 15 PM collection 16 Howard Lester, MMT Observatory 18 Julieta Gonzales, Univ. Arizona 20 PM collection 21 FORS Team/8-2-m VLT/ESO 22 © Anglo-Australian Observatory/ Royal Observatory, Edinburgh, Photograph by David Malin 25 NASA/JPL 26 Novosti/PM collection 27 Paul Doherty/PM collection 28 Viking Project/NASA 29 Viking Project/NASA 31 PM collection 32 PM collection 34 E. L. Wright (UCLA)/The COBE Project/DIRBE/NASA 37 NASA/PM collection 39 PM collection 40 Philip's 43 NOAO/AURA/NSF 44 The Hubble Heritage Team (AURA/STScl/NASA) 47 PM collection 48 © Akira Fujii/DMI 50 PM collection 52 PM collection 55 NASA/PM collection 56 NASA/JPL/Malin Space Science Systems 58 NASA/JPL/Univ. Arizona 59 Dr R. Albrecht ESA/ESO/ ST-ECF/NASA 62 Philip's 64 LEDAS/PM collection 65 NASA/SRON/MPE 66 PM collection 71 PM collection 72 National Astronomy & Ionosphere Center/Cornell Univ./NSF 75 NASA/PSU/G. Pavlov et al. 77 ESA/PM collection 78 PM collection 81 NASA/The Hubble Heritage Team (STScl/AURA) 82 Philip's 84–85 FORS Team/8.2-m VLT Antu/ESO 89 PM collection 90 PM collection 92 PM collection 94 Erich Karkoschka (Univ. Arizona Lunar & Planetary Laboratory)/NASA 96 Lawrence Sromovsky (Univ. of Wisconsin-Madison)/STScl/NASA 97 Voyager Project/JPL/NASA 98 Voyager Project/JPL/NASA 101 Paul Doherty/PM collection 102 NASA/The Hubble Heritage Team (STScl/AURA) 107 T. Boroson (NOAO/USGP)/W. Keel (UA)/KPNO 108 NASA/The Hubble Heritage Team (STScl/AURA) 110 NASA/AURA/PM collection 112 R. Williams & the HDF Team (STScl)/NASA 114 Peter McGregor (Siding Spring)/PM collection 116–117 H. Weaver (JHU)/

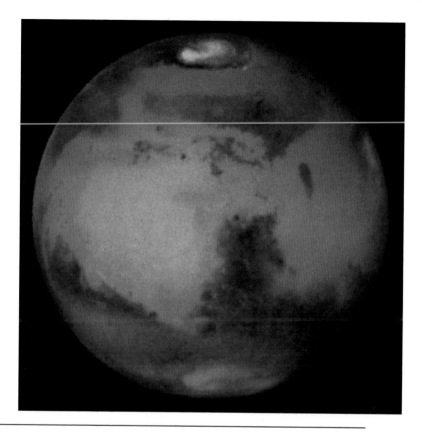

T. Smith (STScI)/NASA 118 R. Beebe (NMSU)/NASA 121 Dominic Cantin 122–123 W. Fukushima/PM collection 125 Kent Blackwell/PM collection 126 PM collection 129 PM collection 130 PM collection 132 PM collection 133 PM collection 134 PM collection 138 M. Karovska (Harvard-Smithsonian Center for Astrophysics)/NASA 140 J. P. Harrington & K. J. Borkowski (Univ. of Maryland)/NASA 142 R. Beebe (NMSU)/D. Gilmore & L. Bergeron (STScI)/NASA 144 Voyager Project/JPL/NASA/PM collection 145 Voyager Project/JPL/NASA/PM collection 146 NASA/JPL 149 Chris Doherty/PM collection 153 ESA/ISOCAM/ISOGAL Team 155 PM collection 156 Paul Doherty/PM collection 157 Philip's 159 PM collection 162 Philip's 163 NASA/The Hubble Heritage Team (STScI/AURA) 165 PM collection 166 PM collection 167 PM collection 169 Rutherford Appleton Laboratory/PM collection 171 Allan Chapman/PM collection 172 (top & bottom) Allan Chapman/PM collection 173 Allan Chapman/PM collection 175 NRAO/NSF 176 PM collection 178 Galileo Project/JPL/NASA 179 PM collection 181 PM collection 183 Viking Project/M. Dale-Bannister (WU St L)/NASA 184 JPL/NASA 187 NASA/James Bell (Cornell Univ.)/Michael Wolff (Space Science Inst.)/The Hubble Heritage Team (STScI/AURA) 188 XMM-Newton/ESA/NASA 191 NASA/SAO/R. Kraft et al. 194 PM collection 197 Paul Doherty/PM collection 198 PM collection 199 PM collection 200 PM collection 203 PM collection 206 L. F. Ball/PM collection 207 Susan Terebey (Extrasolar Research Corp.)/NASA 208 NASA/PM collection 211 SOHO-LASCO Consortium/ESA/NASA 212 Philip's 215 NASA/PM collection 216 Don Trombino/PM collection 218 Courtesy of Cassini Imaging Team/Univ. of Arizona/JPL/NASA 219 Andrew Fruchter (STScI) et al./WFPC2, HST/NASA 220 ESO/PM collection 224 Philip's 227 Philip's 231 Philip's 232–233 Jason Ware 234 NASA/Cosmic Background Explorer (COBE) Project 236 Courtesy ESA/ESO/MACHO Project Team 239 Institute for Cosmic Ray Research, Univ. of Tokyo 243 The Boomerang Collaboration 245 C. Burrows & J. Krist (STScI)/NASA 246 M. J. McCaughrean (MPIA)/C. R. O'Dell (Rice Univ.)/NASA 248 JPL/NASA 249 Peter H. Smith & Mark Lemmon (Univ. Arizona Lunar & Planetary Laboratory)/STScI/NASA 251 NASA/PM collection 253 NEAR Project/JHU APL/NASA

Foreword

The second is the duration of 9,192,631,770 periods of the radiation corresponding to the transition between the two hyperfine levels of the ground state of the caesium 133 atom.

SI Definition of Time

Each second of every day there are almost 10,000 million beats in the gaseous hearts of our global atomic timekeepers. Yet, in this stream of anonymous, recurring ticks of caesium 133, one particular transition was destined to draw the world's attention to Greenwich, the home of time, as 1999 became 2000.

On the eve of millennium year, as a record-breaking, international television broadcast linked over 60 countries, the world's viewers were reminded of the stories of time and astronomy that sprang from the Royal Greenwich Observatory and many were reacquainted with their natural fascination for the night skies.

Anniversaries usually provoke reflection, and so it is particularly timely to remember the television phenomenon that is *The Sky at Night*. This remarkable television programme has continued to feed viewers' astronomical fascination for what is approaching 1/20th of the last millennium. In April 2002 the programme celebrated 45 unbroken years of broadcasting. Patrick Moore has not missed a single episode.

From the first programme, about the Arend–Roland comet of 1957, the series has continued to follow the events and observations of the night skies, and reflect upon our understanding of the universe. Patrick has witnessed the beginning of the space age, watched mankind take its first giant leap to the Moon, and seen our first deep-space probes leave the Solar System.

In this 11th *The Sky at Night* book, Patrick reviews the programme from 1992–2001. It reflects the range of both the subject and the series: the search for extra-terrestrial life; potentially catastrophic Near Earth Asteroids; exploding stars; pulsars; black holes; the pleasure of naked-eye stargazing; and even advice on which binoculars and telescopes will reveal more of the beauty in the heavens.

In April 1995 the 500th programme was broadcast and, in Chapter 14, Patrick recalls some personal highlights. Sputnik 1, the satellite which ushered in the space age; Lunik 3's first pictures of the far side of the Moon; his visits to the world's, ever bigger, great observatories. It is interesting to remember how much our knowledge of the cosmos has widened while *The Sky at Night* has been transmitted. The planet Pluto, a close cosmic neighbour, was discovered only 27 years before the first broadcast and, in 1957, many believed that we would find life on Mars.

A thousand years ago we thought the Earth was the centre of the universe and that the planets were moved around the skies by angels. Today, we can only wonder how our view of the heavens will have changed by the year 3000 and if each episode of *The Sky at Night* will still begin with its familiar theme, *At the Castle Gate* by Sibelius.

Ian Russell
BBC TV Producer *The Sky at Night*

Introduction

This collection of articles based on *The Sky at Night* programmes – the 11th book in the series, though the first to be published by Philip's – covers the period from mid-1992 to the start of 2001. It follows the same pattern as in the earlier books, so that we have a variety of topics; some of the articles are more technical than others, but I hope that there is 'something for everybody'.

I am most grateful to all those distinguished astronomers who have joined me in the programmes; I have listed them below. Meanwhile, there is one point I must make. In most of the programmes given here, I have been joined by guests, and inevitably the texts in the present book are based upon these discussions, though of course any errors and omissions are my responsibility alone. This is particularly true of the following astronomers:

The late Colin Ronan (1)
Professor Sir Francis Graham Smith (3)
Iain Nicolson (6, 18, 28 and 45)
Professor Chris Kitchin (8 and 15)
Dr Fred Watson (9)
Dr Phil Charles (11)
Dr Paul Murdin (13)
Professor Richard Ellis (19)
Professor Garry Hunt (20)
Dr Helen Walker (24 and 27)
Professor Jasper Wall (30)
Dr Allan Chapman (31)
Ian Morison (32)
Martin Mobberley (33 and 37)
Dr Peter Cattermole (34)
Dr John Mason (36)

Much has happened since that first *Sky at Night* programme, 45 years ago. And I am sure that there will be plenty more to say when I start to compile *The Sky at Night* book, issue 12!

Patrick Moore

Sir Patrick Moore
Selsey, April 2002

The Very First Telescope?

Most books tell us that the first telescope was made in 1608 by a Dutch spectacle-maker, Hans Lippershey, and that the first man to turn a telescope skywards was Galileo, in 1610. The second of these statements is definitely wrong. Thomas Harriot, one-time tutor to Sir Walter Raleigh, drew a telescopic map of the Moon months before Galileo completed his primitive 'optick tube'. It may be that the first statement is also wrong, and that the original telescope was made in England some time between 1550 and 1560. Research by the British science historian Colin Ronan has opened up a whole new series of possibilities.

▲ **A portrait of Galileo,** *painted in 1636 by Justus Sustermans. Galileo lived from 1564 to 1642, and was one of the first to use the telescope for making astronomical observations.*

Galileo's telescope was, of course, a refractor, collecting its light by means of a lens known as an object-glass. The first surviving reflector, using a mirror to collect the light, was presented to the Royal Society by Isaac Newton in 1671. It has been suggested that the prototype English telescope was a curious mixture of the two types.

The study of reflecting light by mirrors goes back a long way. Euclid wrote about it as early as 300 BC. There were also reports of telescopes – of a kind – well before Galileo. Robert Grosseteste, who wrote a series of books from 1220 to 1235, alludes to 'making things a long distance off appear very close', but admittedly this is very nebulous. Other hints came during the 11th century from Witelo, in Eastern Europe, and John Pecham in England. Then there was the 'Forerunner', Leonardo da Vinci, who was born in 1452 and died in 1519. He knew a great deal about lenses, and wrote the significant sentence 'Make lenses in order to see the Moon large.'

It appears that in 1514, when he was working on the Vatican Hill, he constructed some optical device which was so secret that he would not let even his craftsmen helpers grind the lenses involved in it. All in all, I find it hard to credit that Leonardo can have failed to develop a telescope of some kind, but I am the first to admit that there is no proof.

So let us now turn to Leonard Digges, who was born in or about 1520 and had a decidedly chequered career. He came from Kent, and was unwise enough to take part in a rebellion led by Sir Thomas Wyatt against the reigning monarch, Mary Tudor, who – to the fury of many of her subjects – had married Philip, King of Spain. Queen Mary was not noted for her mildness and *bonhomie*, and in April 1554 Wyatt was summarily executed. Leonard Digges was lucky to escape the same fate. He did so probably because of an influential friend (Lord Clinton), but he lost all his estates. Eventually he managed to buy them back, but in 1559 or thereabouts he died.

He had been educated at Oxford, and was a good mathematician. He was, it was said, 'devoted to scientific pursuits'. He published mariners' almanacs, and also wrote a best-seller, *Prognostication*, which came out in English rather than Latin. It was an almanac-cum-perpetual calendar, with all kinds of scientific information.

Leonard Digges had one son, Thomas, born probably in 1546. He too was a good mathematician and surveyor; he became a Member of Parliament, and from 1586 to 1593 was Muster Master General to the English forces in Holland.

Because his father had died early, Thomas' education was entrusted to Dr John Dee, who was a skilled scientist but also a convinced astrologer; he became official adviser to Queen Elizabeth I. Dee lived at Mortlake, outside London, and possessed a fine library, but, sadly, all his books were destroyed by fire in 1583, when his house was attacked and burned by a mob.

In 1571 Thomas Digges published a book, *Pantometria* (an abbreviation for a very long title), which was mainly an account of his father's work. In this he told his readers that Leonard had used lenses and mirrors to make what sounds like a description of a reflecting telescope. In his own words (I have modernized the spelling): 'Glasses duly situated in convenient angles, not only discovered things far off, read letters, numbered pieces of money with the very coin and superscription thereof, cast by some of his friends upon

► *Colin Ronan and Gilbert Satterthwaite,* seen here together with the 'reconstructed' Digges telescope in 1992, built specially for our Sky at Night TV programme.

Downs in open fields, but also seven miles off declared what had been done at that instant in private places . . . . By these kinds of Glasses, or rather frames of them, placed in due angles, you may not only set out before your eye the image of every town, village, etc . . . you may by application of Glasses in due proportion cause any peculiar house, or room thereof, dilate and show itself in as ample form as the whole town first appeared.' He also referred to a more detailed book written by Leonard.

Moreover, in 1576 Thomas published a new edition of his father's *Prognostication everlastinge*, and added an appendix of his own, supporting the Copernican Sun-centred theory of the universe and arguing that the universe itself was probably infinite. Digges' description of how the stars extend outwards until they become too dim to be seen is surely just what would have been expected from telescopic observations of them.

Another key figure in the story is William Bourne, an expert mathematician as well as a specialist in marine and military affairs. Apparently Lord Burleigh, Queen Elizabeth's chief adviser, asked Bourne to report on Thomas Digges' claims, because a telescope would be of tremendous importance in war, and the Queen was only too well aware of the chance of an eventual Spanish attack. (Remember, the Armada came in 1588.) Bourne did a good job. He reported to Burleigh, and it seems definite that he had looked through a Digges telescope, because he said that 'its greatest impediment is that you cannot behold and see but the smaller quantity at a time'. In other words, the telescope had a small field of view. Had Bourne not used one, he could not possibly have known that. And realizing that it was of military value, Burleigh may well have ordered it to be kept secret – a sort of Tudor D-notice.

In 1758, however, Bourne published a book, *Inventions and Devices*, in which he gave the first description of a telescope that we know (Device 110). It needs two optical components: a lens and a mirror. Light enters through a lens, and is then reflected in a curved mirror; there is no eyepiece, and the observer has to 'look backwards', so to speak. It was remarkably awkward to use, but apparently it did work.

For our *Sky at Night* programme, Colin Ronan and Gilbert Satterthwaite built a 'Digges telescope' which they had made in the Optics Department of Imperial College, London. We looked through it, and showed an image on the television screen; later, a photograph of a distant church spire was taken through it. Whether the model looked anything like Digges' original we do not know, but the optical design was the same. (Another model was made about the same time by Joachim Reimitz in Germany, and it too worked.)

True, it is all very shadowy; we lack information about both Leonard and Thomas Digges (no pictures of them have ever been found), and the loss of Dee's library was indeed a disaster. We cannot be sure that Leonard produced a workable telescope, but the evidence that he did so is undeniably strong. Whether he turned it towards the sky is another matter – and we will never know unless, by some miracle, a long-lost manuscript turns up. Yet there is at least a chance that the telescope was known long before Lippershey or Galileo, and that the very first telescope was made not in Holland, but in England.

Six Into One Will Go

In late October 1992 I found myself in the Sonora Desert of Arizona, driving along a most unusual mountain road – by no means a racetrack, to put it mildly. It led up the side of a high peak, Mount Hopkins; atop the peak I could see what looked almost like a doll's house, but which was in fact a major observatory. This was the home of the MMT, or Multiple-Mirror Telescope.

The dome itself is not conventional. It spins round on rails, so that the telescope is always in front of the slit, and the telescope itself moves only in declination. The rails have to be kept clear; snow can be an occasional problem, and squashed ladybirds produce a perennial hazard. (These seem to be French ladybirds, and, incidentally, I am told that they bite!) The MMT did not look like a telescope at all; it was a mass of steel wires and girders. It used six 72-inch mirrors, which worked together, and made the equivalent of a single 176-inch mirror, one of the largest in the world.

But why use six mirrors when one would do? Well, there were two main reasons. First, making six relatively small mirrors is a great deal easier than making one very large mirror. Secondly, cost. When the MMT was built it cost much less than a conventional 176-inch would have done.

The MMT has been in action since 1979 (you may remember a programme we presented about it then). Yet in 1993 a radical change was

▼ **The old MMT,** as it appeared in 1992. I took this photograph to show the six mirrors.

announced. The six 72-inch mirrors were to go, to be replaced by a single 256-inch or 6.5-metre mirror. (When I went there, the new plan had only just been announced. The single large mirror was eventually installed in 1999.)

This is not to suggest that the MMT was a failure; it was in fact an unqualified success. First, the site. This is excellent. For one or two months each year the MMT Observatory has to be shut down because of the monsoon pattern which hits Arizona (this happens mainly in August, and affects most Arizonan observatories), but otherwise the seeing is very good indeed, as can be seen from the quality of the star images. Secondly, the telescope itself gave surprisingly few technical problems once the teething troubles had been overcome.

The mirrors had to be kept in perfect adjustment, and the first system involved a laser co-alignment arrangement, whereby an artificial star was created in the centre of the structure and sent out to each of the six mirrors. For a number of reasons, this did not work, and in the early 1980s it was abandoned. Moths tended to interrupt the laser beam at night, shutting down the co-ordinating system, and the computers were quite incompetent at moth identification. There were other drawbacks, too, and the laser was

▼ **The new MMT.** The six mirrors have gone, to be replaced by a single 6.5-metre mirror. The new MMT was dedicated on 20 May 2000.

replaced by a much more straightforward system, in which the images at the focal plane were digitally recorded – six in all, one from each mirror. The position of the centre of the image was worked out electronically, and the secondary mirrors were commanded to bring all six images together.

The mirrors themselves were among the first lightweight mirrors to be used for a large telescope. The mounting was of the altazimuth type, which in 1979 was decidedly unusual; at that time there was only one other large altazimuth telescope, the Russian 236-inch. The MMT proved to be a very accurate tracker. The rotating building was also a marked success.

Researches of all kinds were carried out. Quasars came under careful scrutiny, for instance, and so did gravitational lenses, which were fairly new discoveries when the MMT was built. A gravitational lens is a phenomenon which occurs when the light from a distant quasar or galaxy passes by some massive object during its trip to Earth. The massive object may be another quasar, or another galaxy; the image of the background object is distorted, and there may in fact be several images instead of only one.

Now comes the vital question. If the MMT was such a success, why remove the six 72-inch mirrors and substitute one of larger diameter?

The discussion went back to 1985, when the American optical pioneer Roger Angel developed a revolutionary manufacturing process which had far-reaching results, and could facilitate the construction of very large mirrors. There were already plans for building huge telescopes, and it was clear that by the end of the century the MMT would go from being the third largest telescope in the world down to something like the 12th largest. This is still a respectable size, of course, but it meant that some kinds of frontier research would be unavailable; a larger aperture would be needed. There are various ways of making telescopes of tremendous light-grasp (for example, the Keck telescopes on Mauna Kea in Hawaii, with their segmented mirrors), but Angel's method was quite new.

Underneath the University of Arizona football stadium there is a most unusual astronomical laboratory. It is here that the new mirror for the tele-scope was built: 6.5 metres or 256 inches in diameter. It was essential to make a honeycomb, to give both stiffness and lightness of weight; the mirror had to be made of borosilicate glass, which is very easy to melt. The mirror contained 10½ tons of this glass, in chunks; the chunks were put on top of a mould which was the reverse of the honeycomb. The mould was made out of aluminium silica fibre, in hexagonal shapes; these produced the hexagonal voids in the honeycomb. There were 1020 of them, bolted down on to the floor of the mould. The glass was placed on top of them, and when melted it ran down the sides of the mould to form the ribs of the honeycomb. Roger Angel described it to me as follows:

'Besides being a honeycomb, this is also a very fast focal ratio mirror, and so it has quite a steep sag from the centre to the edge of the mirror. To get that sag without grinding off another 10 tons of glass, which would be expensive both for grinding and for buying another 10 tons of glass, we spin the furnace containing the mirror; by spinning the furnace we form a parabolic shape for the mirror. For this mirror – a 6.5-metre, with a focal ratio of 1:25 – the rotation speed is 7.4 rpm. This has to be held to about a thousandth of an rpm for three days or so, while the glass is liquid.'

The mirror was cast on 2–3 April 1992. When the glass was actually molten, and running down into the mould, came the most difficult part of the whole operation. The cooling had to be at a rate of one-eighth of a degree per hour through the temperature range of 500°C, when the glass annealed and relaxed to relieve the stresses and strains which had been built up during the casting. By the time I arrived, in November, the temperature was down to that of an ordinary room, and so there was no longer a need for a 24-hour watch; the glass could even be touched, and certainly it seemed to be a perfect honeycomb.

Everything depends upon a really effective furnace, and this one was indeed large. It could attain a temperature of well over 1000°C, and it could spin at 10 revolutions per minute.

Normally, a single mirror thick enough to be stable must be heavy and unmanageable. To quote Roger Angel again:

'The idea of spinning is very simple. If you take a pool of liquid – whether it is water, glass or anything else – and spin it around, the liquid is thrown on to the sides of the container, and produces the dish shape that you want for a mirror. Actually, this is fairly easy to do; it just means building a furnace which spins. The more difficult problem is in making the honeycomb structure. There are therefore two things going on at once when we make the mirror. We spin the liquid glass, and we also fill the liquid glass with blocks of material that will later be removed to make cavities. Learning how to do this is the really tricky part. The mirror is about 2½ feet thick, and of that thickness about 80% of it is air. If we melted the glass, the mirror would be only 6 inches thick when spread evenly around. If the honeycomb technique had not been developed, the only option would have been to make one thin solid glass sheet.

'We heat to about 1200°C (2200–2300°F). This temperature is reached in two to three days, but the cooling takes a long time, because if the glass is not cooled very slowly it cracks. The cooling rate is down to just two or three degrees per day.

'There are two big hurdles to overcome. One is to prevent the mould from coming apart. All the blocks are held below the surface, and if something breaks they will simply bob up to the surface of the glass; we had to watch very carefully to make sure that none of those thousand blocks had bobbed up.

▲ **The new mirror cell**, *being positioned in the MMT observing chamber in August 1998. (Photograph by Julieta Gonzales, University of Arizona.)*

'The next step is to lift the mirror to the vertical, put it in a stand, and then go in from the back and remove all the blocks of material that have made the honeycomb structure. Then we are left with the required lightweight honeycomb.'

He went on to say that it would be quite practicable to make a larger mirror, using more glass and heating it for longer. 'There is no conventional way to make, for instance, an 8-metre mirror. You could make it from a single piece of glass, thick and solid, but it would weigh 60 tons, as opposed to 10 tons for a honeycomb. Moreover, not only would it be heavy and unwieldy, but glass takes a very long time to cool to the same temperature as the surrounding air; if the mirror is too warm you get convection off the surface, and this causes shimmer. So the very thing you are trying to do with a big telescope – make the sharpest possible image – is spoiled by the heat which is stored in the thick piece of glass.

'The Palomar 200-inch mirror took about 20 years to make; the blank was cast in 1934 and the telescope was finished in 1948. The 4-metre mirror for the Kitt Peak telescope took ten years, from the melting of the blank to putting it in the telescope. The spin-casting method is very much quicker.'

Naturally, replacing six smaller mirrors with a single large one posed many problems. The observatory building on Mount Hopkins had been designed specially for the MMT and so had to be modified, while the entire support structure of the telescope had to be lifted bodily out of the dome and replaced by a different one to hold the 6.5-metre mirror. But as Roger Angel said when I was at the Observatory:

'There will be two main advantages of the new telescope. One is the simple collecting-area increase – more than a factor of two in the light-gathering power of the telescope – so that we can see objects twice as faint as before. Also, the new telescope will have a much wider field of view than the MMT – 1 degree as against 3 arc-minutes. In terms of the area of the sky that you can cover, you are looking at 400 times as much area of the sky at once as was possible with the MMT.'

Everything went according to plan. In 1998 the old MMT came to the end of its career, and by 1999 the great new mirror was in place. What about the name? Many ideas were put forward – in the end the acronym was retained; the Multiple-Mirror Telescope became the Mono-Mirror Telescope.

In a way it was sad to see the end of the MMT in its old form; it had been a pioneer telescope. But science moves on, and at least the MMT has its place in history.

A Glitch In The System

Zeta Tauri – sometimes, though rarely, referred to by its old individual name, Alheka – is an ordinary-looking star. It is of the third magnitude, and has a B-type spectrum; it is 150 light-years away, and about 1300 times as luminous as our Sun. But it has one point of special interest. It is the 'guide' to one of the most important objects in the sky – the Crab Nebula.

The Crab is much too faint to be seen with the naked eye – I can just glimpse it with my 20 × 70 binoculars, but not easily. A telescope of small aperture shows it with no trouble at all, and photographs taken with large instruments reveal an immensely complicated structure. We know what it is: a supernova remnant – the wreck of a star, which was seen to blaze out in the year 1054 and was recorded by Chinese and Korean astronomers. (It was not documented in Europe, though in America there are some old Indian cave drawings which may show it.) The star became brilliant enough to be seen with the naked eye in broad daylight. After it faded below naked-eye visibility, nothing more was thought about it until 1731, when a gas-patch in the same position was noted by John Bevis. It was rediscovered by Charles Messier on 12 September 1758, and – fittingly –

◄ *The Crab Nebula,*
as sketched by Lord Rosse
in 1845. This drawing was
made using observations
from his great Birr Castle
reflector. It was he who
nicknamed it the Crab.

▲ The Crab Nebula – *viewed here using the 8.2-metre VLT – is the result of a spectacular supernova explosion* *recorded in* AD *1054. In the centre of the nebula lies a pulsar – a neutron star rotating at a rate of 30 times per second.*

listed as No. 1 in his classic catalogue of clusters and nebulae. The nickname by which we now know it was bestowed by the Earl of Rosse, who in 1845 observed it with his great Birr Castle 72-inch reflector and likened its shape to that of a crab.

Deep inside the gas-cloud there lurks the Crab's 'power-house' – a neutron star or pulsar, which is spinning round rapidly and is the actual core of the progenitor star. It was identified visually in 1989 by a team of astronomers at the Steward Observatory in Arizona, and catalogued as NP 0532. The mean magnitude is about 17, so that it is faint – but not excessively so, as judged by modern standards. It is much brighter than the second pulsar to be visually traced, PSR 0033–45 in the far-southern constellation of Vela, the Sails, whose mean magnitude is below 24.

The Crab's main importance is that by cosmic standards it is close. The distance is a mere 600 light-years. Also, it radiates over almost the whole range of the electromagnetic spectrum; it sends out long-wavelength radio waves, visible light, ultraviolet, X-rays and also gamma-rays.

A supernova of this type (II) is the result of the collapse of a very massive star. Stars draw their power from nuclear reactions, and when all these sources are exhausted there is a sudden change in structure. The core collapses in a matter of seconds. There is an 'implosion', followed by a shock wave which disrupts the entire star; for a while, the luminosity may rise to 100,000 million times that of the Sun. Heavy elements manufactured in the supernova then enrich the interstellar medium. Eventually all that is left is the neutron-star core, which has a solid, iron-rich crystalline crust and a superfluid liquid interior. The density may be well over a million million times that of water. The spin produces 'pulses' of radio emission, rather in the manner of a rotating lighthouse. There is, of course, an immensely powerful magnetic field.

▼ **The Large Cloud of Magellan,** 169,000 light-years away in the constellation of Dorado.

Photographed by David Malin (Anglo-Australian Observatory/Royal Observatory, Edinburgh).

Because a neutron star is radiating, it is gradually slowing down. The Crab remnant is the youngest and quickest-spinning of the known normal pulsars, and its slow-down rate has been carefully monitored by radio astronomers all over the world. For 23 years now it has been measured daily from Jodrell Bank (not with the 250-ft Lovell telescope, but with the 40-ft dish nearby), and the rate of spin has fallen from just over 30 revolutions per second to just under 30. If this continues, the pulsar will cease to radiate in around 10,000 years' time. There must be many dead pulsars in the Galaxy; the slowest rotaters we have so far found have periods of about 4 seconds.

However, there is one complication. Sometimes the rate of spin changes abruptly – not by much, but by a measurable amount. This is termed a 'glitch'. In the case of the Crab, a glitch may amount to as much as one-tenth of a second. Many glitches have been recorded, both with the Crab and with the Vela pulsar; with Vela, indeed, Jodrell Bank observers have identified 39 glitches over a period of eight years.

The cause of a glitch is a slight change in the rate of rotation. The interior of a pulsar is a superfluid liquid, and when this is rotated it does not behave in the way that an ordinary liquid would do; it produces 'eddies', and when these press against the rigid crust a glitch results. Obviously, they are important, because in studies of this sort physics and astronomy 'come together', and we can compare phenomena available in the laboratory with what is happening in the Crab Nebula, 6000 light-years away.

Since 1054 there have been only two naked-eye supernovae in our Galaxy: Tycho's Star of 1572 and Kepler's Star of 1604, though in 1987 a naked-eye supernova flared up in the Large Cloud of Magellan, 169,000 light-years away. When the next supernova will blaze forth in our part of the universe, we do not know. Meanwhile, the Crab Nebula continues to fascinate us. It is a timely reminder that though most things in the cosmos happen slowly, there can be times when the universe becomes a very violent place.

Comparative Planetology

The Solar System is divided into two well-marked parts. First we have the four small, solid inner planets: Mercury, Venus, the Earth and Mars. Then comes a wide gap, in which move many thousands of dwarf worlds known as minor planets or asteroids; beyond, we meet the giants Jupiter, Saturn, Uranus and Neptune, plus the enigmatic Pluto.

Obviously, the close planets are bright. Venus is much the most brilliant object in the sky apart from the Sun and the Moon, and at its best it can cast appreciable shadows. Mars cannot rival this, but it outshines all the stars, even Sirius, when it is well placed. Only Mercury, of our nearer neighbours, is never very prominent.

Mercury is not a great deal larger than the Moon, and always keeps in the same part of the sky as the Sun, so that we never see it against a really dark background. Its atmosphere is very rarefied, and any kind of life there seems out of the question. But Venus and Mars might be expected to be more welcoming, so let us try a little of what is termed 'comparative planetology', and see where the main differences and the main similarities lie.

First, size and mass. Venus and the Earth are very similar; Earth is 12,756 km (7926 miles) in diameter, as measured through the equator, whereas Venus is 12,104 km (7523 miles) in diameter (represent the Earth by a snooker ball, and Venus will be another ball so like the first that Stephen Hendry and John Parrott could quite happily use them!). In mass there is a similar likeness; Venus has 86% of the mass of the Earth. Mars, with a diameter of 6794 km (4222 miles) and a mass 15% of that of the Earth, is much smaller and less substantial. Here, we can make our initial comparisons.

The Earth, with an escape velocity of 11.2 km/s (7 miles/s), can hold on to a dense atmosphere – which is fortunate for us, otherwise we would not be here. Venus, with an escape velocity of 10.4 km/s (6.4 miles/s), can also retain a dense atmosphere, and in fact it is much more substantial than might be expected, for reasons to be discussed shortly. But Mars has a weak pull – escape velocity only 5 km/s (3.2 miles/s) – and this is not enough. Unlike the Moon, it has managed to retain an appreciable atmosphere, but the ground density is below 10 millibars everywhere, so that from our point of view Mars might just as well be airless. We can never live there except under enclosed conditions – in spacesuits, in rockets or in the Martian Bases of the future.

Then the movements are different. Venus is an inferior planet – that is to say, closer to the Sun than we are – and so it shows phases similar to those of the Moon. When closest to us, at around 39 million km (24 million miles), it is 'new'; its dark side is facing the Earth, and we cannot see it at all except when it passes directly between the Sun and the Earth, showing up in transit as a dark spot crossing the solar disk. The last of these transits took place as long ago as 1882, and the next is not due until 2004. When Venus is full, it is on the far side of the Sun, and is again virtually unobservable. In fact, Venus is a most awkward object; as the phases increase, the apparent diameter shrinks, and Venus is actually at its most brilliant when it is in the crescent stage. (*En passant*, binoculars will show the crescent easily, and I know a few lynx-eyed people who can detect it without any optical aid at all.) Venus can sometimes be on view for as much as 5½ hours after sunset or 5½ hours before sunrise, but it can never be seen throughout the night. The orbit is more or less circular, and the mean distance from the Sun is 108 million km (67 million miles), as against 150 million km (93 million miles) for the Earth. The orbital period is 224.7 days.

Mars has a more eccentric orbit; the mean distance from the Sun is 228 million km (141.5 million miles). The Martian 'year' is 687 Earth days or 668 Martian days (sols), because Mars spins rather more slowly than our world; a sol is equal to 24 hours 37 minutes. This is easy to measure.

▼ **The surface of Mercury,** *photographed by Mariner 10 in 1974–5.*

Superficially, the planet's surface looks very like that of the Earth's Moon.

▲ *A panoramic view of the surface of* **Venus,** *from the Venera 13 Lander in 1982. Part of the spacecraft is visible at the bottom of the image, together with a camera lens cover.*

Telescopes show surface markings on Mars, and we can watch the planet rotate; it is not often that dust storms in the Martian atmosphere cover the whole disk sufficiently to hide the surface markings (though occasionally this does happen). When we go to Mars we will not find the calendar very unfamiliar, apart from the fact that the seasons are so much longer than ours.

Venus is different. Before the Space Age we did not know the length of the axial rotation period, because telescopes cannot show us the true surface; all we can see are the upper clouds, and the vague shadings are too impermanent to give reliable clues. But thanks to space-probes, we now know that the axial rotation period is 243 Earth days – longer than a Venus 'year', so that the solar day there is 118 Earth days long. Moreover, Venus spins from east to west, in the sense opposite to the Earth or Mars. If you could see the Sun from the surface of Venus, it would rise in the west and set in the east – though in fact this would never be possible, because the open sky could never be seen at all. There is no such thing as a sunny day on Venus.

Why does Venus behave like this? We can probably explain the slow rotation by the braking effect exerted by the pull of the Sun (Mercury, too, is a slow spinner), but the 'wrong-way' rotation is a real puzzle. The favoured explanation is that at an early stage in its history Venus was hit by a large body, presumably an asteroid, and literally tipped over. I find this hard to credit, because it seems likely that a collision on this scale would shatter planet and impactor alike, but I have to confess that I cannot think of anything better.

Next, the atmospheres – and here the three planets differ widely. Our air is made up of 78% nitrogen, 21% oxygen, and smaller amounts of other gases such as argon and carbon dioxide. The thin Martian air is almost pure carbon dioxide, and this can be understood, because carbon dioxide is a heavy gas and less likely to escape than lighter elements. But Venus, too, has an atmosphere which is mainly carbon dioxide, with virtually no free oxygen; the ground pressure there is about 90 times that of the Earth's air at sea-level.

Because Venus and the Earth have similar escape velocities, one would expect them to have similar atmospheres. The difference must surely be due to the fact that Venus is more than 32 million km (20 million miles) closer to the Sun. It is thought that at the earliest period in the story of the

Solar System the Sun was less luminous than it is now, in which case Venus, Earth and Mars may have started to evolve along similar lines, with the same kinds of atmospheres and probably broad oceans. We can still see the results of water action on Mars, with dry riverbeds and 'islands', while some areas were affected by flash floods; but when the Martian atmosphere leaked away, the seas dried up. (All this was amply confirmed by the probes of the late 1990s. Ares Vallis, the landing site of the Pathfinder mission to Mars in 1997, is unquestionably an old flood-plain.)

Then the Sun increased in luminosity. The Earth was just clear of the danger-zone; Venus was not. The water molecules in Venus' atmosphere were broken up into hydrogen and oxygen by short-wave solar radiations. The light hydrogen rose to the top of the atmospheric layer and escaped, while the oxygen combined with the surface rocks. The net result was that Venus lost all its seas, and became bone-dry. The carbonates were then driven out of the rocks, and the present dense, choking atmosphere developed – also creating a super-greenhouse effect, ending in a surface temperature not far short of 480°C (1000°F). The same fate did not overtake the Earth because the surface temperature was never high enough; the water vapour was more or less confined to the lower layers of the atmosphere, and the seas were safe. In them life appeared, evolving eventually into you and me.

▼ *A volcano on Venus – an impression by Paul* Doherty, though probably very near the truth!

Next, we come to the overall surface conditions. Mars is a barren world, so far as we can tell, and if there is any life it must be very primitive, probably underground (there is no chance that Mars can support anything as advanced as a blade of glass). The landscape is cratered, and there are tall peaks and deep valleys; the most impressive features are the volcanoes, which are much loftier and more massive than ours. Olympus Mons, in the volcanic region known as Tharsis, towers to an altitude of 24 km (15 miles), three times the height of Everest. It is topped by a complex 60-km (40-mile) caldera, and there are abundant lava-fields. Olympus Mons is a typical shield volcano of exactly the same type as Mauna Kea in Hawaii, but much larger and more massive; the width of the base is 480 km (300 miles).

Whether any of the Martian volcanoes are active now is very dubious. The general consensus of opinion is that they are extinct. I am not so sure;

▼ **Olympus Mons on Mars.** *This image, taken from Viking, shows how large and flat the volcano is, with a gently sloping surface.*

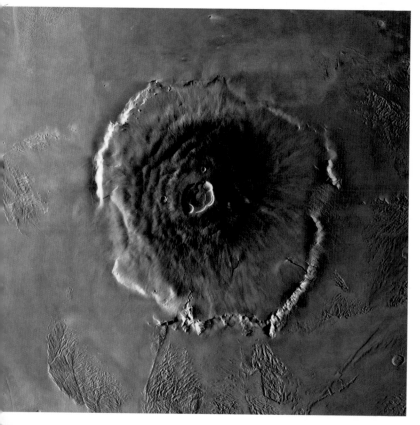

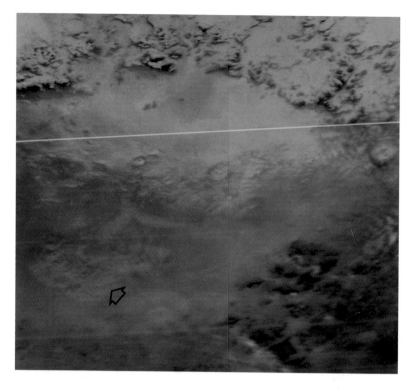

▲ **Mars: a dust storm in Argyre,** seen from Viking. Argyre (arrowed) is one of the largest of the Martian impact basins.

we will not be able to give a final verdict until we have more information. At least it likely that mild 'Mars-quakes' occur.

On to Venus, where we have to rely upon radar results – largely from the very successful Magellan probe, which orbited Venus and mapped the entire surface. Here we have two main uplands, Ishtar and Aphrodite, and again there are craters, valleys and mountains, with lava-flows everywhere. The highest peaks, in the Maxwell Mountains, are very lofty and massive. The volcanoes are also largely of the shield type, but differ from those of Mars inasmuch as they are certainly active. Vulcanism plays a major role in the Venus scene.

On Earth, a volcano develops over a 'hot spot' in the mantle, below the crust. The crust itself is divided into large plates, which shift around; the science of plate tectonics, ridiculed only a few decades ago, has come to dominate the whole of geological theory. When a volcano is carried away from a hot spot, it ceases to erupt. This is what has happened to Mauna Kea, which has been extinct for at least 4000 years and will never erupt again;

its place over the hot spot has been taken by Mauna Loa, which is very active indeed. In time Mauna Loa, too, will move away and become extinct.

This does not happen on Mars or Venus, where there are no comparable shifting plates; when a volcano is born it can stay over its hot spot for an immense period, and can therefore grow to tremendous size. This is why the Venus and Martian volcanoes dwarf ours, and it also explains why the volcanic regions on those planets are more localized than those of Earth.

What else? Well, the Earth has a powerful magnetic field, Mars a very weak one, and Venus apparently none at all, so that magnetic compasses will not work there. It follows that the heavy, iron-rich cores of these planets are smaller than those of Earth, not only absolutely but also relatively. The slower spin may also play a part here, at least with regard to Venus. Radiation belts similar to our Van Allen zones must also be absent, which so far as the space-planners are concerned is a distinct relief.

Finally, we can now try to decide whether or not manned expeditions will be practicable in the foreseeable future. For Venus the answer is a definite 'no'. The clouds are rich in sulphuric acid, and in every way conditions there are about as hostile as they could possibly be; even the spacecraft which have made controlled landings there have been unable to survive for more than an hour or so before being put permanently out of action. There have been suggestions of 'seeding' the atmosphere, breaking up the carbon dioxide and sulphuric acid to release free oxygen; I suppose this may be possible eventually, but certainly not at the moment.

Mars is more promising. We cannot provide it with breathable air (even if we could, Mars could not retain it), but at least there is plenty of ice, so that in some ways Mars will give us some help. Whether the thin atmosphere will provide a useful screen against short-wave solar radiations is problematical, but it may serve to some extent. Mars is a cold world, but not impossibly so. All in all, there may well be a fully-fledged Martian Base within the next few decades.

Earth, Mars and Venus are so alike in some ways, so very different in others. We know much more about them than we did when I presented the very first *Sky at Night* programme, in April 1957, and Mars at least offers a real challenge to Man's ingenuity during the 21st century.

The Radio Watchers

Go to Green Bank, in West Virginia, USA, and you will find a replica of one of the most important scientific instruments ever built. It was made by a radio engineer named Karl Jansky, who was studying 'static' on behalf of the Bell Telephone Company. In 1931 he found that he was picking up emissions which he could not identify. Before long he traced them to the Milky Way – and this was the start of the science of radio astronomy, though for some reason or other Jansky never followed it up as he might have been expected to do.

Today there are huge radio telescopes, which are really in the nature of aerials (one certainly cannot look through a radio telescope!). At Green Bank there is, for instance, the 'dish' which was used in 1960, to listen out for intelligent signals from radio operators living on planets of other stars. Not surprisingly, the results were negative, but the experiment has since been repeated with much more sensitive and far-ranging equipment; SETI – the Search for Extra-Terrestrial Intelligence – is very much a part of official programmes. At Green Bank there are also three 85-ft dishes, and one 140-ft dish mounted equatorially. A former telescope, with a 300-ft dish, came to a strange end. On 15 November 1985 it suddenly collapsed, and in a matter of seconds was reduced to scrap-iron. The trouble was traced to a single faulty gusset, which failed abruptly after years of use. Nothing daunted, the Green Bank radio astronomers set to work to build a new and better telescope (it was completed in 1999).

In the desert of San Agustin there is what must be regarded as the most important radio installation in the world: the VLA, or Very Large Array. There are 27 radio dishes or antennae, and when working together they can synthesize a single dish with a diameter of 32 km (20 miles)! The dishes are arranged in a Y-formation, with three arms; the south-east and south-west (each 27 km [17 miles] long) and the north (19 km [12 miles] long).

▶ **Green Bank Radio Telescope**, *used in the original SETI programme (Project Ozma). It subsequently collapsed! I imaged it in 1992.*

The antennae can be moved about on rails, which is no easy task, since each 82-ft dish is 94 ft high and weighs 235 tons. When the dishes are close together, in what is termed the D-configuration, they act as a 'wide-angle lens', and can scan wide areas of the sky; in the A-configuration, when some of the dishes are moved out almost to the horizon, the array acts as a zoom, giving more detailed information about smaller areas of the sky. The total track length is 137 km (85 miles).

When the VLA is being used, all the dishes point to the same region of the sky, and each pair of telescopes gives an enhanced signal. The reason why the dishes are arranged in a Y-formation is purely for convenience.

All kinds of researches are carried out with the VLA. For example, attention is paid to the jets coming from active galaxies, such as M87 in the Virgo cluster, which is truly immense and is far larger than our own Galaxy; its distance is around 50 million light-years. The jets are best studied at radio wavelengths; they indicate violent activity in the nucleus of the galaxy, where there is probably a massive black hole. Then there is a galaxy where the jets are 'bent' in identical fashion, due probably to 'winds' in the interstellar medium – so that the jets are being blown around rather in the manner of smoke. Even the Hubble Space Telescope cannot tell us as much about the jets as the VLA is capable of doing.

Another branch of investigation concerns the spiral arms of galaxies. For example, it is widely believed that the spiral arms of the famous galaxy M81,

▼ **The Very Large Array (VLA),** *as I photographed it in 1992. Located in New Mexico, USA, the* VLA is one of the world's foremost astronomical radio observatories.

in Ursa Major, are due to the gravitational pull of its smaller, irregular companion M82, though opinions differ. It is possible to measure Doppler shifts at radio wavelengths by tuning the receivers to different frequencies and looking at different parts of the target galaxy; these parts have different velocities, and we can find out just how the galaxy is rotating.

One special study concerns that mysterious region, the centre of the Galaxy, which we can never see at optical wavelengths because there is too much obscuring material in the way; it lies beyond the lovely star-clouds in Sagittarius. Radio waves are not blocked, and with the VLA it has been possible to locate a small, compact, very powerful radio source which is called Sagittarius A-★ (pronounced Sagittarius A-star).

It may well be that Sagittarius A-★ is the actual centre of the Galaxy. The VLA is so sensitive that it can measure the apparent motion of the source against background quasars, thousands of millions of light-years away. The shift is only 5/1000th of an arc second per year, but this ties in with the accepted rotation period of the Sun round the galactic centre, which is of the order of 225 million years.

Closer objects are not neglected. Careful studies are made of the Sun, with special reference to flares – which involve tremendous bursts of energy, usually associated with sunspot groups. Though the VLA was not designed for solar work, it has proved to be very useful, and is providing data which may help us to improve our admittedly scanty knowledge about the nature of the Sun's 11-year cycle of activity.

Another important radio telescope – this time a 12-metre dish – has been set up at the US national observatory, Kitt Peak, in Arizona. It operates mainly at millimetre wavelengths, and has been concerned largely with studies of interstellar carbon monoxide, which leads on to the investigation of cold dark matter – such as the hydrogen clouds spread between the stars. This telescope is also one of a network of radio telescopes making up the VLBI, or Very Long Baseline Interferometer; this includes instruments in Europe and Japan as well as in the United States. It operates at short wavelengths, and the resolution goes down to about 50 micro-arc seconds. If our eyes were of equivalent sensitivity, it would mean that a man in London could read the print of a newspaper held up by a friend in New York (naturally allowing for the curvature of the Earth's surface!). There is also the VLBA, or Very Long Baseline Array, with instruments extending from Hawaii in the Pacific Ocean to the Virgin Islands in the Caribbean. Each installation is equipped with a hydrogen maser clock, and the results are brought to Socorro in New Mexico for detailed analysis. The accuracy obtainable is about a millionth of a millionth of a second, which is remarkable by any standards.

Radio astronomy is a young science, but today it is of paramount importance. We have come a long way since Karl Jansky's accidental discovery of radio waves from the Galaxy.

Just a Moment!

I suppose that over the centuries there are two questions to which Mankind passionately wants to know the answers. One concerns the possibility of life elsewhere. The second is, perhaps, even more fundamental. How did the universe come into being?

We know that the Sun is a star and that there are around 100,000 million stars in our Milky Way Galaxy; beyond, we can see thousands of millions of other galaxies. The furthest known objects in the universe – quasars, the nuclei of very active galaxies, plus 'proto-galaxies' which have not been fully formed – are well over 10,000 million light-years away, so that we are seeing them as they used to be long before the Earth or the Sun existed. Outside our local group of systems, all the galaxies are racing away from us; the further away they are, the faster they are going. The remotest systems are receding at well over 90% of the speed of light. Expansion has been in progress for a long time, and it is therefore logical to assume that the galaxies were once much closer together than they are now; it is generally believed that the entire universe was created in a 'Big Bang', probably at least 13,000 million years ago. If so, then the Big Bang was a hot, dense, explosive event in which space, time and matter came into existence simultaneously. The universe has been expanding ever since, which demonstrates the violence of the initial event. (When I broadcast this programme in 1993, with Iain Nicolson, the universe was thought to be considerably older than we now believe – at least 15,000 million years, and probably rather more. To bring the chapter up to date, I have therefore modified the figures, and give them as we believe them to be in 2002.)

▼ **The Milky Way in infrared,** as imaged by the COBE satellite. The thin disk of our Galaxy is clearly visible, with stars appearing white.

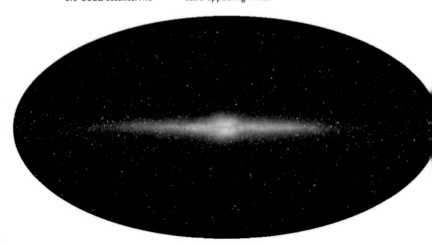

The Big Bang was not like an ordinary explosion. Matter did not suddenly erupt from a particular point into a pre-existing empty space, scattering fragments in all directions. Instead, space, time and matter as we know them all came into existence at the same moment, and expansion began at once. It is not easy to explain the situation in everyday language, but a useful analogy – even if not a very accurate one – is to represent galaxies (or, rather, groups of galaxies) by labels stuck on to the surface of an expanding balloon. As the balloon swells, an observer on any one of the 'galaxies' will see all the others receding from him, the more distant ones moving away faster than those that are closer. The pattern of the labels on our balloon does not change, but the separation between them increases, and there is no unique 'centre'. In fact, it is best to think of the galaxies being at rest in an expanding space, rather than picture them rushing apart through space itself.

But what happened before that? The only answer must be that there was no 'before'; time had not started, and so the question is not valid.

The early universe was incredibly hot. At 10^{-43} seconds after the Big Bang, the temperature was about 10^{32} degrees. (Note: 10^{-43} means a decimal point followed by 43 zeros and then a 1; 10^{32} indicates a 1 followed by 32 zeros.) The universe cooled rapidly at first, and then more slowly.

Around 10^{-35} seconds after the Big Bang, many astronomers (though not all) assume that the universe went through a brief but dramatic period of accelerating expansion (that is, inflation), which blew up each tiny region of space to an immense size. If so, then the observable universe, within range of present-day telescopes, is no more than a microscopic fraction of the whole, and all we are seeing is a tiny portion of a hugely-inflated bubble of space. At the end of the inflationary period, the universe reverted to expansion at the rate we find today. Yet if this is so, what caused the inflation?

In the current universe, matter is controlled by four distinct forces: gravitation, the electromagnetic force, and the weak and strong nuclear reactions. At extreme temperatures it seems that these distinctions vanish, and the forces merge together. If at the beginning of time all four forces were united, then, as the universe cooled, first gravitation and then the others would separate out. The change from grand unified to separate strong and electroweak forces corresponded to a change in the universe which has been likened to the change which occurs when water turns to ice. The difference in energy between the unified- and separate-force condition is what is thought to have driven inflation. When the changeover was complete, inflation ceased.

Initially, space was filled with highly energetic photons – tiny packets of light energy – plus elementary particles and anti-particles. For each particle, there is an anti-particle with mirror-image properties. For example, an electron is a lightweight particle with unit negative electric charge; its anti-particle is the positron, which has the same mass but has unit positive electric charge. When a particle collides with its anti-particle, both are annihilated and turned into photons. Einstein showed that matter and energy are equivalent; particles can be converted into energy and energy into particles.

In the early universe, collisions between energetic photons produced pairs of particles and anti-particles, while collisions between particle/anti-particle pairs produced photons. This kind of interchange was going on all the time.

But as the universe expanded and cooled, the photons became less and less energetic. By the time the temperature had fallen to a mere million million degrees – about a millionth of a second after the beginning of time – there was not enough energy left to make heavy particles (protons, neutrons and their particles). Collectively, these are known as baryons, and are constituents of the nuclei of atoms.

Baryons and anti-baryons collided with one another and annihilated each other. A couple of seconds later, when the temperature had fallen to a few thousands of millions of degrees, electrons and positrons were annihilated.

If there had been exact equality between the numbers of baryons and anti-baryons, all matter would have been destroyed, and there would be no galaxies, stars or planets today. Fortunately, there was a very slight imbalance. For every thousand million anti-baryons, there were a thousand million *and one* baryons. The stuff of which stars, planets and men are made is the one-part-in-a-thousand-million remnant of the orgy of self-destruction which occurred when particles and anti-particles destroyed each other.

After 100 seconds or so, when the temperature was down to about a thousand million degrees, protons and neutrons began to weld together to form nuclei of the lightest chemical elements. The nucleus of a hydrogen atom consists of a single proton; a helium nucleus contains two protons and two neutrons. During the first three minutes or so, all the neutrons were mopped up into helium nuclei. Because a neutron is slightly heavier than a proton, there were fewer of them, and as a result only one helium nucleus was formed for every ten hydrogen nuclei. When we look around the universe as it is today, we do indeed find that for every helium atom there are about ten atoms of hydrogen. The fact that the Big Bang theory correctly predicts the relative abundance of these lightweight elements is a powerful argument in its favour.

For the next few hundred thousand years the universe consisted of an expanding, cooling 'soup' of particles and radiation, and radiation was dominant. Space was opaque to light, because light photons could not travel far without colliding with something; hordes of fast-moving electrons were the main obstacles. But after around 300,000 years, when the temperature had dropped to 4000–3000 degrees, there was another dramatic change. Atomic nuclei were able to capture electrons, and to form complete atoms of hydrogen and helium (at higher temperatures, the electrons were moving too fast to be trapped). The free electrons were quickly captured, space became transparent, and photons were able to travel unhindered for great distances. This period was known as the 'decoupling' of matter and radiation; the radiation released at that time has been travelling through space ever since.

Some time later – we are not sure of the time-scale – galaxies were formed. A vital piece of evidence was the discovery in 1964, by Arno Penzias and Robert Wilson, of the cosmic background radiation. Using a large horn-shaped radio antenna, they found that the whole sky was a faint but

▲ **Artist's impression** *of COBE* – *the Cosmic Background Explorer* *satellite, launched in 1989 to study leftover radiation from the Big Bang.*

remarkably uniform source of microwave radiation – the last remnant of the Big Bang. Subsequent observations indicated that the background radiation was very smooth indeed, with no variations anywhere as great as one part in 10,000. This implied that the early universe must itself have been very smooth and uniform. Yet if galaxies were to form, there must have been variations in density – that is to say, some degree of 'clumpiness'. If this clumpiness existed, it should show up as slight variations in the temperature of the microwave background, which was measured at about 3° above absolute zero. Theoreticians were worried, but were very relieved when, in April 1992, the results of a precise survey carried out by COBE – the Cosmic Background Explorer Satellite – were announced. There were indeed tiny variations in temperature from one place to another. These 'ripples' amounted to no more than about one 30-millionth of a degree, or one part in 100,000, but this was enough.

We have learned a great deal. Accept the Big Bang, and we can work through a complete evolutionary sequence of events, ending up with you and me. On the other hand, we cannot pretend that we know how the Big Bang itself happened; we may be strong on details, but we are still woefully weak on fundamentals.

Consider an intelligent observer from, say, Alpha Centauri C, who pays a brief visit to Earth and spends an hour in Piccadilly Circus, London. He will see babies, children, adults and older people; and if he is sufficiently acute, he will be able to work out that a baby turns into a child, a child into an adult, and so on. Eventually he will build up a reliable picture of the career of a human being – but unless someone has told him the facts of life, he will not know how the baby appeared. In cosmology, at least at the present moment, our 'baby' is the Big Bang.

Town Astronomy

Over the past few years I have had countless letters from people who ask me, 'Where have all the stars gone? I used to be able to see them shining brightly, but now I can't. What has happened to them?' The answer is, of course, that the stars are exactly the same as they have always been, but the skies are not.

Light pollution is an ever-increasing problem. A television programme I presented recently about it did lead to the Government Minister sending a circular to all local authorities suggesting that replacement street lights should be designed to shine down, not up, but this is only part of the problem. Towns and cities have to be well lit, particularly in view of the fact that law and order have to a large extent broken down. And once you live in a densely-populated area, your view of the sky is bound to be affected.

Stand in the middle of a town and look upwards; you will not see very much. But after a while you may realize that things are not quite as bad as they seemed at first; it takes minutes to dark-adapt. What will happen, of course, is that you will miss the fainter stars; for example, you may see nothing of Orion apart from its two brightest stars, Betelgeux and Rigel. Consider also the two Bears, Ursa Major and Ursa Minor. If conditions are not intolerable, you will be able to see the seven stars of Ursa Major which

▼ *Light pollution –* *note the bright glare* *in the sky! I took this* photograph on the outskirts of Dublin, at midnight, in 1993.

make up the famous Plough (Big Dipper) pattern; the Bear's 'tail' points to Arcturus in Boötes, which is the fourth brightest star in the entire sky. But what about Ursa Minor? Only two of its stars – Polaris and Kocab – are as bright as the second magnitude, and only one other is above the third, so that in a light-polluted sky the main pattern cannot be made out at all. This sort of situation can make star identification decidedly tricky.

Next, what about telescope siting? It may be tempting to consider putting an observatory on a rooftop, but this is not a good idea. It is only a question of time before something gets dropped, and if an eyepiece makes a rapid descent on to a pavement there is bound to be considerable damage. Moreover, heated air rising from the house below will ruin the seeing. The ideal is to set up your telescope as far away from your house as possible. Poking a telescope through a window is most unsatisfactory, though there are occasions when it is inevitable.

There is always the Sun, which is less affected by light pollution (though, of course, there remains the problem of unsteady seeing). I well remember Bill Baxter, who retired from a career in tea planting, settled in Acton in Outer London, established an observatory equipped with a modest 4-inch refractor, and earned himself an international reputation as a solar observer. In fact, the Sun is an obvious target for the town-dweller. (Let me repeat yet again: *never look straight at the Sun through any telescope or binoculars*, even with a dark filter, because eye damage will most certainly result.) Solar sketching and photography can be done, and so can more sophisticated work involving spectroscopy and electronics.

The Moon is next on the list. Here the problem of light pollution is more serious than with the Sun, but mainly because of loss of definition. Still, you can have good views provided that you can see the Moon at all through the maze of adjoining houses. It does not take very long to find one's way around

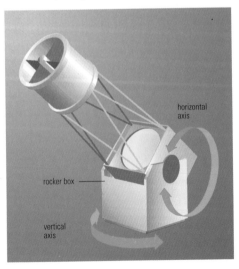

◀ *A Dobsonian telescope:* the simple altazimuth mounting is easy to move around, but the disadvantage is that it has to be hand-driven.

horizontal axis

rocker box

vertical axis

the lunar surface; my method, adopted when I was very young, was to make several drawings of each named formation, on different nights. Craters and other features show marked apparent changes according to the angle at which the sunlight strikes them.

Planets are more difficult, but at least you will be able to see the phases of Venus, the rings of Saturn, and the belts and moons of Jupiter if you have even a small telescope. Jupiter is particularly rewarding; you can follow the Galilean satellites as they move round the planet, showing eclipses, occultations, transits and shadow transits. Again the main problem is lack of definition. With a light-polluted sky you will not be able to use a high magnification, but at least you will manage to obtain reasonable views.

What can be done to improve matters? Shading lights does no harm if it can be achieved. (I recall one old friend of mine who was plagued by a street lamp by his fence; it shone right across his observatory. One night he crept out and painted the nearside of the lamp black. To the best of my knowledge, the local Council has yet to realize this; in any case, they have caused no trouble about it.)

The best course is to remove oneself and one's telescope away from the polluted area, and this involves a careful choice of telescope. A refractor of 3-inch aperture is portable; a 4-inch marginally so, but anything larger simply cannot be moved around. With a Newtonian reflector on a conventional mount the portability limit is about 8 inches, but with a Dobsonian mount things are much less restricted, and a portable 24-inch Dobsonian is quite feasible. It has to be said that a Dobsonian is a 'light bucket' and cannot easily be driven, so that it is limited to low powers and is not of much use to planetary observers, though ideal for the deep-sky enthusiast. Dobsonians can be computer-driven, but this does lead to complications.

Undoubtedly the best answer of all is the 'folded' telescope – a Schmidt-Cassegrain or a Maksutov – because here we can combine large aperture with portability. Modern telescopes of this type (Meades and Celestrons) are extremely good, and, mercifully, much less expensive than they used to be.

How can we sum all this up?

We have to admit that the town-dweller is at a grave disadvantage. Unless he can take his telescope into the country, he can do no proper deep-sky work; probably he will not even be able to see the Milky Way. He must resign himself to concentrating on the Sun, and perhaps the Moon. If he wants a powerful telescope, he must select one which can be moved around. But there are ways and means of coping with the situation.

Above all, do not give up. Astronomers are nothing if not resourceful, and even if you have to put up with an unhealthy glare there is still much that can be done.

Exploding Stars

At 21:30 hours GMT on Sunday, 28 March 1993, a Spanish amateur astronomer named Garcia Diaz was using his telescope to look at a spiral galaxy, Messier 81, when he noticed something very unusual. A relatively bright star had appeared where nothing conspicuous had been seen before. Diaz realized what it was – a supernova, a huge stellar outburst involving the death of a star. By Monday the news had reached the observatory on La Palma, in the Canary Islands, and the 100-inch Isaac Newton telescope was turned towards the star, obtaining the first spectra. Astronomers all over the world were excited. Apart from Supernova 1987A in the Large Cloud of Magellan (too far south to be seen from Europe, or from the Canaries), this was the brightest supernova to appear since the invention of the telescope.

Messier 81 is one of the closer galaxies. It is a fine spiral in the constellation of Ursa Major and is easy to find, as it lies in the same binocular field as the 4½-magnitude star 24 Ursae Majoris. Binoculars show it as a misty blur. Close beside it is the smaller galaxy M82; this, too, is said to be a binocular object, though I admit that, personally, I have never been able to see it without a telescope. Both systems are over 8 million light-years away, but are not so very far from the edge of our Local Group. M81 (NGC 3031) was discovered in 1774 by Johann Elert Bode. Its integrated magnitude is 7.9 and it is a typical spiral of class Sb. It was, incidentally, the first spiral to be proved to be rotating; this was demonstrated spectroscopically by Max Wolf as long ago as 1914. The mass is thought to be of the order of 90,000 million Suns.

Supernovae are among the most colossal outbursts known in nature; at its peak the new supernova – 1993J – was about 182,000 million times as powerful as the Sun. Though there have been no naked-eye supernovae in our Galaxy since 1604, they are often seen in external systems, and it has been found that they play a key role in the ecology of the universe. During the explosion, the heavy elements that the star has manufactured during its lifetime – carbon, silicon, iron, titanium, gold and so on – are thrown out into space, ready to mix with the interstellar gas to form new generations of stars. The very heaviest elements are made during the course of the explosion. Moreover, the shock waves generated by the supernova trigger the collapse of nearby interstellar clouds, causing fresh stars to form. There is even some fairly reliable evidence that our Solar System may have been formed soon after a nearby supernova explosion. Certainly everything on Earth – including the Earth itself – was made inside a supernova, and has passed through several generations of stars before producing our world.

There are other reasons why astronomers are so interested in supernovae. Explaining the mechanism of the outburst is a challenge to physics, and as the explosion proceeds the expanding fragments enable us to work out how the original star was put together; this in turn is a key to theories of stellar evolution. Luckily, the luminosity is so great that supernovae can be seen out to immense distances across the universe, allowing us to gauge the distances of the galaxies in which the supernovae flare up.

▼ **M81,** a type Sb spiral galaxy in the constellation Ursa Major. This image was taken using the KPNO Mayall telescope, in 1975 – aperture 3.8 metres (153 inches).

There are two distinct types of supernovae. In Type Ia, what we are seeing is the total destruction of a white dwarf star. The white dwarf is one component of a binary system, and pulls material away from its less evolved, less dense companion until it becomes so massive that it passes over the 'critical limit'; as soon as this happens, there is a nuclear explosion which literally blows the star to pieces. It is important to note that all Type Ia

▼ **A bright star,** *similar to others in this starfield imaged by the Hubble Space Telescope, exploded as a supernova that was seen from Earth in 1987.*

SN1987A occurred in the Large Magellanic Cloud – its rings are currently excited by light from the initial explosion.

supernovae reach about the same peak luminosity, so that they are very useful for distance-measuring. The original binary companion of the doomed white dwarf may be either a hot blue supergiant or a cool red supergiant.

However, both 1987A, in the Large Magellanic Cloud, and 1993J, in M81, are of Type II, and here the mechanism is quite different. The whole story of a star's evolution is concerned with a battle against the force of gravitation. It is gravity which causes clouds of material to condense into a star, and it is also gravity which heats and compresses the gas until the central temperature is high enough to trigger off nuclear reactions. Hydrogen reacts – we say, rather misleadingly, 'burns' – which not only makes the star shine but also, by heating the gas, raises its pressure, which balances the force of gravity. Once the hydrogen has been used up and has been converted to helium, gravity takes over once more, heating and compressing the core and raising the temperature sufficiently to ignite the helium and 'burn' it to carbon.

While this is going on in the core, the outer layers of the star are expanding and cooling; the star changes into a red giant. The reasons why the outer layers expand while the core contracts are decidedly complicated, but at least we know that the future of the star is determined by the events in the core, though we can see only the outer layers.

After about 10 million years, the interior of the star is layered in the manner of an onion. The outer layer is still hydrogen, but beneath this there are successive layers of spent 'fuel' of increasing atomic weight. Over time intervals ranging from a few years to a few days, the core is heated and compressed, and successively burns neon, oxygen and silicon. It is when silicon burns to iron that the crisis comes. Burning iron does not produce heat to fight off the gravity; instead, it absorbs heat. Within seconds, the star's core collapses from a body about the size of the Sun to a diameter of no more than about 13 km (8 miles), forming a neutron star and releasing an enormous amount of energy in the form of neutrinos – strange particles which have no electrical charge and no rest mass (or virtually none). These neutrinos carry off most of the energy of the explosion. They were detected from Supernova 1987A because the Large Magellanic Cloud is 'only' 169,000 light-years away, but they were not detected from 1993J; a distance of 8,500,000 light-years is too far.

Once the core has collapsed, there is nothing to support the outer layers of the star. These layers fall freely under the effect of gravity until they collide with the rigid, superdense core. They bounce back, and this causes a huge shock wave to develop; this wave races back up through the outer layers of the star, triggering off still more thermonuclear reactions. It is only when the shock wave reaches the surface of the star, and heats it to a very high temperature, that we see evidence of the explosion. The surface of the star is torn apart, and material is hurried out into space at velocities of up to 20 km/s (12 miles/s).

Therefore, 1993J was of special interest, and before long many telescopes were directed towards it – including the Kapteyn Telescope on La Palma in the Canary Islands, and even the Carlsberg Transit instrument also on La Palma. Visiting astronomers willingly gave up some of their hard-won telescope time so that the changing brightness and spectrum of the supernova could be closely monitored. Of course, M81 was well known. Observations made a day and a half before Diaz's discovery showed that the supernova was already bright, but two days before discovery it was still faint, and from this it can be deduced that the core collapse, when the great burst of neutrinos occurred, happened on 25 March, while the shock wave reached the surface of the star, making it brighten, around 27 March. Moreover, images taken with the Isaac Newton Telescope enabled astronomers to identify the progenitor star. It was of around magnitude 20, and seemed to be a binary system made up of a blue supergiant together with a red supergiant. It was the red star which 'went supernova', though the progenitor of 1987A was a single blue supergiant.

The light-curve of 1993J showed an initial rapid drop in brightness, followed by a slow rise to a secondary maximum and then a decline. This was a little like the behaviour of 1987A, though the peak luminosity was much greater and the timescales were different. The star had a relatively thin atmosphere; the initial decline in brightness was due to the star's atmosphere expanding and cooling after the original shock heating, while the secondary maximum was due to the build-up of energy released by the radioactive decay of nickel-56 to cobalt-56, which itself then decayed to iron-56.

What seems to have happened is that the star began life on the Main Sequence, with a mass about 12 times that of the Sun and a companion at a distance of 3 astronomical units (a.u.), or roughly 480 million km (300 million miles). Then the progenitor became a red supergiant, it started to lose mass rapidly, partly to its companion but also out into space. Just before the explosion, the progenitor's mass was between 3 and 4½ times that of the Sun, and the companion was now the more massive of the two; the separation was about 5 a.u., or 740 million km (460 million miles), and the diameter of the progenitor was about 595 million km (370 million miles). The shock wave took about two hours to reach the surface, and burst out at a temperature of around 220,000°K. One hour later the temperature had dropped to 130,000°, and after three hours it was no more than 21,000°. As the shock wave passed through the star, it created a quantity of nickel-56. The mass of this was probably about 7% of the mass of the Sun, and it was this which controlled the later light-curve.

A great deal can be learned from studying changes in the spectrum. Elements such as hydrogen and sodium can be detected, and their movements measured. The early spectrum showed that the peak luminosity was in the blue, indicating great heat; later came the signature of hydrogen gas moving at over 14,500 km/s (9000 miles/s), while helium appeared still later. However, the appearance of helium at a relatively early stage demonstrated that 1993J was not a typical Type II supernova, but showed some of the characteristics of a Type Ia.

The comparative closeness of M81 has meant that the spectrum of 1993J has been examined at very high resolution, and this has given us information about the cold interstellar gas lying between the supernova and ourselves. Some of this gas is in our own Galaxy, some of it in M81, and some of it is intergalactic. The high-resolution spectra also allow us to see the very narrow emission lines coming from the very hot gas close to the surface of the supernova; this was gas which had been steadily boiling off the surface of the red supergiant for the last few thousand years, and was heated by the flash from the shock. The supernova was soon detected at

▼ *The Jacobus Kapteyn Telescope,* situated on La Palma in the Canary Islands, which was used to observe SN1993J.

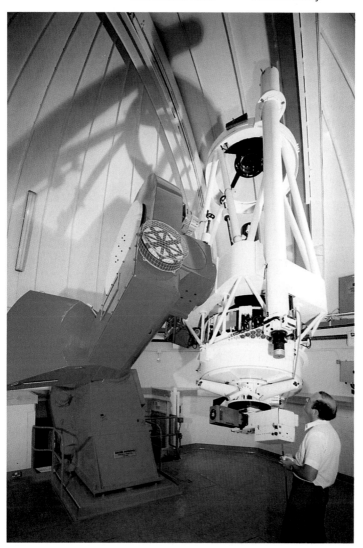

radio wavelengths by the Ryle Telescope at Cambridge, England, in X-rays by the ROSAT satellite, and in the ultraviolet by the International Ultraviolet Explorer satellite (IUE). All these detections arose from the shock-front ploughing into the very low-density gas surrounding the supernova.

When will we next see a supernova in our own Galaxy? The southern star Eta Carinae is one candidate. Another is Betelgeux, the red supergiant in Orion, and this would indeed be spectacular; if Betelgeux turned into a supernova, it would become as brilliant as the full moon. At least we can be sure that our Sun will never 'go supernova'; it is not nearly massive enough.

Certainly astronomers all over the world welcomed 1993J. If we cannot yet hope for a supernova in our Galaxy, then an outburst only 8,500,000 light-years away is almost the next best thing.

▼ **The constellation Orion,** photographed by David Malin, showing orange-red Betelgeux at top left, while Rigel is the bright white star at bottom right. It is possible to see the red glow of the Orion Nebula (M42) below the middle star of Orion's Belt in this image.

Tubes of Light

M any new techniques have been developed over the past few years to help the astronomer in his work. One of the most bizarre is that of fibre optics. It is possible to pass a beam of light through a glass fibre which looks rather like a nylon fishing line; the light-beam will emerge virtually undimmed at the far end, which means that it can be aimed with great precision. Of course, the light has also to be aimed at the source very carefully – in fact, to an accuracy of about a hundredth of a millimetre.

The story began with Roger Angel, who also developed the spin-casting method of making large telescope mirrors (*see Chapter 2*). Angel hoped to use fibre optics to blend together the light-grasp from a hundred 2.5-metre diameter mirrors. This was never achieved, but it did lead on to the present-day fibre optics techniques.

Once the light has been sent into the optical fibre, it 'bounces' along its length in a zigzag path, being reflected from opposite walls of the fibre. It is the accuracy of these boundaries, and the purity of the fused glass silica from which the fibre is made, which allows the light to be transmitted without being dimmed. One important point is that the fibres are flexible, and so the light from distant stars and galaxies can be 'moved around' under control.

The advantages of this are obvious. Imagine that you point a huge camera at the sky – and after all, a modern telescope is essentially a camera; it is seldom that anyone actually looks through an eyepiece. (Not long ago I was at Palomar Observatory, in California, for a *Sky at Night* programme. It so happened that the 60-inch reflector was not in use one night; it was 'between programmes' by visiting astronomers. At my instigation, we put in an eyepiece and looked directly at Saturn. Nobody could remember the last time when this had been done!)

Now arrange a series of fibres to intercept the light from the objects under study – one fibre for each target object. You can bring all the fibres back to a single point and then rearrange them – in a straight line, for example, which is ideal for leading them into a spectrograph. The main point is that all the objects can be examined simultaneously instead of one at a time, so that only one exposure is needed, and there is enormous saving in the all-precious 'telescope time'.

The first practical test was made by John Hill, one of Roger Angel's post-graduate students, in 1979. His device was called Medusa; it was used on the 90-inch Cassegrain reflector at the Steward Observatory, Tucson, Arizona. Hill used an aluminium plate with holes in it, each hole matching the position of a galaxy (or group of galaxies) that he wanted to study. By inserting a short length of fibre into each hole, and leading it back to the entrance slit of the spectrograph, he could observe all the galaxies at once – about 20, in the initial test. Naturally, he used a CCD (Charge-Coupled Device) instead of an 'old-fashioned' photographic plate.

The experiment worked well, and was soon extended to larger telescopes, notably the Anglo-Australian Telescope (AAT) at Coonabarabran in New South Wales, Australia. Here a young engineer, Peter Gray, built a system called Focap. This involved a 'plug-plate' method, in which the fibres were fitted with metal ferrules on their ends, so that they could be reused many times on different plates. This is all very well, but it does mean a new plate for each observation, and plugging the holes in for the separate objects is very time-consuming, even though the holes can be made with a computer-controlled drilling machine. With the AAT, the cost of producing the plug-plates became greater and greater with Focap's increasing success. Another drawback was that no plug-plate could be used for any area of the sky except that for which it had been specifically made.

Angel's group therefore looked round to see if they could hit upon something which would be more economical in time. They developed the MX technique (named after a famous Cold War ballistic missile system). This

◀ *The Anglo-Australian Telescope at Siding Spring.*
It has a 3.9 metre (153-inch) mirror.

involved fibres mounted on the tips of 32 computer-actuated rods which could be moved around individually in the focal plane. The rods met the plane in a way rather reminiscent of the rods of fishermen round a pond, so that the computer could tell each fibre just where to go in order to catch the light of the target object. No holes had to be drilled beforehand; all that was needed was a list of target positions for feeding into the computer.

This is still not perfect. MX needs a separate robot actuator for each fibre, which adds to the cost. Accordingly, Ian Parry, of Durham University, devised a different computer-controlled positioner, known as Autofib. ('Fib' stands for 'fibre', and has nothing to do with prevarication!)

Imagine that the input-end of each fibre is fitted with a tiny right-angled prism, smaller than a pin's head, and that it is placed on a steel plate held there by its own magnetism. If the steel plate is put in the focal plane of the telescope, you can have a large number of buttons to pick up the light from their target objects and send it down the fibres. To move the fibres around for different sets of targets, you have to use a robot positioner capable of picking them up and positioning them correctly. The robot must be able to check exactly where it has landed, and it also has to be quick-moving, since, unlike MX, it has to deal with one object at a time. The main advantage of Autofib is that it needs only one robot, and so this single robot can be made to a very high degree of sophistication. The first Autofib was fitted to the AAT in 1987, and has been working there successfully ever since. Bear in mind, of course, that each fibre is only about the thickness of a human hair.

Fibre optics are particularly suited for Schmidt telescopes (such as the UK Schmidt at Siding Spring, Australia), which have fields at least 40 times greater than that of a conventional reflector. On the UK Schmidt, Fred Watson and his team have developed a fibre-optics system which is interchangeable with the photographic which is still carried on with the telescope. This system is known as Flair, for Fibre-Linked Array Image Reformatter. It uses 90 fibres with a maximum diameter each of a tenth of a millimetre, positioned by a manual version of Autofib called 'Autofred' after its inventor (Fred Watson). Flair was the world's first wide-field fibre-optics spectroscopy system, and it also pioneered another development: instead of using short fibres to couple the focal plane to a spectrograph riding on the telescope, the Australian team used longer fibres and took the spectrograph off the telescope altogether, mounting it in a stationary position on the floor of the dome. There it is immune to any tendency to bend as it would do if it had to ride on the telescope; it is consequently very stable.

Flair has been able to provide large amounts of data for statistical work which would be difficult, or even impossible, to obtain in any other way. The great beauty of the method is that it can be used to cover a large area of the sky with a single exposure.

All in all, this new technique has already become of tremendous importance. It is truly remarkable that we can now take a hair-thin fibre, lead light through it, and use it to obtain spectra of objects so far away that their light has taken thousands of millions of years to reach us.

What's In A Name?

Have you ever heard of Quetzalpetlatl, Hwang-chi or Erxleben? Do you know where to find Hell? And where would you look for Zubenelgenubi? Well, the answer to all these is: 'In the sky' – and we have to admit that some celestial names are decidedly bizarre. Therefore, it seems a good idea to say something about them, and where better to start than the Moon?

Look at the Moon, and you will see dark patches and bright regions. Initially, it was natural to believe that the dark patches were seas – and they were named accordingly; obviously the Latin forms were used, since Latin was (and in some ways still is) the international language. The names given were romantic: Mare Crisium (the Sea of Crises), Mare Tranquillitatis (the Sea of Tranquillity, where the Apollo 11 astronauts landed), Sinus Iridum (the Bay of Rainbows), Oceanus Procellarum (the Ocean of Storms), and so on. One of the earliest lunar maps, dating from 1610, was Galileo's. It may be that he knew the 'seas' to be waterless; only later was it proved that the Moon is bone-dry.

In 1647, Hevelius, a city councillor of the Polish town of Danzig (now Gdansk), used one of the strange 'aerial telescopes' to produce a Moon map.

◀ **Names on Mars.**
This photograph is of a Mars globe, made by the Belgian astronomer Niestern in 1877. The old names are marked in red, while the new ones are in black. Thus 'Kunowsky Land' has become 'Noachis'.

It was much more detailed than Galileo's, and shows many features in recognizable form. He introduced some names, mainly terrestrial analogies; thus the crater we now call Copernicus was his 'Etna', and the 96-km (60-mile) crater known to us as Plato was his 'Greater Black Lake'. Mountains were named after terrestrial ranges, such as the Apennines and the Alps. However, the system was never popular, and only four of Hevelius' names are now in use – including the Lunar Alps, which are cut through by the great Alpine Valley; I have no doubt that during the 21st century this valley will become a popular tourist attraction.

In 1651 new studies of the Moon were made by Giovanni Riccioli, an Italian Jesuit. He drew a lunar map, based largely on observations by his pupil Grimaldi, and introduced an entirely different system of nomenclature. Craters were named after famous people, mainly – though not always – astronomers. Thus Ptolemy, the last great astronomer of Classical times, was given a vast walled plain near the centre of the Moon's disk; we call it Ptolemaeus. The Greater Black Lake became Plato, and a very brilliant crater was named after Aristarchus, the Greek astronomer who was one of the first to maintain that the Earth is a planet moving round the Sun. Tycho Brahe, the Danish astronomer, was allotted the most prominent crater on the Moon, striking because it is the centre of a system of bright streaks or rays. And, of course, two very conspicuous dark-floored walled plains were named after Grimaldi and Riccioli himself. However, Riccioli had his quirks. He did not believe the Copernican theory, which put the Sun in the centre of the Solar System rather than the Earth, so he 'flung Copernicus into the Ocean of Storms'. He had no time for Galileo, who was fobbed off with a very obscure, semi-ruined crater. Later astronomers came off second-best, though admittedly this was not Riccioli's fault! Even Newton has a crater which is hard to locate. In fact, Newton was originally given a 'ghost ring' near Plato, but the name was later transferred to a deep formation too near the Moon's South Pole to be well seen. In 2000, at my instigation, the old 'ghost ring' was renamed Bliss, after Nathaniel Bliss, a former Astronomer Royal.

In the 1830s two Germans, Wilhelm Beer and Johann Mädler, drew what remained the best lunar map for several decades, and augmented Riccioli's nomenclature. Today the decisions are made by the International Astronomical Union (IAU), the controlling body of world astronomy, but we still find some unusual people on the Moon; Julius Caesar is one, not because of his military prowess but because of his association with calendar reform. There are a couple of Olympians, Atlas and Hercules. There is Birmingham, named after a 19th-century Irish astronomer, and there is Hell, commemorating the Hungarian astronomer Maximilian Hell. (I assure you that the crater is not exceptionally deep!)

Long before the start of the Space Age, I was doing my best to map the Moon's 'libration regions', which are close to the edge of the Earth-turned face of the Moon and are very foreshortened. I was using my 12½-inch reflector, then at my home at East Grinstead in Sussex, when suddenly I came across something which I did not know. It looked like a small 'sea', right at the limit of visibility. I charted it as well as I could, and contacted other observers, asking them to confirm it. I suggested a name: Mare Orientale, the Eastern Sea, because it lay at the extreme eastern edge of the disk. Much later it was found to be a huge ringed formation, extending on to the hemisphere of the Moon which we can never see from Earth because it is always turned away from us.

Then, in 1966, a decree of the IAU reversed lunar east and west, so that my Eastern Sea is now on the Moon's *western* limb as seen from Earth. I feel that I cannot be blamed for the confusion. At the IAU General Assembly, when the switch was proposed, I voted against it, but was heavily defeated . . . .

When Lunik 3 mapped the far side of the Moon in 1959, many new features were seen for the first time, and of course names had to be found for them. One turned out to be distinctly embarrassing. What looked like a towering range of peaks turned out to be nothing more than a bright ray. The Russians had given the feature the name of the Soviet Mountains – but then discreetly forgot about it. However, they did, rightly, name a vast crater on the far side in honour of Konstantin Eduardovich Tsiolkovskii, who was writing sanely about space-travel over 100 years ago.

So much for the Moon. Next there is Mars, where telescopes show many permanent features. Here, too, the dark areas were originally taken for seas. Reasonable maps were drawn up between 1860 and 1877; one was the work of the English astronomer R. A. Proctor, in 1867. Following Riccioli's example he named the Martian features after famous people, usually astronomers who had been particularly concerned with Mars: Mädler Land, Lockyer Land, Beer Continent, and so on. The most obvious dark feature, triangular in shape, was the Kaiser Sea, named after the Dutch observer Frederik Kaiser, though its form led many people to refer to it as the Hourglass Sea.

In 1877 G. V. Schiaparelli, from Milan, Italy, drew new maps of Mars. He described the 'canals', which we now know to be non-existent; he also threw out all Proctor's names, and went back to mythology and terrestrial analogies. Thus Lockyer Land became Hellas (Greece), and the Kaiser or Hourglass Sea became Syrtis Major, after a Libyan gulf. Proctor's Schiaparelli Sea was changed to Mare Sirenum (the Sea of the Sirens); there too was Lacus Phoenicis, the Phoenix Lake. One white patch was named Nix Olympica, the Olympic Snow.

Many of these names have survived, but the space missions have led to changes. Lacus Phoenicis is not a lake; it is a volcano, now known as Phoenicis Mons, while the Olympic Snow is really Olympus Mons, which towers to 40 km (25 miles) and is the greatest volcano on Mars (or anywhere else, so far as we know). Craters have been named after people, which is fair even though the names have been duplicated, and this can cause problems; for example, there is a crater Ptolemaeus on Mars as well as on the Moon.

The other planet with permanent surface features is Mercury, but from Earth these details are difficult to make out, partly because Mercury is so near the Sun but also because it is not a great deal larger than the Moon and never comes much within 80 million km (50 million miles) of us. The best pre-Space Age map was drawn by the Greek astronomer Eugenios Antoniadi, who spent most of his life in France and used the 33-inch refractor at Meudon, near Paris (which I know well – I used it for Moon-mapping before the Apollo missions flew). Antoniadi produced a map of Mercury in which he named various features; for example, one dark patch was christened Solitudo Hermae Trismegisti, or the Wilderness of Hermes the Thrice Greatest. But when Mariner 10 flew past Mercury, in 1974–5, it became clear that Antoniadi's map was not accurate enough for his names to be retained. The IAU produced a hybrid system. The main feature on Mercury is a huge ringed basin; this was called the Caloris Basin, for one good reason. 'Caloris' indicates heat; when Mercury is at its closest to the Sun it is noon in the Basin, and the temperature rockets to over 370°C (700°F). Valleys are named

▼ **The Moon's far side.**
The large dark-floored lunar crater (centre top) has been named Tsiolkovskii, after the Russian space pioneer, Konstantin Tsiolkovskii, who lived from 1857 to 1935.

after radar installations such as Arecibo, because Mercury had been mapped by radar; craters are again named after people – for example, Gerard Kuiper, a pioneer of the exploration of planets by spacecraft, has been given a bright ray-crater (in fact this was the first feature to be identified on the Mariner 10 images). Astronomers do not have the monopoly; the largest known Mercurian crater is named Beethoven.

Things are less easy with Venus, because the surface is hidden by the cloud-laden atmosphere, and before the Space Age we had no idea what Venus was really like. In fact there are plains, ridges, volcanoes, craters and lava-flows. To be 'politically correct', the IAU decreed that all names of features on Venus should be female. We have Callas (Maria Callas), Halle (Austrian violinist), Marsh (Ngaio Marsh, New Zealand authoress), and so on, but in some cases things have become rather obscure. Who was Quetzalpetlatl? Answer: an Aztec fertility goddess. Xiao Hong was a Chinese novelist; Erxleben was a German scholar, and so on. I wonder what would happen if we ever managed to terraform Venus and settle there? Imagine driving down Titibu Road and coming to the junction of the Taymuriyya and Hwang-chi motorways!

What about other satellites? The two dwarf moons of Mars have been named Phobos and Deimos, after attendants of the mythological War-God. Phobos shows one major crater, and this has been given the rather

◀ **The small Martian satellite Phobos,** *which was discovered in 1877 by Asaph Hall. This image was taken by the Mars Global Surveyor probe in 1998.*

unexpected name of Stickney. Phobos itself was discovered by the American astronomer Asaph Hall, in 1877. Using the Washington telescope, Hall had been making a search for Martian satellites, but was about to give up when his wife persuaded him to have one final try – and it worked: Stickney was Mrs Hall's maiden name. The outer satellite, Deimos, has two main craters, Swift and Voltaire. Both of these novelists had predicted that Mars ought to have two moons, though at that time there was no telescope powerful enough to show them. In his *Voyage to Laputa* (one of Gulliver's Travels), Swift predicted that one of these moons would go round Mars more quickly than the planet spins, as Phobos actually does. According to Swift, the discovery was made by the lynx-eyed astronomers of the flying island of Laputa, which we may regard as the first fictional UFO. But Swift's reasoning was simple enough. Venus has no moon; Earth has one, Jupiter four – and so how can Mars possibly manage with less than two? (Mind you, both are real midgets, less than 32 km (20 miles) in diameter, and would give very little night-time during the dark Martian nights.)

The four large satellites of Jupiter are named Io, Europa, Ganymede and Callisto. For a long time these names were not widely used, because they had been given by Simon Marius, who claimed (probably with justification) that he had discovered the satellites well before Galileo saw them. The names are mythological; for example, Ganymede was the cup-bearer of the gods, while Europa was a maiden who was carried off by Jupiter (Zeus) for somewhat discreditable reasons. Surface features on the satellites have also been given names from mythology or folk-lore: on Callisto, for example, the names are Norse, so that the greatest ringed basins are called Valhalla and Asgard. The smaller Jovian satellites have also been given mythological names; thus Satellite 5, discovered by E. E. Barnard in 1892, commemorates Amalthea, the goat which had a great deal to do with Jupiter's early up-bringing. (The planets were named after the Greek gods, but we use the Latin names, so that, for example, Zeus has become Jupiter, while Hermes has become Mercury.)

Saturn was Jupiter's father, though not a loving one; the planet is slow-moving, as is appropriate for the God of Time. Most of the Saturnian satellites have names connected with the mythological Titans – for example Rhea, who was Saturn's wife (and also his sister; the morals of the ancient Olympians were a little odd even by the standards of AD 2002).

The next planet was discovered in 1781, by William Herschel, and was named Uranus, after Saturn's father, though not without a good deal of argument. Herschel was born in Hanover, though he spent almost all his life in England. At that time England and Hanover were united under one crown; King George III was Herschel's patron, and so it was suggested that the new planet should be named the 'Georgian'. However, foreign astronomers objected. For some time the planet was known simply as 'Herschel', but finally, at the suggestion of the German astronomer Johann Elert Bode, it was renamed 'Uranus'. Strangely, the British *Nautical Almanac* changed over only in 1851, by which time the outer giant, Neptune, had been discovered and had been named after the Sea-God.

▲ **Jupiter:** *an impressive view assembled from four images obtained by the Cassini probe in December* 2000. The Great Red Spot *is at lower right, while the shadow of Europa is a dark spot at lower left.*

The satellites of Uranus form one departure from the mythological system. The names for the first four were suggested by John Herschel, William Herschel's son, and came from Shakespeare and from Pope's poem 'The Rape of the Lock' – Ariel, Umbriel, Titania and Oberon. To me this has always seemed peculiar, but the satellites discovered more recently have also been given Shakespearean names – as with the strangely-surfaced Miranda, found in 1948 by Kuiper. Neptune's satellites have been given names linked with marine mythology; for instance, Triton was a minor sea-deity. Of course, Triton was mapped from Voyager 2, in 1989, and we now have another crop of unfamiliar names; what do you make of Bubembe Regio, Uhlanga, Namazu Macula and Kikimora Maculae? No doubt we will become used to them in time.

The ninth planet was discovered in 1930 by my old friend Clyde Tombaugh, from the Lowell Observatory at Flagstaff in Arizona. A name had to be found. T. J. J. See, an American astronomer, suggested 'Minerva', after the goddess of wisdom – but to say that See was unpopular with his colleagues is to put it mildly, and the final choice was 'Pluto', proposed by an Oxford schoolgirl named Venetia Burney. (She is now Mrs Phair; I talked to her about it quite recently.) The name is apt enough. Pluto is a remote, gloomy world and Pluto or Hades was the God of the Underworld. The one satellite is called Charon, after the sinister ferryman who took departed souls across the River Styx into Pluto's kingdom. (Naming recommendations nowadays are proposed by the Nomenclature Commission of the International Astronomical Union; it has 17 members, of which I am one.) The proposals then go to the General Assembly of the IAU for ratification. The Hubble Space Telescope can now show some details on Pluto, and I have suggested that these should be named after Underworld deities.

Of the minor bodies of the Solar System, we have the asteroids or minor planets, the first of which was discovered in 1801 – on 1 January, the first day of the new century. The discoverer was Giuseppe Piazzi, from Palermo in Sicily, and he named the asteroid Ceres, after the patron goddess of the island. The next asteroid names were all mythological: Pallas, Juno, Vesta, Astraea, and so on. But by now we have thousands of asteroids, and the supply of mythological names ran out long ago. It is the privilege of the discoverer to suggest a name for his asteroid, and we have some oddities; for example Asteroid 2309, Mr Spock, is named after a ginger cat which was itself named after the sharp-eared Vulcan of *Star Trek*. When the Italian astronomer Palisa discovered Asteroid 250 he offered to sell the name – and this was accepted by Baron von Rothschild, who named it Bettina after his wife. I cannot resist adding that when Dr Edward Bowell, at the Lowell Observatory, discovered Asteroid 2602 he named it 'Moore' after me . . . so

▼ **Pluto** *(left) and its satellite Charon (right), as seen by the Hubble Space Telescope. This image was taken by the* European Space Agency's Faint Object Camera in 1994 when Pluto was 4.4 billion km (2.6 billion miles) from Earth.

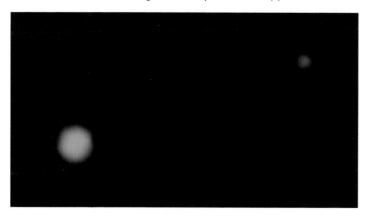

that, as Clyde Tombaugh said in 1980 when he was given an asteroid, I now have a piece of real estate which nobody can touch, even though it is well over 320 million km (200 million miles) away and no more than 5 km (3 miles) wide. (I hasten to point out that the name was approved well before I was elected to the Nomenclature Commission!)

Comets are easy; they are named after their discoverers or co-discoverers, so that we have tongue-twisters such as Schwassmann–Wachmann and Tuttle–Giacobini–Kresák. Occasionally, a comet is named after the mathematician who computed the orbit; for example, Edmond Halley, who was the first to realize that the comet now bearing his name has a period of 76 years. The same is true of Encke's Comet, which was found by Johann Encke to have a period of 3.3 years. This is the shortest period known; the comet never recedes as far as the orbit of Jupiter, and with modern telescopes it can be kept continuously in view.

When we come to the stars, we again begin with mythology. Ancient peoples such as the Chinese and the Egyptians worked out their own constellations, but we follow those drawn up by the Greeks, though we use the Latin names. Of course, a constellation has no real significance, because the stars are at very different distances from us, and we are dealing only with line-of-sight effects (one of many reasons why the pseudo-science of astrology is such nonsense). However, the patterns can be striking. There is Orion, the Hunter, which is dominant in the evening sky from October through to April; according to legend, Orion boasted that he could kill any creature on Earth – but he forgot the Scorpion, which crawled out of a hole in the ground, stung Orion on the heel and caused his untimely demise. The gods decided to bring him back to life and put him in the sky. To be fair, they also elevated the Scorpion to celestial rank, but Scorpius was sited on the far side of the sky, as far away from Orion as possible, so that the two can never meet again.

Ursa Major is different. Here we have a beautiful maiden, Callisto, whose charm was greater than that of Juno, queen of Olympus. Juno was unkind enough to change her into a bear. Years later Callisto's son, Arcas, was out hunting and came face to face with the bear. Not realizing that it was his fond mother, he was about to shoot it when Jupiter intervened, turned Arcas into a bear also and swung both animals up into the sky by their tails – which is why both Ursa Major and Ursa Minor have tails of decidedly un-ursine length.

We have a nickname for Ursa Major: the seven main stars make up the pattern which we call the 'Plough', while Americans refer to it as the 'Big Dipper'. Certainly, it looks more like a dipper than a bear . . . .

Many legends are pictured in the sky; for example, most people know about Perseus, who killed a sea-moaster by petrifying it when he showed it the head of the Gorgon, whose glance would turn any creature to stone. But there are also modern constellation names, mainly because the stars of the far south can never be seen from Greece. We have, for instance, the Octant, covering the south celestial pole, as well as the Airpump (Antlia) and the Telescope (Telescopium). There was a time when all compilers of star catalogues felt bound to form new constellations, many of which seem to have no claim to separate identity. One typical example is Leo Minor, the Little Lion, introduced by Hevelius; it has no bright star, and no particular shape. Hevelius also formed Lynx, allegedly because the area is so barren that you need lynx-like eyes to see anything there at all. Leo Minor and Lynx have survived; Quadrans, the Quadrant, has not. It was formed in 1775 by J. E. Bode, out of stars near Ursa Major. It has been deleted from modern maps, but we still remember it, because it marks the radiant of the meteor shower seen in early January every year. The radiant is now in Boötes, the Herdsman, but we call the shower the Quadrantids.

I am rather sorry about Felis, the Cat. In 1805 it was added to the sky map by the French astronomer Joseph Lalande, who wrote: 'I like cats. I'll let this figure scratch on my chart. The starry sky has worried me quite enough in my life, so now I can have my joke with it.' Alas, current maps show no Cat. We have also lost Noctua, the Night Owl. I do not care about other abandoned constellations, such as Sceptrum Brandenburgicum (the Sceptre of Brandenburg), Globus Aerostaticus (the Balloon) and Officina Typographica (the Printing Press), but it does seem a pity to eliminate the Owl and the Pussycat!

Individual star names are mainly Arabic. In Orion we have Rigel, from Rijl al Jawzah, the leg of the giant. There is also Betelgeux, the 'hand of the giant'; this really ought to be Yed al Jauzah, and 'Betelgeux' instead of 'Yedelgeux' is due to a mistranslation. It can be pronounced in many different ways: 'Beetlejuice' is common. It can also be spelled in different ways (Betelgeuse, Betelgeuze). Of course, nobody really knows how these old names were pronounced.

In general, individual names are used only for the brightest stars and a few special cases. There are a few which stand out. The brightest star in the sky is Sirius, in Canis Major, the Great Dog, and for once we have a fair idea of the true pronunciation, because the name is not Arabic; it is Greek, and means 'scorching'. Scholars say that it should be pronounced 'Sy-rius', rather than the usual 'Si-rius'. They may or may not be right! We are much more confident about Polaris, the Pole Star. It may be just as well that we have dropped many of the individual names for fainter stars – such as Zubenelgenubi (Alpha Librae) in the Southern Claw; the Zodiacal constellation of Libra, the Balance or Scales, was originally Chelae Scorpii, the Scorpion's Claws.

One point should be made here. No new star-names are now given. Unfortunately, some unscrupulous and totally bogus agencies have been 'selling' star names; pay £×, and they will name a star after you. They prey upon people who have been bereaved; the names mean nothing, and nobody will ever know about them. On no account have anything to do with these schemes.

It seems fitting to end with a story which I believe to be true. A dear lady had been listening intently to a lecture given by an astronomer. At the end, she stood up and said, in a puzzled tone, 'Yes, I understand how you discover these stars – but tell me, how do you find out their names?'

The Swan's Nest

Cygnus, the Swan, is one of the most prominent constellations of the northern sky. Its leader, Deneb, is a true cosmic search-light, about 70,000 times as powerful as the Sun, and so remote that its light – travelling at 300,000 km/s (186,000 miles/s) – takes 1500 years to reach us. Look at Deneb this evening, and you will see it as it used to be in the days when Britain was occupied by the Romans. It is far more luminous than either of the other two members of the 'Summer Triangle', Vega and Altair, though its greater distance makes it look the faintest of the three.

Cygnus is often nicknamed the Northern Cross, for reasons which are obvious at a glance; the main stars really are arranged in an X-pattern, far more cruciform than the kite-shaped Southern Cross. One member of the X, Albireo or Beta Cygni, is dimmer than the rest and further away from the centre, so that it rather spoils the symmetry; but, to make up for this, Albireo is a glorious coloured double, with a golden-yellow primary and a vivid blue companion. The magnitudes are 3 and 5; the separation is 35 seconds of arc, so that any small telescope or even good binoculars will split the pair. I always regard Albireo as the loveliest double star in the entire sky.

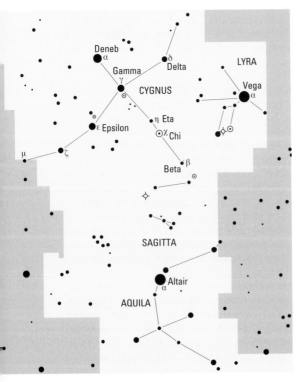

◀ **Cygnus, the Swan,** showing Alpha (Deneb), Beta (Albireo), Gamma (Sadr), Delta, Epsilon (Gienah), Eta, and the red variable Chi. Deneb forms a large triangle with Vega and Altair; my name for it of 'the Summer Triangle' is now widely used.

Cygnus is crossed by the Milky Way, and the whole region is very rich. Several novae have been seen here, but one is of special interest. It is normally very faint, but in 1938 it flared up to the 11th magnitude, not far below binocular range, remaining near maximum for some time before fading back to its former obscurity. Because it was the 404th variable star to be identified in the Swan, it is known as V404 Cygni.

Initially, it caused no excitement. Novae are not genuinely new stars; each is a binary system, of which one member is a white dwarf and the other a normal Main Sequence star. The white dwarf pulls material away from its larger, less dense companion; this matter accumulates round the white dwarf in an accretion disk. Eventually the situation becomes unstable, and there is a relatively mild explosion, after which things revert to normal and there is no permanent change. V404 Cygni behaved like this. But in 1989 it erupted again – and this time the outburst was initially detected in X-rays.

Light is a wave motion, and the colour of the light depends on the wavelength; the longest wavelengths are red and the shortest violet, with orange, yellow, blue and green in between. Shorter wavelengths cannot be seen visually, though they can be detected in other ways; we have ultraviolet, X-rays and finally the ultra-short gamma-rays. Most of these radiations are blocked by layers in the Earth's upper air, so that space research methods have to be used; for example, the International Ultraviolet Explorer (IUE), launched in the late 1970s and operated well into the 1990s, surveyed the whole sky in UV. There have also been many X-ray satellites; the first known discrete X-ray source (apart from the Sun) was Scorpius X-1, found in 1962 by equipment carried in a rocket. This was the real start of X-ray astronomy.

The Sun is 'bright' in X-rays only because it is so close to us; it is not really a powerful source, and neither are ordinary stars. In our Galaxy, the really strong sources are either supernova remnants (such as the Crab Nebula) or binary X-ray pairs, in which we again have a normal star associated with a compact object – either a neutron star or a black hole. The compact object pulls material away from its companion, and as this material falls into the compact object it is heated to tens of millions of degrees, making it emit strongly in X-rays. Neutron stars have powerful magnetic fields, and this leads to X-rays being pulsed as the star rotates; the situation is not unlike that of a man on the sea-shore being periodically illuminated by the beam of a distant lighthouse. Generally, the pulses are regular; as the normal star orbits the neutron star, the period can be determined. In some cases there are eclipses, when the normal star passes in front of the neutron star and temporarily blocks its radiations.

Other sources are far from regular; these are known as X-ray transients. They were first detected from the rockets of the 1960s, but at that time the resolving power of the equipment was poor, and it was impossible to pinpoint the positions of the X-ray transients, so that little could be found out about them. At least it was clear that we were dealing with objects which suffered massive X-ray outbursts, fading back after a few months to quiescent states and remaining faint for as long as ten or 20 years. During

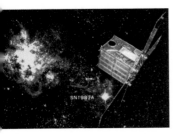

SN1987A

▲ Artist's impression of Ginga, the Japanese X-ray satellite. The background shows the Large Magellanic Cloud, with SN1987A, the supernova that appeared a few days after the launch of Ginga and which was extensively studied by the satellite.

outbursts, they can be caught by X-ray cameras carried in satellites, as was first achieved by the British satellite Ariel 5 (Exosat).

The main problem is that we never know when or where a transient will flare up – so where do you look? The answer is: 'Everywhere'. Specially-designed 'all-sky monitors' have been flown in satellites. The Japanese vehicle Ginga has been particularly successful, and was able to monitor a large fraction of the sky every day in a search for new X-ray transients. It could also fix the positions to an accuracy of about one-fifth of a degree, good enough for ground-based observatories to search for a visible counterpart. And it was from Ginga, in 1989, that a transient was found, and lettered GS2023+338 (because its right ascension was 20h 23m and its declination +33°.8, putting it in Cygnus, close to the star Gienah or Epsilon Cygni).

Dr Phil Charles of Oxford University studied the X-ray variations of the source, and realized that it was something unusual. It showed enormous fluctuations and it flickered. Obviously, it was important to find out whether anything could be seen at optical wavelengths in this position.

When short-lived phenomena are found, they are announced in the circulars of the International Astronomical Union, issued from Harvard in America and run by Dr Brian Marsden, an English astronomer who has been based in the United States for many years. It did not take Marsden long to realize that the position coincided with that of the 1938 nova, V404 Cygni. This was promptly confirmed telescopically; it was found that the nova had again flared up from its normal 19th magnitude to the 12th. It was a splendid example of collaboration between space-borne and ground-based astronomical techniques.

Curiously, the next step was to wait for a year! Though many astronomers all over the world were observing V404 during its 1989 outburst, not much could be found out, simply because virtually all the light was coming from the accretion disk. The disk was being violently heated by the massive flux of X-rays, and the companion star could not be seen at all. Yet it was essential to observe the companion star in order to measure the orbital period and obtain the mass of the compact object. It was not until 1990 that V404 returned to its normal magnitude of about 19. This is very dim, so that a large telescope had to be used. Fortunately, Dr Charles and his colleagues were able to use the 165-inch William Herschel telescope on La Palma, which had been equipped with ISIS, a new type of spectrograph. With this, they were able to see the spectral signature of the companion star, which proved to be rather smaller and less massive than our Sun. More importantly, the orbital period was found to be 6.5 days.

Once this was known, a mass determination could follow simply by using Kepler's Laws. If the two components of a binary system are of equal mass, they will orbit a point midway between them and move by equal amounts, but if the masses are unequal then the centre of gravity will be displaced towards the heavier object. If the heavier object is a black hole, then obviously it is not possible to detect its motion and work out a minimum mass for the compact object merely by disregarding the mass of the normal star (the situation is different for a pair of bodies such as the Sun and the Earth, because the mass ratio is 1:350,000). The normal star in the V404 Cygni system must be of appreciable mass, probably about half that of the Sun; from this estimate, the mass of the compact object must be well over six times that of the Sun.

We can measure the masses of objects which we know for certain to be neutron stars, because they pulse at radio and X-ray wavelengths. The masses are all about the same: 1.5 times that of the Sun. So what is the maximum mass which a neutron star can possibly have? Most theorists would give an upper limit of between two and three times that of the Sun, but years ago it was shown that if Einstein's Theory of Relativity is correct a neutron star cannot be more than three times as massive as the Sun. Searches were then made for a compact object – that is, a strong X-ray source – with a minimum mass of about five times that of the Sun. V404 Cygni meets these requirements, and a black hole is the only logical answer.

Next, look at the situation with an X-ray binary. The normal star is losing mass, and is not spherical; it has been drawn out into the shape of a pear by the powerful pull of the compact object. This can be demonstrated with V404 Cygni, because as the star travels around in its orbit it shows changes in brightness; when we see the side view of the 'pear' we are viewing a larger

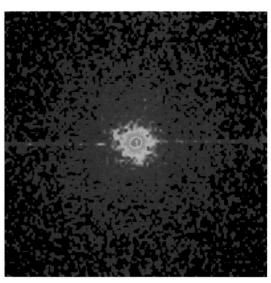

▶ **Cygnus X-3** – *a close binary system in which material from a normal star is being pulled into a neutron star or black hole. This image was taken by the Chandra X-ray Observatory – it shows a halo of emission (beyond the yellow ring in the centre) which is due to the scattering of interstellar dust.*

surface than when the pear is 'end-on' to us. There are two maxima and two minima in each cycle, which is ample confirmation that we are seeing what is termed 'ellipsoidal modulation'. To get the best view of this effect, V404 was studied in infrared together with other X-ray transients, using the UKIRT telescope in Hawaii and the Anglo-Australian Telescope in New South Wales. The distortion was very evident, and the results were combined with those from La Palma to show that the mass of the black hole is actually 11 times that of the Sun.

Other cases of the same kind are known. For many years the most famous black hole candidate was Cygnus X-1, though this was a different sort of binary inasmuch as the mass-losing star is itself very large, hot and massive (it is within easy binocular range). In order to determine the mass of the compact object here, we would have to know the mass of the main star very accurately. This is not easy, but the limiting mass of the compact object seems to be only three times that of the Sun. It will probably turn out to be a black hole, but the evidence is not so clear-cut as with V404.

Interestingly, transient-like behaviour is not confined to black holes. One such transient is Centaurus X-4 in the far south of the sky; here, the detection of X-ray bursts during the main X-ray eruption tells us that the compact object must be a neutron star. This was regarded as an ideal test case. The same infrared techniques were used, and the mass proved to be 1.5 times that of the Sun – precisely as expected for a neutron star. In fact, for the first time we can now make accurate measures of the compact objects in these binaries, and decide whether we are dealing with a neutron star or a black hole. More cases are being examined, with the aim of obtaining really good spectra of the secondary stars; this will tell us how binaries of this kind form and evolve, and also about the formation of black holes and super-massive stars.

We may not be able to see inside a black hole, but at least we can start to have some sort of insight as to what happens. In this field British astronomers are playing a leading role, and are exploiting the outstanding optical and infrared telescopes which Britain has developed in recent years. It is interesting to recall that when *The Sky at Night* began, in 1957, black holes were no more than vague theoretical possibilities; now, we are virtually sure that they do exist, and that they are more bizarre than anyone can really visualize.

Astronomy of Australia

Southern-hemisphere astronomy is particularly significant today, if only because some of the most important celestial objects – such as the Clouds of Magellan – lie in the far south of the sky, and are inaccessible from Europe. One of the first major observatories to be set up in Australia was at Mount Stromlo, near Canberra, and there are now several very large telescopes there. Pride of place goes to the 74-inch reflector, naturally used with the latest electronic equipment and concentrating mainly upon spectrographic research.

Seeing conditions at Mount Stromlo are not ideal, because of the closeness of Canberra, but they are good enough for important researches to be carried out, and the 74-inch is in use every clear night.

The history of the Observatory closely parallels Australian history since federation. The Australian Constitution states that laws must be made regulating astronomical work, so that within about ten years of federation a site-testing party was sent out in Australian capital territory, looking for a site for the Commonwealth Solar Observatory.

As well as the 74-inch, there is a 26-inch refractor used for astrometry, and also a 50-inch reflector. The 50-inch, known as the Great Melbourne Reflector, has had a decidedly chequered history, going back to the 1850s when the Royal Society of London was looking for a suitable site for a large reflector to be devoted to studies of nebulae. In the 1860s the colonial government of Victoria set up the Melbourne Observatory, and wanted to acquire a major telescope, so they commissioned a large mirror from the Grubb firm in Ireland. It was made of metal (large glass mirrors lay in the future) and was beset by problems from the very start; in particular, it expanded and contracted by an unacceptable amount according to daily changes in temperature, producing aberration. After a few decades the telescope fell into disuse, and was eventually transferred to Canberra. In 1944 it was moved to the Commonwealth Solar Observatory and was completely refurbished, with a pyrex spherical mirror; it was put to work on astrophysical programmes. In its modern form it has been involved in a fascinating project: the search for MACHOs, or Massive Astrophysical Compact Halo Objects.

It has been suggested that MACHOs may be responsible for much or more of the 'dark matter' which seems to exist in the universe – though proof is lacking, and there is considerable disagreement among astronomers. Professor Alex Rodgers has been using the telescope to monitor the many millions of stars in the Large Cloud of Magellan, around 170,000 light-years away. Most of these stars will shine steadily; some will be known variables, but, occasionally, it may be possible to see the characteristic brightening of a star by gravitational lensing. After being of constant brightness for many days, weeks or months, the star may show an increase which is symmetrical. The Australian workers expect a rate of one MACHO event for 2 million stars in each year, and they have claimed that after examining 5 million stars they have tracked down one definite case.

What are MACHOs? They could be of any size, from low mass up to many times the mass of the Sun, but in terms of the present experiment the

▼ *The great 74-inch reflector at Mount Stromlo.* The Mount Stromlo and Siding Spring Observatories together form one of the leading optical astronomical observatories in the world today.

MACHOs most easily detected will have masses comparable to Jupiter or Saturn, or perhaps rather more. The method depends upon gravitational lensing of background stars by MACHO objects. By the end of the experiment at least 10 million stars will have been monitored, and even during the first 15 months of work more data about the Cloud had been collected than had ever been done before.

However, Mount Stromlo's closeness to Canberra made it imperative to find a better site. There are no high mountains in Australia, but at Siding Spring, near Coonabarabran in New South Wales, seeing conditions are good; there are no large towns anywhere in the area, and Coonabarabran itself is not big enough to be a problem. Moreover, the Siding Spring Observatory is very accessible; there is no need to climb a volcano or battle your way across hundreds of kilometres of desert. The only real problems are kangaroos, which have absolutely no road sense!

The main instrument, the Anglo-Australian Telescope (AAT), has a 153-inch mirror and is extremely versatile, because it is used with a very wide range of sophisticated electronic equipment. Every few nights a different party of astronomers turns up to do some specialized research, ranging from measuring the distances of remote quasars and galaxies down to Solar System studies. David Allen, whose early death from cancer was so tragic, paid particular attention to Venus, and was even able to record surface details at infrared wavelengths.

Fibre optics have become increasingly important, and indeed the AAT was one of the first telescopes to be used with this technique. You can collect the light from 50 or 100 stars or galaxies simultaneously, putting the light from each object down a separate fibre. Also at Siding Spring is the 2.3-metre telescope of the Australian National Observatory, which is smaller than the AAT but even more modern. There are two or three smaller telescopes, and also the UK Schmidt (UKS), which was originally built and operated from the Royal Observatory Edinburgh but which has now become part of the Anglo-Australian Observatory.

The AAT itself was never designed for infrared work, but it has been used in this way by means of the latest instrumentation. Great attention has been paid to that mysterious region, the centre of the Galaxy. We want to know what is going on there, but at optical wavelengths it is impossible to see through the 'smog' – that is to say, dust and dirt. Luckily, infrared can pass through. At the galactic centre one would expect large numbers of old cool stars, but in fact it seems that there are stars in all stages of their evolution. It is widely believed that the centre is marked by a massive black hole, known as Sagittarius A-$\star$ (pronounced Sagittarius A-star).

Much nearer home there is the Orion Nebula, a stellar nursery. When David Allen was taking pictures of the Nebula he chanced upon a feature, at the northern end just above the infrared group, which had been vaguely known but had not been examined in detail. Allen found that what we now see is the result of a gigantic explosion, throwing blobs of gas out into the northern part of the Nebula. Behind each blob there is a sort of wake – recalling a boat going through water – which shows up in molecular light;

it is due to hydrogen. Nothing like this has been seen before, and it makes us modify our theories about what happens to massive stars.

Naturally, the AAT concentrates upon electronic equipment, but, unusually for a major telescope, it is also used for traditional photography. David Malin is the photographic expert, and his pictures of galaxies and nebulae are superb. There is nothing old-fashioned about Malin's methods; for example, he has devised a technique which is now called 'photographic amplification'. It is a straightforward contact copying process which extracts the faint images from the photographic plate and produces a very thin-looking film positive of the plate. Malin then adds together large numbers of these thin film derivatives, and combines the information to yield images much deeper than those obtainable from a single plate alone.

Yet there are some things beyond the scope of even the AAT or the UKS. Remember, a star is so far away that it looks only like a dot of light. In Australia a new piece of equipment has been built which will, for some purposes, be equivalent to a 640-metre telescope. It is called SUSI – the Sydney University Stellar Interferometer – and it has been set up by Professor John Davis at Narrabri, some way north of Siding Spring.

SUSI is an instrument for measuring the angular diameters of stars, that is, the angle drawn from Earth to the two sides of the star. This angle is incredibly small. Measuring the angular diameter of the star with the greatest known apparent diameter (Betelgeux) is equivalent to measuring the diameter of a human hair from a range of over 90 metres (300 ft). There are only half a dozen stars which show measurable disks, even with the world's largest optical telescopes. To measure the sizes of other stars we would need a telescope with a mirror hundreds of feet in diameter, which is out of the question – so we use an interferometer. Here we have a number of small-aperture telescopes, and we can combine two apertures at once; in other words, bring the light from two small mirrors together and combine them. By making a series of measurements with different separations we can, in effect, build up the same angular picture as would be obtained with a single huge telescope. At SUSI there are baselines, or separations, ranging from 6 metres (20 ft) right up to 640 metres (2100 ft).

Once you know a star's size, you can find out a great deal about its make-up. The measurements made with SUSI are used together with measurements made with conventional telescopes, mainly photometric techniques which measure the brightness at different wavelength bands; also used are measurements made with spectroscopes. We can measure the distribution of the light through the spectrum, and note the way it changes when, for example, we are dealing with a binary system, with two stars orbiting round their common centre of gravity. By combining this information with SUSI data, we can determine the energy actually cooling out from each square metre of the star's surface; this gives us the surface temperature. It is even possible to measure the changing sizes of pulsating stars, such as Cepheid variables. Linking this with spectroscopic measurements, we can then find out the star's distance, and thereby provide a completely independent calibration which is essentially geometrical.

Remote even from Australia is an area which has great astronomical potential: the South Pole, where seeing conditions are very good indeed. The main problem, of course, is that it is a somewhat chilly place. It is the combination of the extreme cold, the very dry conditions and the tenuous air on the high plateau that makes it so suitable. The cold reduces the thermal radiation ('heat'), which is a tremendous advantage for infrared work. The extreme dryness means that transmission through the atmosphere is better than anywhere else on Earth, and the stable air means that star images are perfectly steady. In fact, the Antarctic plateau is the ultimate place for doing ground-based astronomy. Overcoming the cold is really an engineering problem; temperatures down to $-68°C$ ($-90°F$) have to be expected.

The fact that the polar night lasts for six months helps some branches of observation and hinders others. Some optical researches need very long-period observation, and the six-month winter will be an advantage, though nothing can be done in the summer with regard to these particular programmes. The greatest gain will be for radio astronomers, who do not care whether the sky is dark or not. From the Pole, no bodies rise and set apart from those in the Solar System.

Naturally, environmentalists are concerned. Antarctica is a fragile eco-system and not one to be disturbed. However, astronomy is one of the most peaceful of all operations; all that has to be done is detect the photons falling into the telescopes. Once the Observatory has been set up, impact will be minimal.

The Polar Observatory will be complete early in the 21st century. It will be unique, and certainly there is a great deal to be learned from studying the skies of the far south.

▼ **SUSI:** the Sydney University Stellar Interferometer, at Narrabri in New South Wales, as I photographed it in 1994. Difficult to believe that it is a precision scientific instrument!

Planets of Pulsars?

It now seems definite that many stars are the centres of planetary systems, and in this case the Sun's family is in no way exceptional. One solar-type star, Upsilon Andromedae, is thought to be attended by at least three planets. But there are oddities, too, and as long ago as 1990 it was claimed that there might even be planets orbiting pulsars.

Let me say at once that I was sceptical then, and I am sceptical now (June 2002). However, let us look carefully at the evidence.

A pulsar is the end product of a supernova explosion, a colossal outburst involving the death of a very massive star; most of the star's material is blown away into space, leaving only a tiny, super-dense core made up of neutrons. In our Galaxy no supernova has been seen since 1604, but in 1987 we were lucky enough to observe one in the Large Cloud of Magellan, 169,000 light-years away. This supernova – 1987A – reached the second magnitude. We expected it to produce a pulsar; so far this has not happened, but there is still time.

Pulsars are spinning neutron stars. Although as massive as the Sun, they are very small – say around 20 km (12 miles) across. They spin at high speeds, up to 100 times per second. Radio astronomers detect them because they flash radio waves; these emissions are in the form of beams, and each time a beam sweeps over the Earth we detect a pulse of radiation (the 'lighthouse effect'). Not all neutron stars are pulsars; it depends upon whether their beams are suitably angled towards us.

In a supernova outburst of this sort, the core of the massive star collapses and releases an immense amount of energy. The collapsed core shrinks from a radius of several thousand kilometres down to no more than half a dozen kilometres; the neutron star picks up spin and rotates quickly, initially at around 100 times per second. The collapse compresses the magnetic field that is trapped in the core, so that the field becomes very strong – hence the generation of the radio beams. As it ages, the pulsar loses energy and slows down, so that the spin rate is reduced to several seconds. Yet there are exceptions.

◀ *The Arecibo Radio Telescope, in Puerto Rico, as used by Alexander Wolszczan in his research on millisecond pulsars.*

Sometimes we come across a supernova explosion in one of the two members of a binary star system. The binary system may or may not be disrupted; if not, the result is a pulsar orbiting the companion star. The companion evolves in the usual way, and grows in size, so that the pulsar can capture most of its atmosphere, which is pulled across in a stream. The impact of the stream on the surface of the neutron star heats it up, so that it begins to emit X-rays. Also, the effect of the stream is to increase the spin rate (just as you can make a table-tennis ball spin by suspending it on the end of a string and blowing on it through a drinking straw). Eventually, we have what is termed a millisecond pulsar, spinning up to 1000 times per second or even more. Radio astronomers have found several millisecond pulsars in orbit round ordinary stars.

Because it is rotating so quickly, the pulsar becomes very energetic again, and may heat up so much that it starts to evaporate the companion – a case of cosmic murder well worthy of Miss Marple! In other cases, the companion may itself explode as a supernova and disrupt the binary system, so that we now have a lone millisecond pulsar. Note that millisecond pulsars are old, not young. Normal pulsars may be of the order of 10 million years old, but the really fast ones are much older, perhaps dating back 1000 million years.

Millisecond pulsars are important because their periods can be measured very accurately indeed, and they are superb 'clocks', but there are also some subtle effects. For example, if a millisecond pulsar is orbiting another body, the pulses will arrive late when the pulsar is on the far side of its orbit relative to Earth, and early when the pulsar is on the near side.

One astronomer who has been working on the problem is Alexander Wolszczan, of Penn State University; with him is his colleague Dale Frail. In 1990 Wolszczan was working at the Arecibo Radio Astronomy Observatory in Puerto Rico, and was lucky enough to have the exclusive use of the 'dish' for a few weeks when it was undergoing structural modifications. It was able to survey the sky at the zenith, and Wolszczan found a millisecond pulsar in Virgo, now catalogued as 1257+2. It is at least 1500 light-years away (perhaps as much as 3000), and it has a period of 6.2 milliseconds, so that it beats 161 times per second. (If you could 'hear' it, it would sound like a lowish note on the piano – G flat below the C an octave down from middle C.)

Wolszczan monitored the pulsar for a couple of years, and found that it was not quite regular. Sometimes the pulses arrived a whole beat too early, sometimes a whole beat too late. In musical terms, the note was a complex vibrato.

What was the answer? Wolszczan came to the conclusion that the pulsar was orbiting with some other body, or rather two bodies. The two invisible bodies in the system corresponded to the double vibrato; the periods were 2 and 3 months respectively.

The great surprise was that the two additional bodies were not nearly so massive as the pulsar, so that we were not dealing with a triple-star system. The new bodies were planetary in mass, and were separated from the pulsar by 'planetary' distances. Then, early in 1994, Wolszczan announced that he had found a third body in the system, from another subtle effect which had taken a long time to emerge because it was so small. In fact, the latest object (A) was comparable in mass with the Moon. So the system as Wolszczan believed it to be is as follows:

WOLSZCZAN'S PULSAR SYSTEM				
	Period	Mass	Separation a.u.	millions of km
Pulsar	6.2 ms	1.4 Sun		
A	25.3 days	0.014 Earth	0.19	28.5
B	66.6 days	2.8 Earth	0.36	53.9
C	98.2 days	3.4 Earth	0.46	68.9
Compare these with the inner part of the Solar System:				
	Planet	Mass	Separation a.u.	millions of km
	Mercury	0.055 Earth	0.38	58
	Venus	0.815 Earth	0.72	108
	Earth	1	1	150
	Moon	0.012 Earth		
	Mars	0.107 Earth	1.52	228

Wolszczan also believed that there could be more planets in the system; there remained anomalies which could be due to planets with longer periods.

There had been a false alarm in 1990, when astronomers at Jodrell Bank reported a 'pulsar planet'; this turned out to be erroneous. But Wolszczan maintained that this could not be the case again; he found that the orbits intersect, with every three revolutions of B corresponding to two of C. The planets pass close to each other every 200 days, and as they do so they perturb each other. Wolszczan believed that it is hard to see how anything other than planetary dynamics could mimic this effect.

Obviously we cannot say much about the nature of the planets, assuming that they really exist. They could have Earth-like surfaces, and B and C could have dense atmospheres, though it is also possible that the pulsar will have swept any atmosphere away. Object A is the closest-in and the least massive, and is the least likely to have an atmosphere. They could have magnetic fields, and the interactions of the magnetic fields of the planets with that of the pulsar would be interesting – perhaps producing brilliant aurorae, with surface rocks fluorescing and showing discharge phenomena.

What about the origin of the planets? They can hardly have been formed in the same way as those of our Solar System, because they could not have survived the supernova outburst. They could have been captured, with a millisecond pulsar passing close to another star and 'stealing' its planets – though this is unlikely inasmuch as the two bodies would have to pass very close to each other, and such an event would not lead to near-circular orbits which seem to be the case.

Could they be second-generation planets, formed directly round the pulsar? In this case, we must assume that after the millisecond pulsar was formed in its binary system it evaporated most of its companion, so that the debris left over formed first a planetary disk and then true planets. Or the companion may have exploded as a supernova, so that some of the debris fell back and was captured, again producing a disk from which planets evolved.

If these findings are confirmed, we may have to modify some of our ideas about planetary formation. In the *Sky at Night* programme transmitted on 10 November 1994, Paul Murdin said: 'My bet is that radio astronomers will see more; it just takes time to see the effects of the orbits. If this is right, then this is the first discovery of planets outside our Solar System.'

We must wait and see. We are dealing with almost incredibly small disturbances, and surely the region of a pulsar is the very last place where we would expect to find planets? I find it hard to credit, but I may well be quite wrong, and in any case Wolszczan's work is fascinating in the extreme.

▼ **Compact nebula around the Vela pulsar,** imaged by the Chandra X-ray satellite. Perpendicular to the bow-like structures at the leading edge of the nebula, embedded in the Vela supernova remnant, are jets emanating from the central pulsar, or neutron star. The jets point in the same direction as the motion of the pulsar (indicated by the arrow).

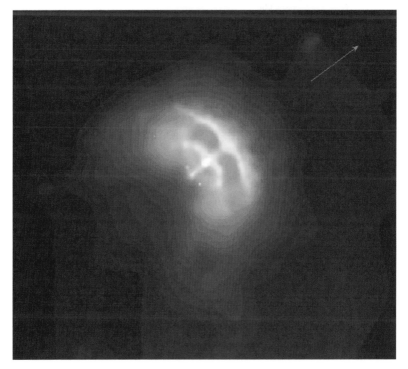

The 500th Sky at Night

In a way, our programme of April 1995 was a landmark: it was the 500th *Sky at Night*. The first programme went out in April 1957. We transmit every four weeks, adding a few 'specials', such as that at the discovery of Halley's Comet in 1982, and we have never had a break (now, in the year 2002, we still haven't).

Things were very different in 1957. The Space Age had not started; the electronic revolution was barely under way; computers were primitive, and there were many sceptics about manned flight beyond the Earth. Television was different, too. Everything was black-and-white, and all our programmes were 'live', which could give scope for total disaster. The time when I swallowed a large fly during transmission is still remembered. For our 50th programme we went to George Hole's observatory in Brighton to show Jupiter, Saturn and the Moon direct; both immediately before and immediately after the transmission the sky was beautifully clear, but during the programme itself there was total cloud – and every time we tried to aim the telescope, George would proclaim: 'Totally obscured.' On another occasion we were filming in the Canary Islands when my newly-acquired Canaries hat blew off. I chased it, and was duly recorded by the camera . . . .

What have been some of the highlights?

We began with the Arend–Roland Comet, which shone down at the precise time when our first programme went out. This was the brightest comet for some years, even though it did not rival the splendour of some past visitors such as the comets of 1811, 1843, 1882 and even 1910. The comet had a curious forward 'spike', which was not in fact an anti-tail, but was due to the sunlight catching the thinly-spread material in the comet's orbit. Alas, we will never see Arend–Roland again; it was perturbed by the planets and thrown into a hyperbolic orbit, so that it will wander unseen among the stars until disaster strikes it.

Then, of course, came Sputnik I, the Russian artificial satellite which ushered in the Space Age. We then had to make a decision, and I am sure that we made the right one: we deal with 'space' only in its purely astronomical context. Thus, a probe to the Moon or Mars is very much our business, whereas an Earth-surveying or a communications satellite is not. Neither are we a 'news' programme as such. Rather than try to 'get in first', we tend to wait until we have positive results, and then discuss them in more depth. For example, there was the time when the Giotto probe, having surveyed Halley's Comet, went on to study a much smaller comet, Grigg–Skjellerup. The news media covered the encounter as it happened; we waited a week or so, and then presented the full results. We followed the same procedure when Comet Shoemaker–Levy 9 impacted Jupiter in July 1994. Our programme, with the relevant experts, came out ten days after the last fragment of the shattered comet had plunged to its doom; by then, we knew exactly what had been learned.

The 'other side of the Moon', in 1959, was particularly special for me. Until then, the far side had never been seen; it is always turned away from us.

The Russians dispatched Lunik 3 to take the first pictures – and to link them with the familiar hemisphere they had used my own charts of the 'libration zones', the extreme edges of the disk as seen from Earth, where the features are so foreshortened that it is often impossible to tell a crater from a ridge. The Russians had promised to send me the results as soon as they came through, and they kept their word. The first images were actually received in

▼ **The far side of the Moon,** which was unknown in 1957. The dark-floored crater in the centre of this image is Tsiolkovskii.

the studio during the *Sky at Night* transmission. Mercifully, I recognized one feature, the Mare Crisium, under reverse lighting, and I was able to give what I hope was an intelligible commentary.

Later, we had the first unmanned lunar landings, and also, during the 1960s, the first forays to Venus and Mars. Naturally we covered all these, and also the subsequent missions to the far reaches of the Solar System.

▼ *Total solar eclipse, showing the outer corona, as seen in February 1998, from the Caribbean.*

During the commentary, I took this rather hasty photograph – but it came out!

We were at NASA's headquarters at the Jet Propulsion Laboratory, in Pasadena, for all but one of the Pioneer and Voyager encounters of the giant planets, and also for the Viking landers on Mars; previously we had devoted several programmes to speculations about possible Martian life. We had some model 'landers', and I remember one telling comment by Garry Hunt: 'We can prove one thing, at least. If you drop them too hard, they break!'

We covered the Apollo missions, of course, though the actual real-time commentaries were carried out under a different programme heading; with James Burke, I did all the main BBC commentaries. It was a tense time. I remember my feelings as Neil Armstrong and Buzz Aldrin went down into the waterless Sea of Tranquillity; if they had made a faulty landing, there could have been no rescue, and it was a tremendous relief to hear Neil's calm voice: 'The *Eagle* has landed.' I was broadcasting, live, for 15 hours without a break. I was starting to flag when the floor manager, Joan Marsden (known to all and sundry as 'Mother'), passed me a glass of what looked like water; in fact it was mainly gin, and it revived me at once! Apollo 13 was another dramatic time. We had finished broadcasting for the night, and I decided, for once, to drive back to my home in Selsey. I was just walking indoors when the phone rang, calling me back to the studio. At one stage during the crisis I was able to talk 'off the air' to the NASA controller, and I asked: 'Are you going to get them back?' 'Yes, if nothing else goes wrong, but we've come to the end of our resources.' Mercifully, nothing else did go wrong.

We did a special programme when Halley's Comet was recovered; this was 'live', and on radio we linked with Palomar and talked to David Jewitt, one of the discoverers. I am bound to say that the coverage of the moment when Giotto went through the comet, in 1986, was not a success. We did not have the funds to do a *Sky at Night* programme from the European Space Agency's headquarters in Munich, and *Horizon* more or less took over, doing the bulk of the programme from (for some odd reason) Greenwich. There were no comet experts at Greenwich, and the only participant who really had the right idea was Lee Sproats, aged 14, who was there at my suggestion (he is now a highly-qualified research astronomer). I was cut off every time I tried to tell viewers what was going on, and back in Greenwich the experiment by James Burke did not work. In fact, everything went exactly as I had predicted. Nobody was at all pleased, but to be fair it was not the fault of *The Sky at Night*.

Subsequently, we summarized the Giotto results, this time minus any help from *Horizon*. Our last Halley programme was the only time when we did not end with our usual signature tune, Sibelius' *At the Castle Gate*. The Band of the Royal Transport Corps played us out with the march *Halley's Comet*, which I had composed myself.

Obviously we have to deal sometimes with technical subjects, such as cosmology, and I have one firm policy: when I have an expert guest, I act merely as a 'feed'. The viewers want to see him (or her), not me. Occasionally we have a guest which is a leader in the field, but not very used to television; on these occasions we have to use some skilful editing!

We have travelled far and wide; we have covered total eclipses of the Sun, on one occasion from a ship off the coast of Africa. The nearest town was Nouadhibou, in Mauritania, which is the end of the world, and consists mainly of sand, flies and a chemical manure factory. We wanted to get our pictures back quickly for processing, so we tried to contact the BBC's man in Nouadhibou. We failed, and eventually found that although he remained on the BBC's payroll, he had last been heard of in 1948. I remember, too, that on the homeward voyage there was a ship's concert, in which I gave the only public (or even private) performance of my specially-written song, *Boo, boo, Nouadhibou.*

We have been to most of the world's great observatories; indeed, the Visitor Centre at Palomar still gives several daily showings of the film about the 200-inch reflector which we made in 1982. And I think it is fair to say that a large number of the world's leading astronomers have joined me on the programme at one time or another. Many, of course, are no longer here. I recall Harlow Shapley telling me how he measured the size of the Galaxy in 1917, and I also remember Wernher von Braun giving me his views about the future of space travel. When von Braun was making the V2 weapons at Peenemünde, in 1943, the base was bombed by the RAF. I was not on that raid, but I might have been, as I was at that time a navigator in Bomber Command. All the same, Wernher and I were on very friendly terms.

What of the future of the programme? Well, I hope to keep on as I have done ever since 1957. It gives me immense pleasure to go round and meet famous amateurs and professionals who tell me that they were introduced to the subject by watching the programmes. There are a good many of them . . . .

The 500th programme itself? I merely took viewers on a tour of the night sky as it appeared at the time; we reserved our main celebrations for the 40th anniversary, in 1997. Yet I am bound to admit that I had a great sense of satisfaction in having presented *The Sky at Night* 500 times without a break. Now, I am looking forward to our 45th anniversary, in 2002.

Starbirth

Look up into the night sky, and you will see that the stars are not all alike. Not only do they differ in brightness, they also differ in colour. Thus Betelgeux in Orion is orange-red, while Rigel is pure white and Vega is decidedly bluish. And, of course, our Sun, which is an ordinary star, is yellow.

These colours indicate different surface temperatures, and also different ages. We know that the Earth is around 4600 million years old, and the Sun must be older than that; neither will it last for ever. But going back in time, how were the Sun and other stars formed? Can we see very young stars? The answer is: 'Yes.'

In everyday terms, the lifetimes of the stars are very long indeed, but they are not infinite. Stars come to the ends of their careers, sometimes in spectacular fashion, as with supernova explosions, but often more placidly, losing their outer layers to become planetary nebulae before settling down to become white dwarfs and, ultimately, black dwarfs. There are about 100,000 million stars in our Galaxy, which has been in existence for at least 10,000 million years. It would therefore seem that roughly ten stars per year will have to be born in order to keep the stellar population constant. In fact, we need rather more stars than that, because the hotter stars have much shorter lifetimes. The Sun is about halfway through its active lifetime of about 10,000 million years, but a star with ten times the solar mass will last for only about 100 million years, and true 'search-lights' such as Canopus and Rigel will be more evanescent still. This means that we need about 100 stars per year to be born over the whole of the Galaxy.

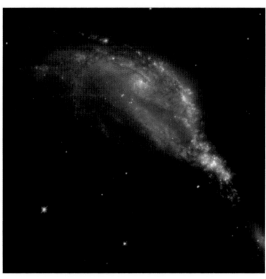

▶ **Starbirth: interacting galaxies NGC 6745.** *Collision between a large spiral and a smaller passing galaxy (lower right), as imaged by the Hubble Space Telescope. Interstellar material is compressed, and star formation is triggered off.*

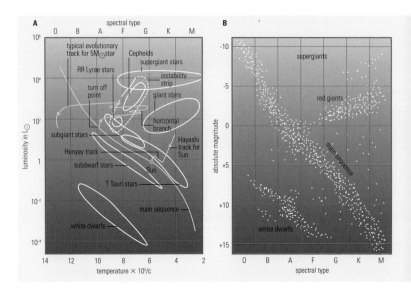

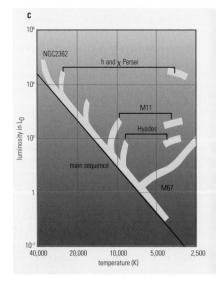

▲▶ The Herzsprung–Russell diagram, plotting stars' luminosity against temperature. Most stars lie on the Main Sequence, running from top left to bottom right. The main regions of the HR diagram are shown in (B), while (C) illustrates some of the evolutionary paths that stars may take as they break away from the Main Sequence.

Of course, stars were formed when the Galaxy itself came into being, but any star of solar mass born at that remote epoch will have disappeared by now. Only the dim red dwarfs can have survived since that time; most of the stars we now see have been born much more recently. The stars in globular clusters are probably the oldest in the Galaxy, and date back well over 10,000 million years.

At least we know that stars are born from a battle between pressure and gravity, and that pressure is the loser. The space between the stars is not empty, but on average contains about a million atoms per cubic metre. In some regions the density can be a thousand times as great as this, and we can sometimes see regions, termed nebulae, which glow because of the stars formed within them.

Gravity tends to pull even single pairs of atoms together, and so there is a constant tendency for the gas to collapse into even denser clumps. This is, however, counteracted by gas pressure, which tends to disperse the gas throughout the universe. An equation known to most school students – the Perfect Gas Law – states that the pressure is proportional to the number of atoms or molecules per cubic metre, and that temperature is involved. In the glowing parts of HII regions such as the Eagle Nebula, where the temperature may be as high as 10,000 degrees at least, it is already too hot for any condensations to occur under the effect of gravity. (Remember that 'temperature' is defined by the speeds at which the atoms and molecules move around, and is not the same as what we normally call 'heat'. HII regions are areas where the hydrogen atoms have been ionized, that is, partly disrupted.) Pressure will increase as the cloud condenses, because its density will grow. If a gas-clump halves in size, the gas density, and hence also the pressure, will rise by a factor of eight. Newton's laws tell us that gravitational force is inversely proportional to the square of the distance between two particles, so that if the same clump halves in size the gravitational force increases by a factor of four. So how can gravity ever overcome pressure, if the pressure always rises more quickly?

The answer lies in keeping the temperature low enough. The conditions under which a clump of material will collapse under its own gravitational forces were first worked out by Sir James Jeans, and summarized in 'Jeans' Equation'. This is decidedly complicated, but shows that for a given density and temperature there has to be a minimum amount of material in a clump before it can collapse. If the mass is greater than this minimum value, the collapse will be much more pronounced.

At the typical density of a clump in an interstellar gas cloud, around 10^{12} atoms per cubic metre, the temperature would have to be a few degrees above absolute zero ($-273°C$) before a clump the mass of the Sun would collapse, and the density would have to be a million million times greater before an Earth-mass clump would condense directly out of the gas, even at such a low temperature. It therefore seems likely that the clumps that do start collapsing are considerably more massive than the Sun, and that the clump breaks up into star-sized fragments only much later on, when the density has increased considerably. We would thus expect star births to be multiple phenomena, with many stars forming close together and at the same time.

Yet it does not follow that if you put enough material into a small enough space at a low enough temperature, you will automatically end up with a star. The crucial factor is not just in starting with a low temperature, but in keeping it that way. And therein lies a major problem. As the clump collapses, it will release potential energy. In effect, the atoms are 'falling downhill', and, as happens with a stone rolling downhill on Earth, the speed will grow and grow. With atoms, these faster movements represent an increase in the gas temperature. As the cloud collapses, the temperature – and hence the pressure – rises, and this tends to halt the collapse.

Fortunately, there is another way of cooling the material (otherwise, there would be no Sun and no Solar System).

The solution lies in radiating the energy away. Initially, the temperatures are so low that the energy is radiated away as radio waves, which can penetrate the cloud material quite easily and therefore allow the temperature

◀ **The Bok globule Barnard 68** appears as an opaque mass against a rich star background field. No stars are seen in front of B68, showing that it is relatively close (around 500 light-years away). This composite image was obtained with Antu, the first component of the VLT, in 1999.

to stay low. Later on, the temperature does start to rise, and the energy comes out as microwaves rather than radio waves, but the collapse still continues. The crisis comes when the collapse pushes the density up to around 10^{18} atoms per cubic metre, which is about 1000-millionth of the density of the Earth's air at sea-level. The cloud then becomes opaque, and the energy can no longer escape. Instead, the trapped energy raises the internal temperature, and this means that the internal pressure also increases. In many cases, the rise in temperature will be sufficient to halt the collapse. The cloud, now perhaps 1/1000th of a light-year across, will simply remain, doing little except to radiate away the energy slowly percolating out from the interior. In fact, if the pressure rises too quickly, no star will form for a very long time indeed.

Then how can stars manage to form at all? The energy being released as the cloud collapses has to go somewhere, so that it does not heat the gas. Paradoxically, this requires the gas temperature to rise to 1000 or 2000 degrees, which is as hot as the centre of a blast-furnace. The hydrogen molecules which make up most of the cloud will then split into their constituent atoms. Splitting or dissociating the hydrogen molecules requires a great deal of energy; in fact, as much as our present Sun radiates in 10,000 years. This means that if the cloud is still collapsing when the internal temperature reaches 2000 degrees, it will continue to collapse; the temperature will remain constant and the released potential energy will be absorbed in dissociating the hydrogen molecules. Of course, there is a vast amount of hydrogen, but eventually all of it will be dissociated. The central temperature will shoot up again, but by now the collapse is too rapid to be stopped. When the temperature has risen to 5000 degrees, the released potential energy will be mopped up by ionizing the hydrogen, that is, breaking up the atoms into their constituent protons and electrons. This requires six times the energy that had been needed in dissociating the hydrogen molecules. Later on in the collapse, the ionization of helium also helps to use up some of the energy. In the end, we are left with the centre of the cloud, collapsed down to a few times the present size of the Sun, with a temperature of the order of 1 million degrees; the pressure has at last become great enough to halt the collapse. We may now think of this as a protostar rather than merely the denser part of a gas-cloud.

The inner parts of the cloud collapse faster than the outer parts; but once the protostar has been formed, the continuing collapse of the outer parts will add to its mass, causing a slow shrinkage down to the final size. The infalling material also releases its energy as it hits the surface of the protostar, so that the protostar becomes many times more luminous than the Sun – the main difference here being that the protostar radiates most of its material in the infrared part of the electromagnetic spectrum.

It is fair to say that a star may be regarded as 'born' when nuclear reactions start inside it. This means a temperature of at least 1 million degrees, but the initial reactions are not the hydrogen-into-helium processes. The protostar will contain small quantities of deuterium (heavy hydrogen) and lithium, which react at lower temperatures than normal hydrogen will do. At first, therefore, deuterium and lithium will be consumed in the same way as happens inside an atom-bomb. These reactions will raise the central temperature to the 10-million-degree mark, and this is enough to spark off reactions involving nuclei of normal helium. It is now that we can place the star in the Hertzsprung–Russell Diagram. It lies low down to the right, with low temperature and luminosity, after which it moves across diagonally as the temperature and luminosity increase. Perhaps rather surprisingly, it will be above its final place on the Main Sequence, because of the effects of the infalling matter. Eventually the star stabilizes, and moves to its rightful place in the Main Sequence.

There are two main problems about watching stellar births. The first is that although some of the stages happen quite quickly on the astronomical scale, they still extend over many hundreds of human lifetimes, and this means that we cannot follow a star as it goes through the whole process. We must study stars in different stages of formation, and try to build up a true picture of the sequence of events.

The second problem is that stars are born deep inside interstellar gas-clouds. This gas – and, more importantly, the dust which is there as well – hides the embryo star. However, there are some stages which we can follow; the earliest stages occur inside giant molecular clouds, and these can be followed in the radio range. The clouds are huge – sometimes over 300 light-years across – and contain thousands of times the amount of material in the Sun. Within them are denser cores, each less than a light-year across, containing a few masses of solar material at temperatures down to $10°$ above absolute zero. These cores seem to mark the start of the collapse process.

The formation of the giant molecular clouds themselves is still not understood, but it has been suggested that explosions near the centre of the Galaxy – similar to those which occur in Seyfert galaxies – may cause concentration of material through magnetic interactions. Also, we can sometimes see concentrations of gas which may represent the early stages in collapse to a protostar; these are silhouetted against bright nebulosity and appear dark because of the amount of dust they contain. They are known as Bok globules, in honour of the Dutch astronomer Bart J. Bok, who first drew attention to them.

The later stages of star formation are hidden by the gas and dust in which the fledgling stars are immersed; however, some infrared sources may well be at the stage when the outer parts of the cloud are collapsing on to the surface of the protostar. We can even 'see round corners', because of the scattering of light. Most interstellar clouds are in slow rotation, and that rotation will be maintained as the collapse continues. The clouds will therefore tend to become flattened by centrifugal forces, and the polar regions will be clearer of dust and gas than the equator. Infrared light can then escape more readily via the poles, and some of this light will be scattered towards us by the remaining gas and dust. When we see it, the scattered light will be mixed up with the light coming directly from the outer parts of the cloud – but the scattered light will be polarized. If we observe with a polarimeter, we can separate the polarized component which is coming from the protostar, and are therefore in effect seeing 'round the corner'.

This is all that can be seen directly, but in the later stages a strong stellar wind develops, and because of the equatorial concentration this wind comes out as jets along the polar axes. When these jets interact with the remains of the gas-cloud, we see faint glowing patches known as Herbig–Haro objects. Later still, after the star has been born, it goes through an unstable phase before settling down on the Main Sequence; this is the T Tauri stage. Irregular variables of the T Tauri type lie just above the Main Sequence, and are often still embedded in the remains of the gas-cloud from which they were formed. We can also see groups of stars which have formed together; these are the galactic clusters, such as the Pleiades.

What about planets? The precursors of the planets could form quite early on during the collapse of the dense cores in giant molecular clouds; alternatively, they might form later in the thick disk of accreting material which forms round the protostar, or even later as the disk evaporates. In any case, we now have excellent evidence that planetary systems are common.

At least we have gained some insight into star formation, and if we look up into the night sky we can see that each star has its own characteristics. We also know that thousands of millions of years ago, our Sun was born in precisely the same way.

The Flying Observatory

A most unusual aircraft has been flying from the Ames Research Centre in northern California. It is a converted C141 cargo plane; it carries a telescope, and is known to astronomers as the Kuiper Airborne Observatory (KAO).

The main enemy of the astronomer is the Earth's atmosphere, which is dirty and unsteady as well as cutting out many of the most important radiations coming from space. Obviously, going up a mountain helps, but there is still a great deal of atmosphere above you even at the top of Mauna Kea in Hawaii. Short of going into space, as the Hubble Space Telescope has done, the only real answer is to use an aircraft. The telescope in the KAO is a 36-inch Cassegrain reflector, carried in front of the aircraft's left wing. The aircraft itself can fly at 41,000 ft (12,000 metres), which is above 85% of the Earth's air and above 99% of the water vapour – which is particularly important.

The observatory is named in honour of Gerard Kuiper, a Dutch astronomer who spent most of his working life in the United States and became a leading planetary authority; he was also the first to use airborne techniques for infrared astronomy. The maximum length of time that the KAO can fly is 12 hours, though in fact the flights are never as long as that

▼ **The Kuiper Airborne Observatory (KAO) –** *a converted C141 cargo* *plane, carrying a 36-inch Cassegrain reflector telescope.*

▲ **Here I am pictured** *only a few months prior*
standing outside the KAO *to the aircraft being taken*
in California in 1995 – *out of service.*

– it is essential to keep something in reserve. The longest flight undertaken, to study an occultation of a star by the planet Uranus in 1977, lasted for 10¼ hours. It was during this flight that the obscure ring-system of Uranus was discovered.

The telescope itself is a Cassegrain; the light comes through the side of the aircraft off the primary and secondary mirrors, but is then deflected to the side by a flat mirror and passes through a hole in the wall of the telescope cavity, so that the instruments can be located comfortably in the cabin.

Navigation is, of course, of paramount importance. We are observing from a moving platform, so that as the stars move across the sky, the telescope has to be flown in a curved path. This means that to ordinary mission flight controllers the KAO's flight plans look very peculiar indeed. The telescope is kept pointing steadily by three separate systems. The first is a vibration isolation system – essentially, a shock absorber. The second system keeps the telescope pointing at the target object at the aircraft rolls and yaws; the telescope is mounted on a spherical bearing with a thin film of air, and there is a gyro-stabilized system for keeping it pointing in the right direction. Thirdly, there is an optical tracking system.

It is clear that the KAO has advantages over ground-based equipment, but – surprisingly – it also has some advantages over a space telescope. The observers can fly in it and modify the instruments *in situ*, which is clearly impossible in space at the present time. Moreover, extra experimentation can be attempted; Dr Edward Dunham, the KAO project scientist, commented that: 'We can be a little riskier with our instruments than is possible with a spacecraft.'

During our *Sky at Night* programme we were able to take part in an actual KAO flight. Bear in mind that each flight is different, and each one needs its own special instrumentation, which has to be installed before take-off. On our flight, the senior scientist was Dr Fred Witteborn. It was in fact a routine operation to establish infrared flux standards for standard stars, using an infrared spectrometer sensitive from 3 to 30 microns and with a spectral resolving power of the order of 200. The instrument needs to be calibrated very accurately, because the aim is to establish stars for use as standards; these stars can be used by space observatories.

To quote Dr Witteborn: 'To get the instrument properly calibrated, we have to look at a standard which we know very well. We have a black-body source which emits a very well-known flux-versus-wavelength radiation. In order to duplicate the conditions of flight, we actually run this radiation through a cold chamber containing some optics which simulate the telescope optics in the aircraft; the temperature of the cold cavity is the same as that of the temperature of the telescope during flight. In this way, we can calibrate the infrared spectrometer very precisely. The advantage here is that the instruments do not have to be completely automated; the observers are there to operate the valves and knobs, and deal with any unexpected development – which would not be possible with a purely automated system.'

Vibration is clearly a problem, but probably no worse than that at a mountain-top observatory. Safety is all-important. For example, oxygen masks are always at hand to guard against sudden decompression.

Following the briefing, we duly took off; several astronomers as well as Dr Witteborn were on board – including an old friend of mine, Dr Martin Cohen, who had made numerous trips in the KAO and knew it as well as anybody. It was noisy; we had to wear ear-plugs, but it was not nearly so uncomfortable as I had expected, and certainly not so uncomfortable as the bombers in which I used to fly as an RAF navigator during the war. There were no alarms; everything went according to plan. We were airborne for seven hours, and it was fascinating to see the cities below; we landed back in the same position as that from which we had taken off, and retired to bed well satisfied.

All in all, it must be said that the KAO has performed better than most people expected it to do, mainly because of the very marked improvements in infrared detectors over the past 20 years. Much has been accomplished. In the field of planetary astronomy, the results include the detection of water in the atmospheres of Mars and Jupiter as well as in comets; in the field of stellar research, star formation has been studied, as well as measurements of stellar magnetic fields, and observations of spectral lines produced in star-forming regions and in the shock waves associated with them. The most spectacular discovery, probably, was that of the rings of Uranus. The predicted track of the occultation was known, so that the KAO could be in precisely the right place at precisely the right time. There were also observations of the atmosphere of Pluto. An occultation of a star by Pluto had been predicted for 1988, but at the last moment new calculations showed that the track would be some way away from the originally expected position. Once again, the KAO's mobility made it possible to get to the right place. During the return of Halley's Comet, in 1986, the KAO was based in New Zealand in support of the Halley Watch programme, and was the first to detect water in the comet.

Sadly, the KAO came to the end of its career in October 1995; it was taken out of service, to save money (yet another instance of scientific short-

▼ **Inside the Kuiper Airborne Observatory.** I took this photograph during our flight. Obviously the conditions were cramped, but not intolerably so. Moreover, the vibration level was much lower than I had expected. During the flights, last-minute decisions could be made – something which was purely automatic.

sightedness). It will eventually be replaced by another flying observatory, a converted 747; this will be called SOFIA – the Stratospheric Observatory for Infrared Astronomy.

The Boeing 747 to be used will require a great deal of modification. There will be a large pressure bulkhead in which the telescope will be mounted; this will separate the telescope from the operating area for the scientists and the aircraft crew. The telescope will look through an open port, and so the back end of the aircraft will be completely depressurized. Facilities for the telescope will have to be approved and installed – a power distribution system, and so on – and there will be structural modifications round the hold, to retain the original stiffness and strength of the fuselage.

The flying altitude will be much the same, but the telescope will be larger; the main mirror will have a diameter of 2½ metres (100 inches), which will be a great advance on the 36-inch Cassegrain of the KAO. The telescope will be mounted at the back of the aircraft, not in the front as with the KAO; this is partly because of financial considerations. The fuselage is practically round, making the door mechanism simple; only one pressure bulkhead will be needed instead of two, and practically every engineering consideration suggests that it is better to put the telescope at the back rather than at the front.

The instrumentation will be very varied, because the telescope covers a wavelength region from about 3/10ths of a micron (on the ultraviolet side of the visible range) through to 1.6 mm (which includes the entire near-infrared, mid- and far-infrared, and the submillimetre part of the electromagnetic spectrum). You need a wide range of instruments to cover all this.

Once again, star formation will be an important part of the programme, because stars are formed in clouds which are opaque because of the dust particles in them; the clouds cannot be penetrated in the ultraviolet or visible range, but can be penetrated at infrared, allowing us to study the ways in which stars are actually formed by the collapse of segments of the cloud. In fact, we can look at the very earliest stages of star formation.

SOFIA should be operating by 2003, but in the meantime there is no flying observatory – and as Fred Witteborn said, the KAO has been indispensable; it could achieve results quite impossible in any other way. Even though its career is now over, it will go down in scientific history as being the first observatory which proved that airborne techniques can play a major role in astronomical research.

The Outer Solar System

We hear a great deal about the familiar planets: Mercury, Venus, Mars, Jupiter and Saturn. But there is much less news about the outer members of the Solar System – and yet these remote worlds are of tremendous interest.

They were not known in ancient times, and as far as astronomers were concerned the planetary system ended with Saturn. Then, in 1781, along came William Herschel – by birth, Hanoverian; he came to England as a young musician and spent the rest of his life here, anglicizing his name from the original Wilhelm. He became organist at the Octagon Chapel in Bath, but his hobby was astronomy. He settled at No. 19 New King Street, Bath, and ground his mirrors for reflecting telescopes in the cellar of his house, sometimes with alarming results! It was with a home-made telescope, in 1781, that he made his great discovery.

He was engaged in what he called a 'review of the heavens', because he wanted to study the shape of our star system or Galaxy; he believed it (correctly) to be flattened. But suddenly he came across something which was clearly not a star; it showed a disk, which no star does, and it moved slowly against the starry background from one night to another. Herschel believed it to be a comet, but when its orbit was worked out it was found to

▼ **Uranus:** this false-colour image was obtained by the HST Wide Field Planetary Camera-2 in 1995. The red around the planet's edge represents a very thin haze at a high altitude.

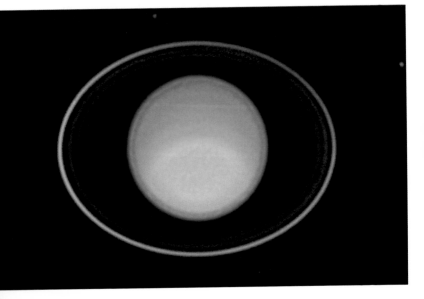

be a planet, far beyond Saturn. After some discussion it was named Uranus, after the first ruler of Olympus.

You can just see Uranus with the naked eye if you know where to look for it, but it seems like a star; with a telescope it shows a pale, greenish disk. Its diameter is around 50,000 km (30,000 miles), far larger than the Earth, but it is a very long way away; its mean distance from the Sun is 2870 million km (1783 million miles), and its 'year' is 84 times as long as ours.

The surface is made up of gas. There may well be a silicate core (we are not sure), but there is nothing solid about most of Uranus; the bulk of the globe is made up of 'ices', with water a major component. Above this comes the hydrogen-rich atmosphere, which we can actually see. All in all, Uranus is rather a bland world, with no belts as prominent as those of Jupiter or even Saturn.

Its strangest point is the way in which it spins. It has a short rotation period of 17.2 hours, but it has a very curious axial tilt. As most people know, the Earth's axis is tilted by 23½ degrees to the perpendicular to our orbit, which is why we have our seasons; the tilt of Mars is much the same, while Jupiter is almost 'upright'. But with Uranus, the tilt is 98 degrees – more than a right angle. This leads to a truly weird calendar. Alternate poles may be turned sunwards, and each pole has a 'midnight sun' lasting for 21 Earth years, with a corresponding period of darkness at the opposite pole.

Why does Uranus have this odd tilt? To be candid, we do not know. The favoured theory is that in its early history Uranus was struck by a massive wandering body and literally tipped over. This does not sound very likely, but there is as yet no other explanation which is even remotely plausible.

In 1977 it was discovered that Uranus has a system of rings (the main credit must go to the astronomers in the Kuiper Airborne Observatory). It was hoped to make a very accurate measurement of the planet's diameter, and one way to do this was to see how long it took to pass over, or occult, a star. There was a favourable occultation in 1977, and it was found that the star 'winked' both before and after occultation by the planet itself, so that clearly a ring system existed. It has been confirmed since, and was well shown by Voyager 2 in 1986; it is also easily within the range of the Hubble Space Telescope. The rings are dark and narrow, and quite unlike the glorious icy rings of Saturn.

Voyager 2 is the only probe to have passed Uranus up to the present time. Of course, the planet was approached pole-on, with the pole in the middle of the disk and the equator all round the edge. Clouds were seen, but were very obscure. A magnetic field was confirmed; it was found that the magnetic axis is displaced by 59° from the axis of rotation, and does not even pass through the centre of the globe. Moreover, Uranus, unlike the other giant planets, does not have an appreciable internal heat source, so that its upper temperature is almost the same as that of Neptune, even though Uranus is more than 1600 million kilometres (more than 1000 million miles) closer to the Sun.

Uranus has a whole family of satellites. Herschel found two, now named Titania and Oberon; Ariel and Umbriel were added in the 19th century, and in 1948 Gerard Kuiper discovered yet another, Miranda. (The Uranus satellites have been given names from Shakespeare's plays and Pope's

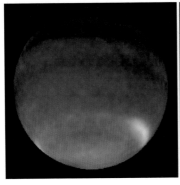
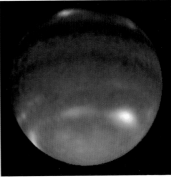

▲ **Neptune:** two Hubble Space Telescope images showing the weather on opposite hemispheres. The highest clouds are in red and yellow.

poem 'The Rape of the Lock', which seems an undesirable departure from the usual mythological system.) All are comparatively small, and even the largest member of the family, Titania, is only 1600 km (less than 1000 miles) in diameter; none can have any trace of atmosphere. Voyager 2 imaged them all. Oberon is icy, with dark-floored craters; Titania is also icy, with tall cliffs; Umbriel is darker and much more subdued, while Ariel has strange branching valleys which look as if they have been liquid-cut, even though there can never have been any water there. Miranda is a real puzzle. It is less than 500 km (300 miles) across, but has an immensely varied surface, with craters, ice-cliffs, scarps, and areas which were nicknamed 'race-tracks'. Planetary geologists are still trying to explain them. Voyager 2 discovered another ten inner satellites, but all are so close to Uranus that they are unobservable from Earth.

With Uranus, the Solar System seemed to be complete, but before long doubts set in. When a planet is found, the mathematicians set to work and compute an orbit for it. They also know how it ought to move. But Uranus refused to behave; persistently it wandered away from its predicted position, and astronomers were forced to realize that something was wrong. Could a more remote planet be pulling Uranus out of position?

One man who believed so was John Couch Adams, a young Cambridge mathematician. He was faced with a cosmic detective problem. He knew the effects on Uranus; what he had to do was work out the position of the unknown planet responsible for them – and then look for it. By 1845 he had made the necessary calculations, and he believed that he could more or less pinpoint the position of the planet in the sky.

You would imagine that he would begin to search – but this is just what he did not do. Instead he reported his results to the then Astronomer Royal, Sir George Airy, and expected that a hunt would be put in hand. Unfortunately Airy was not impressed, and took no action.

Meanwhile, the problem had been taken up in France by another young mathematician, Urbain Jean Joseph Le Verrier. Le Verrier knew nothing about Adams, but he came to almost the same result, and sent his findings to the Paris Observatory. Nothing was done. Patience was never Le Verrier's strong point, and he sent his work to Johann Galle at the Berlin Observatory. Galle went to the Observatory Director, Johann Encke, and asked for permission to use the Observatory's main telescope for the hunt. Encke agreed: 'Let us oblige the gentleman from Paris!' Together with a young astronomer named Heinrich D'Arrest, Galle set to work – and on the first night they located the planet almost exactly where Le Verrier had said it would be.

In the interim Airy had at last acted, and since there was no suitable telescope at Greenwich he contacted James Challis, professor of astronomy at Cambridge University, instructing him to search with the main telescope

▼ **The Great Dark Spot on Neptune,** *as imaged by Voyager 2 in 1989 as it* *bypassed the planet. This storm system rotates anti-clockwise.*

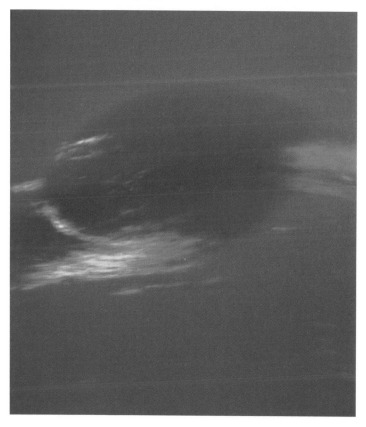

▲ **Ice geysers on
Triton,** *Neptune's largest
satellite. Triton is marked
with great cracks – this
image from Voyager 2's*
*flyby in 1989 shows active
geyser-like eruptions,
throwing nitrogen gas and
dark particles of dust high
up into the atmosphere.*

there (the Northumberland refractor). Challis was not at all energetic; for
one thing he was preoccupied with observing a comet, Biela's, which had
broken in half. The 12-inch Northumberland telescope was good, but Challis
had no up-to-date star maps of the region, and he adopted a decidedly slow
and laborious method. In fact he saw the planet on several occasions, but did
not check on his records until after the announcement from Berlin.

An undignified dispute followed. The French were furious that anyone
could suggest that Le Verrier had not been first in the field, but the fact remains
that the planet – Neptune – was originally identified by Galle and D'Arrest on
the basis of Le Verrier's work. The two results were almost identical.

Neptune is a slow mover, and takes nearly 165 years to go round the
Sun; at present (2002) it is in Capricornus. It is too faint to be seen with the
naked eye, but binoculars will show it as a starlike point. This being so, why
did not Adams (and Le Verrier) look for themselves? They did not need a
large telescope. I found the answer when I was doing the research for my own
book about Neptune (*The Planet Neptune*, Ellis Horwood, Chichester 1989);
neither was an observational astronomer. They were purely theorists.

Some years ago I tried an experiment of my own. I asked a colleague to look up the rough position of Neptune, with an error box similar to that expected by Adams. Using binoculars, I then observed nightly to see whether I could identify Neptune by its movement. It took me less than two weeks! Opportunity missed . . . .

In size and mass, Neptune is almost a twin of Uranus. It is very slightly smaller, rather more massive, and bluish rather than greenish. It does not share Uranus' strange axial tilt, so the calendar there is less alien; like Uranus, it has quick rotation – just over 16 hours – and a magnetic axis which is well away from the rotational axis. But unlike Uranus, it does have a store of internal heat, and it is much more dynamic.

Voyager 2 bypassed Neptune in 1989; by then the probe had been in space for over 12 years and had covered 7000 million km (4500 million miles) – yet it reached its target within a minute or two of the planned time. At once it became clear that Neptune is an active world, with violent winds. There was one huge feature which became known as the Great Dark Spot, and there were other spots too; the so-called Scooter had a more rapid rotation period, so that every five Earth days it overtook the Great Dark Spot and lapped it.

The upper atmosphere was found to be made up chiefly of hydrogen, with some helium and traces of other gases. Below came a layer of what seems to be hydrogen sulphide, overlaid by layers of hydrocarbons with methane 'haze'; some of these methane clouds cast shadows on to the main cloud-deck. Once Voyager 2 passed out of range, nothing more could be done until the repaired Hubble Space Telescope was fully operational. The HST can show details on Neptune, and, amazingly, there is no sign of the Great Dark Spot, which has vanished completely, though new spots have appeared. Neptune is clearly much more variable than had been expected.

Voyager 2 detected a thin ring system, not to be seen from Earth. The main ring is 'clumpy and, before the Voyager pass, had been expected to be discontinuous; it had been traced (more or less) by the occultation method which had been so successful with Uranus.

Two satellites, Triton and Nereid, were known before the Voyager flight. Triton was discovered by the English amateur William Lassell shortly after Neptune itself had been found; it was thought to be larger than the Moon and to have an appreciable atmosphere. The other satellite, Nereid, was very small.

The movements of the satellites are decidedly odd. Triton has an almost circular orbit, but moves round Neptune in a wrong-way or retrograde motion, like a car going the wrong way round a roundabout; Nereid has direct motion, but a very eccentric orbit more like that of a comet than a satellite. Voyager discovered six new inner satellites, all tiny.

Triton was the *pièce de resistance*. Instead of being larger than the Moon it turned out to be smaller, and also very cold – in fact, the coldest world ever encountered by a spacecraft. The pole was covered with ice – not water ice, but nitrogen ice. There were also active nitrogen geysers, which was the last thing that anyone had expected. Further from the pole there was a different type of terrain, with grooves and frozen 'lakes'. There is little surface relief; there are no mountains on Triton, and few craters.

Fittingly, the last view from Voyager showed the crescents of Triton and Neptune together. Voyager had done its work; I well remember a comment from Larry Soderblom, one of NASA's leading planetary scientists: 'Wow! What a way to leave the Solar System!' Voyager 2 will never come back; many millions of years hence it may still be wandering among the stars, unseen, unheard and untrackable. It carries a plaque in case anyone finds it, and also a record of Earth sounds. Since the soundtrack includes a pop group, it may well persuade any aliens to keep well clear of us!

With the discovery of Neptune, the Solar System again appeared to be complete, but then some new small discrepancies were found in the movements of the outer giants, and these caught the attention of Percival Lowell. Lowell is best remembered today, alas, for his admittedly wild theories about the canals of Mars, but he was an expert mathematician, and he worked out a position for a new planet. From the observatory he had set up at Flagstaff in Arizona he started looking for it, using the magnificent 24-inch refractor. There was no success, and when Lowell died suddenly in 1916 the planet had failed to show itself. A brief hunt from Mount Wilson in 1918, carried out on the basis of independent calculations by W. H. Pickering, was equally fruitless.

In 1929 the hunt was resumed from Flagstaff. A young amateur, Clyde Tombaugh, was called in to take charge; he used an excellent 13-inch refractor obtained specially for the purpose, and of course he carried out the search photographically. In 1930 he found Pluto very near the position given by Lowell.

Yet from the outset Pluto was an enigma. It had a period of 248 years, but an unusual orbit; it can come closer-in than Neptune, as it did between 1979 and 1999. However, there is no fear of collision, because Pluto's orbit is tilted at an angle of 17°, and it can go nowhere near Neptune.

The main problem was Pluto's small size. It seemed to be no larger than the Earth, and we now know that it is smaller than the Moon; it has a companion, Charon, with more than half the diameter of Pluto.

Pluto is dim; I can just about see it with a 10-inch telescope. The magnitude never rises much above 14. No space-probe has encountered it, but the Hubble Space Telescope can show a certain amount of surface detail; there are light and dark areas. The surface is coated with methane ice, though Charon's surface layer seems to be of water ice. Pluto spins round in 6 days 9 hours; this is also the orbital period of Charon, so that the two are 'locked'. From Pluto, Charon would appear fixed in the sky.

Pluto has an extensive though very thin atmosphere, but this may not be permanent. Pluto passed perihelion in 1989, and is now moving outwards, so that it is becoming colder and colder. In a few years the temperature may have dropped so much that the atmosphere will freeze out on to the surface. For part of its long 'year' there may be no atmosphere at all.

In many ways Pluto does not seem worthy to rank as a true planet. It may be that both it and Triton come from the Kuiper Belt, made up of asteroidal-sized bodies moving round the Sun in these remote regions; many are now known. It also seems very likely that Triton was once an independent body, and was captured by Neptune long ago; it is larger than Pluto.

Is there another large planet beyond Pluto? There may well be. Pluto turned up close to the position worked out by Lowell from irregularities in the motions of Uranus and Neptune; but as Pluto is so small and so lightweight, it could not possibly produce measurable perturbations in giant worlds. Either Lowell's success was sheer luck (which I find hard to believe) or else the real 'Planet X' awaits discovery.

It is fascinating to go on an imaginary tour of the outer Solar System. Uranus first; from, say, Miranda it would loom large in the sky, but without much detail apart from scudding clouds. Neptune: from close range the Great Dark Spot would have been striking, and though it now seems to have disappeared there will be many clouds and storms on view. Triton will show its spouting geysers in that excessively tenuous atmosphere. And from Pluto – a distant, almost starlike Sun with a black sky dominated by Charon. You would certainly not be able to make out our tiny Earth.

I will not pretend that these outer planets are at all spectacular telescopically. We need space-probes; but at all events, there is plenty to interest us in the furthest reaches of the Solar System.

▼ **The surface of Pluto:** *an impression by Paul Doherty, showing how* Charon, with our Sun in the far distance, might appear from Pluto.

The End of the Universe

Almost 80 years have passed since Edwin Hubble showed that, apart from a few systems in our immediate neighbourhood, all the galaxies are moving away from us, so that the entire universe is expanding. Most astronomers (not all) believe that the universe as we know it was created in a Big Bang, between 12,000 million and 15,000 million years ago. But how will it end – or will it continue for ever?

If we are to look into the future, we must begin by looking back into the past. Matter did not erupt into a pre-existing space; in fact space, time and matter came into existence simultaneously. The expansion began at once, and space has been expanding ever since, carrying all matter – and, hence, the galaxies – with it.

Initially the temperatures were colossal, and the universe was dominated by radiation. Energetic photons were moving around, and some of this radiation turned into particles of matter and anti-matter – including quarks, the building blocks of protons and neutrons, plus the particles which make up the nuclei of atoms today, and also lighter particles such as electrons and positrons. There was a tiny imbalance – more particles than anti-particles – so that most of the anti-particles were quickly annihilated by collisions with particles. About one-millionth of a second after the beginning of time, when the temperature had dropped to a mere million million degrees, quarks clumped together to form protons and neutrons.

There were more protons than neutrons. About 100 seconds later, nuclear reactions took place everywhere, so that protons and neutrons joined together to form nuclei of helium. At this stage the universe consisted of (a) radiation, and (b) atomic nuclei of hydrogen and helium. The universe was opaque, simply because photons of light could not travel far before being blocked by collision.

Then, 300,000 years later, when the universe had cooled to a few thousand degrees, there was a dramatic change. Electrons were captured by nuclei to

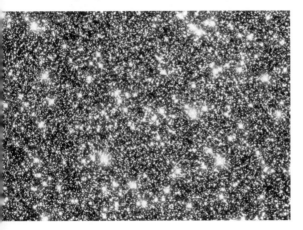

◀ The centre of
Omega Centauri –
a massive globular star
cluster 17,000 light-years
from Earth, which contains
millions of stars orbiting
around a common centre
of gravity, as imaged
by the Hubble Space
Telescope.

make complete atoms. This meant that the universe became transparent; light could now travel vast distances without being blocked. It followed that the radiation content of the universe was free the spread out through the expanding volume of space. The expansion diluted the radiation, and the wavelengths of the light were lengthened. Today, the radiation is still there, diluted and also shifted to the red – into the millimetre and centimetre range. It remains a faint glow filling all space, and is therefore the last remnant of the Big Bang fireball. It was detected in the 1960s by the American astronomers Penzias and Wilson; we call it the cosmic background radiation.

After space had become transparent, matter clumped together to form galaxies and clusters of galaxies, by processes which we do not yet understand completely. Ever since then, the clusters of galaxies have been receding from each other, and the entire universe continues to expand.

Such is the basic picture. Many present-day cosmologists believe that at an early stage, around 10^{-35} seconds after the beginning of time, the universe went through a brief but amazingly dramatic period of inflation, blowing up the universe to such a vast size that the observable universe we can examine today is only a tiny fragment of the whole. In this case, the universe is still much larger than we can see – and it is still expanding.

Whether the expansion will continue indefinitely depends upon gravity. We all know about escape velocity – 11 km/s (7 miles/s) in the case of the Earth – and we can apply this to the universe as a whole. If there is enough material, then the galaxies will be pulled back. We have to fix on a critical density, usually denoted by the Greek letter omega (Ω), which seems to be about 5×10^{-27} kg per cubic metre: that is to say, on average about three hydrogen atoms in each cubic metre of space. We then have several possible pictures. (NB: This programme, with Iain Nicolson, was broadcast in April 1996. Since then (2002) there has been new evidence in support of (a), the open universe. I have modified this article accordingly, but the jury is still out. I must stress that the main text here is based entirely upon what Iain Nicolson said at the time of the programme.)

(a) *The open universe.* The density is too low to halt the expansion. It slows down, but towards a steady speed.

(b) *The closed universe.* The density is greater than the critical value, so that eventually gravity wins the battle, and expansion stops. Subsequently, the universe will begin to collapse on itself – slowly at first, and then more and more rapidly until all the material comes together in a final 'Big Crunch'.

(c) *The 'flat' universe.* Einstein showed that space is curved, or bent, by the presence of matter. Therefore, space in a closed universe 'wraps round' on itself rather like the surface of a sphere. If the density is exactly equal to the critical density, then the galaxies will have just enough energy to continue moving apart for ever; their recessional velocities will get closer and closer to zero, but will not actually become zero until an infinite time in the future. This sort of universe is termed 'flat' because space would have apparent curvature, but would resemble a table-top of infinite extent; rays of light would simply move in straight lines (ignoring local deviations due to individual clumps of matter).

Obviously, then, the first essential is to measure the mean density of matter in the universe. If we assume that all the material is contained in objects which we can see – stars, nebulae, and so on – we can estimate the masses of all the galaxies in a sufficiently large volume of space, and derive a value for the mean density and Ω. If we do this, we find that there is only about 1% of the mass needed to halt the expansion. In fact, Ω for luminous matter is about 0.01.

However, this is by no means the whole story. If most of the mass is concentrated where most of the light is – that is to say, in the central regions of galaxies – then the stars and gas-clouds in those systems should follow Kepler-type laws. The outer parts of the spirals should be revolving round the nucleus more slowly than the regions closer in. This is not what happens. The outer parts of the spirals revolve at least as fast – sometimes faster – than the inner parts. This shows that there must be a great deal of mass in the outer parts, so that most of the mass of a typical galaxy is contained in an outer halo of non-luminous 'dark matter'. A typical spiral may have five to ten times as much dark matter as luminous matter.

The same sort of argument can be applied to clusters of galaxies. Individual member galaxies are moving around inside the cluster, and if there were not a great deal of dark matter present the clusters would have dispersed long ago. Typical clusters need from 30 to 50 times as much dark matter as luminous matter in order to hold them together.

We can also use the new technique of gravitational lensing. Rays of light passing by a massive body are deflected in such a way that two or more images of a more distant object can be produced. If the alignment is perfect, the background object will look like a ring; if not, it will show up as two or more distorted arcs. A cluster of galaxies acts in the manner of a weak giant lens, distorting the shapes of background galaxies into arcs or small arclets. Lensing of this type means that we can probe not only the inner parts of clusters, where the brighter galaxies are seen, but also the outer parts. This again reveals the presence of dark matter – perhaps 50 to 100 times as much as the luminous content.

As yet we cannot claim that we have found enough dark matter to prove that the universe is closed. Yet all the observations show that Ω is remarkably close to 1. The whole universe is dominated by dark matter. The next step is to try to decide just what this dark matter is.

There are many suggestions. For example, brown dwarfs (failed stars), planets, and chunks of interstellar matter could exist in vast numbers and remain undetectable by our present techniques. Luckily, the abundance of the light elements in the universe today – in particular, helium-3 (lightweight helium), deuterium (heavy hydrogen) and lithium, all of which were 'cooked' at the Big Bang – provide important clues. The amounts of these elements which were produced depend upon the density of ordinary matter (known as baryonic matter), and the observed amounts today imply that the total amount of ordinary matter, in the form of protons and neutrons, cannot be more than 10% of the critical value. If there is enough dark matter to close the universe, at least 90% of it must be non-baryonic, which means that its nature is completely different from that of ordinary matter.

It has been attributed to neutrinos with finite mass ('hot dark matter'). Or it could be that most of the dark matter is made up of slow-moving, exotic elementary particles which are nicknamed WIMPs (weakly interacting massive particles). Yet nobody has yet managed to measure the mass of a neutrino, and nobody has found any WIMPs.

Let us now peer into the future, taking one theory at a time. If the universe is open, expansion will go on for ever, with the clusters becoming further and further apart. Recent research (1999) indicates that the rate of expansion is actually increasing, and this would certainly lead to an open universe, though as yet the evidence is far from conclusive. In any case, in an open universe individual stars will use up their nuclear fuel and will die. For example, our Sun will run out of fuel in about 5000 million years hence; it will expand briefly to become a red giant (destroying the Earth in the process) and then shrink to a compact, superdense white dwarf, which over thousands of millions of years will cool down and become a cold, dead black dwarf. More massive stars will explode as supernovae, so that their remnants will become neutron stars. A few will collapse to form black holes. The least massive stars will outlive the Sun many times over; even so, after 10^{14} years or so, all the nuclear reactions in all the stars in every galaxy will have ceased, and the galaxies will be cold, dark places.

Although close encounters between stars are very rare, they do happen occasionally. In such an encounter, one star will gain energy at the expense of the other. The star which gains energy will move further out from the centre of the galaxy, while the other star will fall closer in. Even without such encounters, an orbiting star radiates tiny amounts of gravitational waves, so that it gradually loses energy and migrates towards the centre. Given enough time, most of the individual dead stars escape – that is to say, the galaxy evaporates – while the others coalesce into a gigantic black hole. After about 10^{20} years, which is 10,000 million times longer than the present age of the universe, the universe will consist of vast black holes, individual dead stars, planets, gas, elementary particles such as neutrinos, and photons (light energy), spreading further and further out over the ever-increasing volume of space. By then, the average distance between the gigantic black holes will be more than a million million light-years, which is a hundred times further than the limit of the universe we can see at the present time.

What happens next depends upon whether or not protons are stable, everlasting particles. Current theories suggest that they are not, and that they will eventually decay into lighter particles plus radiation. A proton is made up of three tiny, point-like particles called quarks – two so-called 'up' quarks and one 'down' quark. Very occasionally an up-quark and a down-quark can come together closely enough to interact. The result is that the proton converts into a positron (an anti-electron) and a short-lived particle called a pion, which almost immediately disintegrates into photons, that is, light energy. The average lifetime of a proton must be at least 10^{31} years, and it is not surprising that up to now we have failed to detect a single clear case of proton decay. But if they do decay, then in, say, 10^{33} years, all conventional matter will have disintegrated into positrons and radiation. Dead stars, planets and everything else will have vanished from the universe, to be replaced by positrons and photons to add to the existing electrons, photons and neutrinos.

Even black holes may not last for ever. According to Stephen Hawking, particles and anti-particles form close to the event horizon, that is to say, the edge of the black hole. Usually they will collide again and vanish, but occasionally one of the pair will fall into the hole, while the other – with no partner with which to annihilate – will escape. The black hole will emit particles and radiation in the same way as a 'hot' body. This emission removes energy from the gravitational field of the black hole, and so reduces the mass of the black hole itself. The smaller it gets, the faster it 'leaks', so that eventually it will explode in a burst of particles and radiation, mainly positrons and photons. It will take at least 10^{66} years for a stellar-mass black hole to evaporate, 10^{99} years for a galaxy-sized black hole, and about 10^{110} years for a black hole made up of a supercluster of galaxies; but the final result must be that dark matter will end up as an ever-more dilute mixture of electrons, positrons, neutrinos and photons.

The extent of this dilution is almost impossible to visualize. In 10^{66} years, the average distance between a typical electron and positron will be at least a million million light-years. Yet despite these inconceivable distances, the electrons and positrons will still form pairs, and will orbit around each other, forming 'atoms' of positronium. Gradually, the orbiting pair will lose energy and spiral together until they collide, annihilating each other and turning into photons. This will take about 10^{116} years. As the universe continues to expand, some electrons and positrons will escape this fate. We are then left with a universe of widely separated photons, neutrinos and occasional electrons or positrons, becoming increasingly darker and colder. Nothing else is ever likely to happen. It sounds depressing – but the same situation would eventually occur with a 'flat' universe.

But suppose that the universe expands to a finite size, and then starts to collapse? If the expansion stops in the not-too-distant future (say, in 10^{11} or 10^{12} years' time), some stars in some galaxies will still be shining, and there may even be astronomers to witness what happens next. The red shifts will become blue shifts as the galaxies begin to draw together. Because light takes a long time to reach us from remote galaxies, this will not immediately become obvious. The contraction will already have begun before we start to see blue shifts, and we will see blue shifts in nearby galaxies while very distant galaxies will still be showing red shifts. Many thousands of millions of years will pass before all the galaxies show blue shifts.

During most of the contracting period, life could carry on as before, but then – gradually at first, then more rapidly – the temperature of the background radiation will rise. By about 10,000 million years before the Big Crunch, the temperature will have risen back to its present value of about $3°$ above absolute zero, or $-276°C$ (3K).

A hundred million years before the Big Crunch, galaxies will merge and lose their separate identities. A million years before the end, the whole of space will be warmer than the present-day temperature of the surface of the

▶ **The Sombrero galaxy (M104).** *There is much speculation that a black hole lies at the centre of the Sombrero. This image was taken by the 0.9-m telescope at Kitt Peak National Observatory.*

Earth, and our form of life will find it difficult to survive. By 100,000 years before the Crunch, the temperature everywhere will be about 10,000K, hotter than the present surface of the Sun; stars will explode, and the whole universe will become an opaque mass of plasma (atomic nuclei and electrons), together with radiation – just as before the Big Bang fireball from which the universe first emerged.

A hundred seconds to go; atomic nuclei disintegrate into protons and neutrons, and chemical elements are destroyed. One millionth of a second to go, and protons and neutrons break up into quarks with the temperature now over 10 million million degrees.

Then, one millionth of a second later, comes the Big Crunch. This is the end of everything – the end of space, time and matter. Everything is snuffed out of existence in a state of infinite compression, known as a singularity. This is final. There can be no 'after', because time itself has ceased.

But what about the oscillating universe idea – which I rather irreverently call the Concertina Universe? It has been suggested that because to some extent the Big Crunch replicates the conditions of the Big Bang, the Crunch will be followed by a new Bang and a re-expansion of the universe. In effect, the collapsing universe will bounce and rebound before reaching the state of infinite compression which would terminate space, time and matter. It would enter a new cycle of expansion and contraction, and this cyclic process could go on for ever. If so, there is no reason to assume that the present cycle is the first; there may have been countless previous cycles, and the process may just go on and on in the future.

However, it must be said that we know of no force which could halt the collapse and cause a bounce. If it does happen, then we must depend upon some new and currently unknown force. Our problem is that present-day theories of the universe simply cannot deal with what would happen in the final stages of the collapse. Perhaps space-time breaks down into some kind of turbulent 'foam' from which something new would emerge. . . . We need a quantum theory of gravity to cope with this, and at present we lack anything of this kind.

Moreover, the Big Crunch may not be exactly the same as a Big Bang in reverse. Throughout the lifetime of the universe, stars have been busily converting matter into radiation, so that the radiation content of the universe increases while the matter content declines. If the Big Crunch does not happen until long after stars have died and protons have decayed, even more of the total content of the universe will be radiation. So, whenever the Big Crunch happens, more radiation will be 'going in' than came out of the Big Bang. At the moment, in an expanding universe, light-waves are red-shifted because of the expansion, and this reduces the energy of the photons. But during the collapse, the radiation is blue-shifted, and this increases the energy of the photons; the result is that the universe collapses faster and faster, and becomes even hotter than it was in the Big Bang. It follows that if the universe 'bounces' before space, time and matter are totally annihilated, this bounce should be more energetic than the precious Big Bang. Each successive cycle should be more violent and longer-lasting than the previous one, until, ultimately, the cycles will become so long that the inhabitants of the universe will be quite unable to decide whether their universe is closed or flat.

▼ *A starburst galaxy, NGC 3310.* This is a very active galaxy, which is forming clusters of new stars at an amazing rate. This image was taken using the Hubble Space Telescope.

But if all 'memory' of the precious cycle is completely wiped out in the Crunch, a new cycle will be a completely independent universe, unrelated to ours. Therefore, it would hardly be realistic to think of the process as being a continuous oscillation of *our* universe. Conditions in the next cycle would be totally different: different forces, different laws of nature, perhaps even different numbers of dimensions. There is no guarantee that conditions in a new cycle, or new universe, would permit the existence of life as we know it, or of sentient beings of any kind. Perhaps only a small proportion of cycles, or independent universes, are capable of supporting life.

Whether or not there are other universes, independent of ours, we do not know. But if our universe began as a tiny, so-called quantum fluctuation which inflated rapidly, creating its own space (or space-time) and matter as it went, there is no reason to assume that this event must be unique. There could well be any number, perhaps even an infinite number, of universes, each of which is completely independent, with its own expanding bubble of space-time; and each will be blissfully unaware of all the others. Or perhaps the universe is divided into countless domains, each with different properties and rates of expansion, but where the boundaries of the domains are so far away that it is unlikely that we will ever encounter them. Ideas of multiple or parallel universes sound like science fiction, and perhaps justifiably so; but they represent a speculative possibility which should be taken very seriously.

It has even been suggested that quantum effects could create a new expanding space-time bubble in our own universe. Rather than expanding through our universe, with alarming consequences, these bubbles would branch off from our space-time, creating their own space and time as they went. In this scenario, even if our universe is fated to collapse into oblivion in a Big Crunch, it could give birth to new universes, some of which might be capable of supporting life. Perhaps advanced beings in the far future may be able to concentrate enough energy in a tiny volume of space to make a new universe deliberately, and somehow escape into it, so avoiding the fate of the Big Crunch.

Summing up: we do not yet know what will be the future of the universe. We do not know whether it is open, closed or flat. Everything depends upon pinning down the mean density and the dark matter content of the universe, and so far we have been unable to do so. If the universe is open – and very recent results do favour this scenario – it will expand for ever, becoming colder, darker and more dilute as it evolves. After truly colossal intervals of time, ordinary matter – that is to say, atoms and nuclei – will disappear altogether, and, relative to an infinite future, the era of stars and galaxies will be no more than a short interlude in the history of the universe on its way to a dark, featureless eternity. If the universe is closed, it is fated to collapse in a Big Crunch, and, so far as we can tell, the Crunch will signal the end of space, time and matter. Meanwhile, the speculative prospect of bounces, new cycles and new universes remains tantalizing to those of us who find the bleak emptiness of an open universe or the final annihilation of a closed universe most unattractive.

One thing is certain. At least we have plenty of time to think it over!

The Lives of the Galaxies

The Hubble Space Telescope has proved to be an outstanding success. In 1996 it produced a 'deep sky' image, using an exposure of 100 hours with four filters, which showed galaxies which are fainter and presumably further away than any recorded before. So what can we learn from studies of these far-away systems?

The key question to which we want an answer concerns the ages of the galaxies, and whether it is possible for one type of galaxy to turn into another – for instance, a spiral into an elliptical system, or vice versa. It was Edwin Hubble himself who produced the famous 'tuning fork' diagram, showing ellipticals, spirals and barred spirals, but whether or not this indicated anything in the nature of an evolutionary sequence was by no means clear. It now seems that galaxy types vary with location; clusters of galaxies are dominated by ellipticals, whereas field systems (that is to say, those outside clusters) are dominated by spirals. Therefore, do the galaxies show their rich variety in forms because they were always so, or does the environment shape them after formation? This is often termed 'Nature versus Nurture'.

▼ **The Coma cluster of galaxies,** lying about 330 million light-years away. It is part of the Perseus–Pisces supercluster of galaxies, stretching almost halfway around the sky, as viewed from the Earth. (AURA)

The HST began by looking at distant clusters of galaxies. There were already hints, from data supplied by telescopes such as the Anglo-Australian and the William Herschel, that the galaxy populations in these clusters were bluer than comparable systems closer to us, and, sure enough, the HST images showed many more spirals and fewer ellipticals than exist in regions nearer to the Solar System.

The main information came from clusters showing a red shift of 0.4, corresponding to a distance of 4–5000 million light-years – so that we are seeing them as they used to be a third of the way back to the Big Bang. (Even more remote clusters have been imaged, but less is known about them.) It therefore seems that around 4000 million years ago some spirals were being transformed into ellipticals, in which case the Nurture hypothesis has a clear advantage.

The next question is: 'What happened? What caused this transformation?' There are three basic possibilities:

1. Merging of galaxies. Computer simulations show that when two spirals collide, the result may be an elliptical or an SO system.

2. Removal of gas by external effects. Suppose that a galaxy invades the cluster for the first time. As it falls into the cluster, it encounters a 'brick wall' of gas in between the galaxies which are already members of the cluster, and this produces a pressure which strips the gas off the intruder. This gas is in effect the 'fuel' from which stars are formed, and so its removal leads to a decline in spiral structure and a loss of blue light.

3. Finally, it has been proposed that galaxies may be slightly perturbed and disarranged as they traverse the cluster, due to tidal forces – a process called 'galaxy harassment', which slowly tears the spirals apart, destroying their disks and leaving scattered debris.

All these simulations have been checked against the HST data, and it seems that no one process alone is dominant. More probably all three are occurring, and the HST pictures do seem to support this idea.

The ellipticals, however, make up a very ancient and homogeneous class; it is very difficult either to destroy an elliptical or to change it into anything else. If two ellipticals merge, the result seems to be an even larger elliptical. Even in the most remote clusters, ellipticals look familiar, and are very numerous indeed. Quantitative studies indicate that at least some of these are very old by any standards; indeed, they may be the oldest galaxies of all, so that they formed not so very long after the Big Bang. Can we, then, look back far enough to the time when they were formed?

One HST image, of a small region in Ursa Major, is of special interest here. It was a random area of the sky, chosen so as not to include anything unusual – unlike the clustered fields discussed above. This means that the galaxies in the HST 'deep field' are seen over a wide range of distance, but without follow-up observations it is not clear which systems are remote and which are comparatively nearby. The sheer number of galaxies seen in the picture far exceeds what you would expect if you simply replicated the local universe of nearby galaxies to a great distance, and predicted what you would see.

▼ **Hubble Deep Field:** several hundred galaxies are visible in this 'deepest-ever' view of the universe. There is an amazing variety of galaxy shapes and colours – important clues in our understanding of the evolution of the universe.

There are, in fact, 'extra galaxies' out there – so why do we not see their successors today? What happened to them?

This is what we call the 'faint blue galaxy' problem. Careful analyses of the faintest HST images also show the galaxies to be irregular in form, with knotty structures suggestive of fragments coming together to form larger galaxies. So here too it is possible that merging is going on, and this could explain why in the past we find many more small galaxies than might have been expected. Merging may still be continuing rather than being confined to one particular epoch.

A clever trick has been used here by astronomers at Cambridge. The four filters used to take the deep-field picture enabled the researchers to isolate the most distant objects. Since the galaxies which are furthest away have the greatest red shifts, these are the systems whose spectra are dimmest in the ultraviolet. The spectrum of a typical galaxy shows a steep drop in the far ultraviolet, and when this enters the deep-field filter which records only in the far red, the observed signal drops abruptly.

Of the few hundred galaxies shown in the deep-field picture that are bright enough to provide reliable morphologies and colours, about 10% are being seen beyond a red shift of 2.5, which corresponds to a look-back time of 10–12,000 thousand million years. Therefore, most of the sources appear to be less remote than this. A high percentage of the high red-shift sources are 'lumpy irregulars', but there are also some which are compact. Using the Keck I telescope on Mauna Kea in Hawaii, astronomers have obtained spectra for six of the brightest galaxies, and have confirmed their high red shifts.

In short, we come back to 'Nature versus Nurture'. Some galaxies, notably the ellipticals, are very old, and have maintained their forms from the earliest times. But in clusters, a surprising amount of recent transforming of galaxies has taken place, with spirals being destroyed in various ways. Spirals seem to be particularly vulnerable; it is perhaps fortunate that our own Galaxy is not a member of a rich cluster, so that it has had a relatively quiet history.

However, mergers have occurred in our Milky Way system. There is, for example, the Sagittarius dwarf, a low-mass galaxy identified by astronomers using the Anglo-Australian Telescope, which is actually in the process of colliding with our Galaxy. Merging is still going on, though presumably not quite so abundantly as in the distant past. We have also come across 'black galaxies' in which there are no stars at all; whether stars will ever form in them is not known.

If we could board a time machine and go back into the past, we would find a great deal that is unfamiliar. We cannot achieve this, but by looking back into the past we can at least begin to form some idea of what conditions were like then. And this, in turn, may well help us to look into the future.

Jupiter: The Missing Water

In March 1993 three renowned American comet-hunters, two professional and one amateur, made a remarkable discovery. Eugene Shoemaker, Carolyn Shoemaker and David Levy found what was described as a 'squashed comet'. It was quite unlike anything previously seen, and examination soon showed that something dramatic had happened to it; it had been broken up, and the nucleus had been transformed into a sort of string-of-pearls arrangement. Because it was the team's ninth discovery, the comet became known as Shoemaker–Levy 9 (SL9 for short).

Amazingly, it was not travelling round the Sun at all; it was orbiting Jupiter, and calculations showed that it had probably done so since around 1970 (this was not the first such instance; Comet P/Gehrels 3, for example, had orbited Jupiter temporarily). But it emerged that on 7 July 1992 the comet had skirted only 20,000 km (12,000 miles) above the Jovian cloud-tops, and had literally been torn apart by the gravitational pull of the Giant Planet. A year later, in July 1993, it reached 'apojove' – its most distant point from Jupiter – and solar perturbations put it into a collision path. The disruption had meant that dust and ice had poured out from the fragments of the nucleus, brightening them sufficiently to make them visible from Earth; but the comet was doomed. It would hit Jupiter in July 1994

There was no doubt that impacts would occur, but nobody was at all sure what the results would be. The biggest unknowns were the sizes and masses of the fragments. Depending upon just where the initial break-up occurred, the nucleus could have been as much as 10 km (6 miles) in diameter or as

◀ **Comet Shoemaker–Levy – Fragment G.**
The fireball was seen 12 minutes after impact. On the opposite limb of Jupiter it is possible to see the impact A site. (Photograph by Peter McGregor, Siding Spring.)

little as 3 km (2 miles). Consequently, the largest fragments might have been a kilometre or two across – or they could be much smaller. It was even suggested that the fragments were so weak that they might break apart as they approached Jupiter, so that they would hit the Jovian gas rather in the manner of a shower of shrapnel, and cause relatively little disturbance. Many astronomers believed that far from being solid lumps of 'dirty ice', the fragments were more like piles of rubble; you might imagine a collection of a million house-bricks with room-sized spaces between them. These uncertainties meant that it was very difficult to predict the amount of energy that would be released when the fragments slammed into Jupiter's atmosphere at speeds up to 218,000 km/h (135,000 mph). A loose rubble-pile would not cause a single explosive blast but an intense cosmic hailstorm lasting for an hour or more; a 1 km (half-mile) solid ice sphere would deliver the equivalent energy of 115,000 million tons of TNT. At least 20 fragments were identified, lettered A to W; A would hit on 16 July, W on 22 July. The largest fragments were G and Q, while J and M soon faded out altogether. Subsequently, P and Q split in two; P2 then split again while P1 faded away. By the time they reached Jupiter, the fragments were strung out over some 29 million km (18 million miles), with separate tails and dusty 'wings' extending ahead of and behind the main swarm.

Predictably, the coming event caught the public imagination, and the astrologers and other cranks were very vocal. Perhaps the weirdest statement came from a lady named Sofia Richmond, also known as Sister Gabriel ('Polish, like Copernicus'), who believed that the impacting comet was Halley's (!) and that it was a sign of divine retribution; to save the world we would have to destroy all pornography overnight, abolish all crime, outlaw violence and obscenity on television, replace all beers and wines with non-alcoholic drinks, and reduce all wrong-doing by capital and corporal punishment. Her message was printed in all the quality papers, and was sent personally to dignatories ranging from the Pope to President Yeltsin, Prime Minister Major, King Hussein of Jordan and, of course, the Queen. Whether any of the recipients took heed of her warnings is unclear . . . .

The first impact, A, occurred on schedule on 16 July. Earlier, I had been at Herstmonceux Castle, which had been the site of the Royal Greenwich Observatory, until – against the wishes of all astronomers – it had been removed by command of the Civil Service, and relegated to an office block in Cambridge. (Subsequently, of course, the RGO was disbanded completely – a loss which can never be made good – *see Chapter 30*.) Since then the Herstmonceux telescopes had been unused, so I suggested bringing the 26-inch and 13-inch refractors back into operation specifically to study the cometary collision. It proved to be a Herculean task, because the equipment had been left to rot. In the 26-inch dome the rising floor would not rise, only half the shutter would open, and the drive stuck; however, we managed to overcome all the problems – I provided my own eyepieces – and on 16 July the telescope was turned towards Jupiter; the patch marking the site of the Fragment A impact was visible. The next few nights were cloudy, but on 20 July we had a magnificent view – and it was breathtaking.

The impact sites were blacker than anything I had ever seen on Jupiter, lying along latitude 45° south, and they were big; one of them was larger than the Great Red Spot, which at this time was grey and rather obscure. As other fragments struck, the scene became even more bizarre, and the storms were easily visible in my modest 3-inch refractor. In fact, the effects on Jupiter were much more dramatic than anyone (except possibly Sister Gabriel) had dared to hope.

Obviously, all the world's major observatories were on watch. For example, Dr Jim Scotti was at the Spacewatch telescope at Kitt Peak, Arizona, and was the first to photograph the strange 'wings'; he drew attention to a chain of craters on Jupiter's satellite Callisto, which could well have been caused by an impact of the Shoemaker–Levy type. Dr Steven Miller was atop Mauna Kea in Hawaii, using the telescopes there (America's IRTF or Infrared Telescope Facility and our own UKIRT, United Kingdom Infrared Telescope); predictably, as the heat of the impact faded, infrared radiation was still received. Violent plumes had been reported after the impacts, rising to hundreds of kilometres, but nobody was initially sure how deep the fragments had penetrated. Dr Miller found that A and C could be followed down to the 3-bar level, where the clouds are of ammonium hydrosulphide, and A down to the ammonia clouds at the 1-bar level. The debris due to A soon sank; Fragment B was described as a 'drizzle', but C, G and Q produced tremendous bangs. Material sent up from below Jupiter's cloud-tops gave information about conditions there – the heat of the impacts must have approached 30,000 degrees – and there were reports of effects antipodal to the sites, in which case it ought to have been possible to detect 'ripple' phenomena. In fact, this proved to be very difficult, as it meant measuring temperature differences of only a degree or two, but at least the effects were greater than most people had anticipated. There were also effects on Jovian

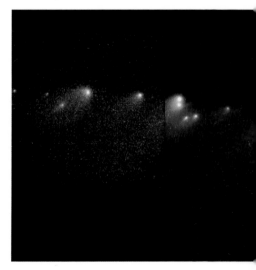

▶ **Pieces of Comet Shoemaker–Levy,** strung out like a 'string of pearls' as the comet's nucleus is fragmented by Jupiter's strong gravity. This is a composite image obtained by the Hubble Space Telescope.

aurorae. Usually, these aurorae are of equal intensity at both poles, but after the impacts the southern aurorae faded, so that possibly the ejected dust was soaking up the electrons and other particles responsible for the aurorae.

Of course, observations were made from space; the various satellites and probes – IUE, EUVE, Galileo, Ulysses and even the remote Voyagers were called in – and superb images were sent back by the Hubble Space Telescope.

Of special interest was the detection of water. It had been believed that a watery layer lay beneath the clouds, and spectroscopic observations did indeed show traces of water, though not as much as might have been anticipated. It was not believed that the comet had penetrated down to the water layer itself, but, naturally, it was assumed that the water was of Jovian rather than cometary origin.

It was an exciting time; the impact scars remained visible for many months, and were still traceable in 1995. There were, however, no dire results on Earth. Sister Gabriel's heavenly informant must have called her up on a crossed line!

The second impact on Jupiter occurred in December 1995. This time the impactor was not a comet, but a man-made vehicle – the entry probe of the Galileo mission.

Galileo was launched in October 1989, from the Shuttle. Unfortunately it did not have the power of a Saturn-5 rocket; after the *Challenger* disaster it was considered too risky to launch a major liquid-fuel rocket from a Shuttle, and so Galileo had to make do with less powerful units. This meant that it had to use the gravity-assist technique, and go on a circuitous journey, rather like driving from Brighton to Bognor Regis by way of Carlisle. In February 1990 it swung past Venus, picking up speed; in the following December it flew past Earth, and then headed out into the asteroid belt. In 1991 it obtained the first close-range image of an asteroid (Gaspra), after which it headed back to another Earth flyby in December 1992. Back into

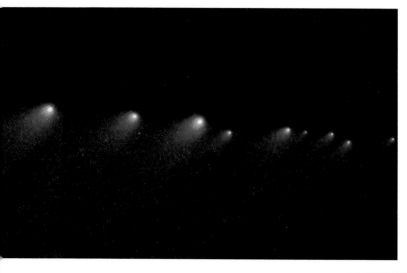

the asteroid belt, so that in August 1993 it was able to image another dwarf world – Ida – and find that it was attended by a satellite, Dactyl, approximately 1.6 km (1 mile) wide. Then, at last, Galileo could make tracks for Jupiter.

There had already been problems. The high-gain antenna, so important for communications, failed to deploy; apparently the constant journeys between laboratory and launching site, due to delays following the *Challenger* tragedy, had resulted in a loss of lubrication which nobody had noticed. All efforts to free the antenna failed, and so the planners were reconciled to

▼ **Target area of the Galileo impact probe,** near the Jovian North Equatorial Belt, as imaged by the HST Wide Field Planetary Camera 2. The probe was released from Galileo in July 1995 and entered Jupiter's atmosphere five months later, transmitting data to Galileo overhead, then back to Earth.

using only the low-gain antenna, which affected the stream of data available. Then, almost at the last moment, there was trouble with the on-board recorder, so that NASA reluctantly sacrificed the pictures of Jupiter and its volcanic satellite Io, which ought to have been taken during the final approach.

Galileo (cost, £900 million) was made up of two parts: an orbiter, and an entry probe. The orbiter, weighing 2½ tons, was scheduled to orbit Jupiter, monitoring both the planet and its satellites, and continuing to transmit data for two years. (In the event it was magnificently successful, and was still operating well in 2002). The role of the entry vehicle was to plunge into the Jovian clouds at a speed of over 170,000 km/h (105,000 mph), and to go on sending back signals until being destroyed; a total of 75 minutes was the target, but nobody could really tell. Neither was it certain how deep the probe could go before being put out of action. If it penetrated to 640 km (400 miles), it would – possibly – reach the water layer. The point of entry was 6° north of Jupiter's equator, at the edge of the North Equatorial Belt (usually the most prominent of all the belts). The angle of entry had to be 8°. Shallower than that, the probe would simply 'skate away'; steeper, and it would burn up before any useful data could be transmitted. The total weight was 340 kg (750 lbs).

In June 1995 Galileo passed through two dense dust-clouds which had not been predicted – at a distance of 180 million km (110 million miles) from Jupiter (that is to say, 2400 Jupiter radii). There was no damage, and on 16 November Galileo passed through the Jovian bow shock; thereafter it was deep inside the planet's magnetosphere. Already, on 13 July, the entry probe had been separated from the orbiter, and was making its own way to its destination – and its doom.

Understandably, there was immense tension at Mission Control during the last stages of the approach. Initially moving at 170,000 km/h (106,000 mph), the probe would first be slowed by parachute to a mere 96,000 km/h (60,000 mph), and would slacken quickly as it descended into the thicker atmosphere. During descent it would monitor the lightning flashes, cloud movements, magnetic effects, temperatures, pressures, and so on. The signals would be relayed by the orbiter, passing 160,000 km (100,000 miles) overhead.

In the event, all went wall. The entry probe plunged into the clouds at the appointed moment, and sent back signals for 61 minutes, by which time it had descended to a depth of 640 km (400 miles) – where the pressure was 20 times that of the Earth's air at sea-level. Meanwhile, the orbiter fired its own motors and was put into a path round Jupiter, ready to begin its 'grand tour' of the satellites, including the dangerously volcanic Io.

It took time for the results to be analyzed, and there were some major surprises. First, the winds. We knew that the Jovian winds were strong – over 640 km/h (400 mph) – but it had been assumed that they were more or less confined to the upper clouds. After all, our own winds are mainly the result of the difference in solar heating at the poles and at the equator, and presumably the same would apply to Jupiter, even though the rotational axis is almost perpendicular to the orbital plane instead of being inclined at an angle of 23½ degrees, as is the Earth's. But Galileo found that as it descended, the winds did not slacken. By the time that contact was lost, the winds were just as strong as they had been at the surface. This indicates that the main force driving the Jovian winds is not the Sun at all, but heat radiating upwards from the hot interior, so that the whole situation is totally unlike anything which had been anticipated,

Secondly, there had been expectations of strong lightning activity. This also turned out to be wrong. Flashes were seen, but far fewer than had been expected.

However, the main shock was the lack of water. Jupiter's atmosphere is dry; it cannot contain more than 5–10% as much water as is found in the Sun. The immediate conclusion was that the water thrown up by the Shoemaker–Levy impact was due to the dying comet, but the dryness of Jupiter still had to be explained. Three theories were proposed, none of which seem to be particularly convincing.

One idea was that Galileo plunged into the Jovian equivalent of a desert region on Earth. It entered near the edge of the North Equatorial Belt, which was – as usual – very prominent. In this theory, Jupiter's atmosphere at the equator is heated by the Sun, and rises until clouds form and water is lost. The dry atmosphere then flows north and south, descending in these 'desert' regions. This would cause a violent downdraught – but could such a downdraught penetrate down to 640 km (400 miles), particularly in view of the fact that there is so much heat flowing upwards from the core?

In Theory No. 2, water does exist, but is locked up in the deep interior of Jupiter, far below the depth reached by Galileo. This means that we must, to some extent, revise our ideas about how the planet was formed.

Assume that it began as a solid, rock-and-ice protoplanet, which grew until it had 8–10 times the mass of the Earth, and collected ice-grains and dust from the solar nebula. Water ice was concentrated in the solid body, while the surrounding regions dried out. As the solid body grew and grew, it pulled in the dry surrounding gases by its gravitational force, and mixed them in with the existing atmosphere. This atmosphere would contain carbon and other gases which had originally been locked up in the core, but had escaped in the form of methane, ammonia, hydrogen sulphide and other volatiles as the core heated up.

Certainly this theory accounts for the present-day composition of Jupiter's atmosphere, and also for the lack of detectable water. Yet how could ice remain in the hot core while carbon-containing gases escaped? This does not seem reasonable.

In Theory No. 3, Jupiter's inner heat is sent out only in isolated 'hot spots' very roughly analogous to terrestrial volcanoes. But there are major problems here too, and for the moment we have to admit that the lack of water in Jupiter remains very much of a puzzle.

The entry probe was destroyed at the end of its transmissions, but the orbiter was still in full working order in 2001, and has provided a mass of information about the four Galilean satellites. Despite the loss of the high-gain antenna, which never did unfurl, Galileo has been in every way an outstanding success.

The Zodiacal Light

Of all the various 'sky-glows', one of the loveliest – and so far as people in general are concerned, one of the least-known – is the Zodiacal Light. It can be seen after sunset, rising from the west from the region in which the Sun has set; it takes the form of a tapering cone of radiance, almost ghostly in appearance, about as bright as the Milky Way but much 'softer'. It can remain on view for two hours after sunset, and it can also be seen in the east before sunrise. From Britain it 'leans over' towards the south, but from the tropics it stands almost vertical to the horizon.

It has been known for a long time. It is mentioned in ancient Arabic texts, and is important in Islam because religious devotees had to pray at dawn – and were all too often deceived by the 'false dawn' of the Zodiacal Light.

▼ **The Zodiacal Light –** Dominic Cantin you can
in this photograph by see Venus at bottom right.

It was also known as 'the wolf's tail' or 'the dawn's left hand'. In the famous *Rubiyyât*, Omar Khayyám speaks of 'dreaming when dawn's left hand was in the sky'. Shakespeare alluded to it in *Romeo and Juliet*; Romeo says: 'Night's candles are burned out and jocund day stands tiptoe on the misty mountain-top', to which Juliet replies: 'Yon is not daylight. I know it. It is some meteor which the Sun exhales.'

What could it be? The first scientific observations seem to have been made by G. D. Cassini, the Italian astronomer who was summoned to Paris to become the first director of the new observatory there (incidentally, he discovered four of Saturn's satellites as well as the main division in the Saturnian ring system). Writing in the *Journal des Scavans* in May 1683 Cassini claimed, quite correctly, that it was a kind of cloud, not around the Earth but around the Sun.

We now know that there is a large dust cloud in the Solar System; it is centred on the Sun, and is lens-shaped, so that it tapers out into the far reaches of the System. It lies along the ecliptic plane, marked by the constellations of the Zodiac, hence the name. The light shines by reflecting the light of the Sun, and its spectrum shows the familiar dark Fraunhofer lines. Not surprisingly, Doppler shifts can be measured, but there is one rather unexpected result. The dust which produces the Light is moving round the Sun in the same sense as the Earth, but its speed is considerably less than was anticipated. At present the reason for this is not known.

Photographs of the 'morning' Zodiacal Light show that it is not quite regular in outline. Apparently there is a belt of dust particles trapped in the Earth's wake, so that there is a dust tail making the morning Light less brilliant than the evening Light. It has also been found that the Light is not

◄ *The Gegenschein –*
a photograph of this
elusive glow, taken by
W. Fukushima in 1999.

symmetrical; it is tipped to the north of the main plane, and at the moment this is a complete mystery.

Until very recently it was thought that the Zodiacal Light particles – which are tiny by any standards – were cometary debris. Certainly it has to be replenished regularly, as otherwise it would have disappeared long ago, sucked into the Sun by the slight dragging action of sunlight, which makes small particles spiral slowly inwards. It would take a mere 10 million years to remove all the dust. But now it seems that comets do not provide the main source; the particles come from the results of collisions between asteroids, with the result that dust is sprayed all over the Solar System. The asteroids hit each other, grind away at each other and scrape dust off their surfaces. Meteoroids can contribute, but in general it appears that the Light is due to the very numerous, very small particles.

For many years observers have claimed to be able to see a slight glow in the sky in the direction exactly opposite to the Sun; it has become known as the Gegenschein, the English equivalent of which is 'counterglow'. It is very elusive indeed (from Britain I have seen it only once – in 1943, when the whole country was blacked out as a precaution against German air-raids). It is hard to capture on film, but CCDs can image it easily enough. From Britain it appears due south at midnight, at the point in the sky where the Sun will be six months later. There is also the Zodiacal Band, a continuous, very faint belt of light going right along the ecliptic and joining the Zodiacal Light proper. Oddly enough, recent work has shown that the Gegenschein is not exactly opposite to the Sun, but is displaced by 2° to the south, again for reasons which are unknown. It may possibly be due to light scattered by dust in the asteroid belt.

From Britain, the best time to see the evening Zodiacal Light is in the spring, when the ecliptic is most upright to the horizon. You must not have any lights to the west, so that ideal sites are the west coasts of Devon or the Channel Islands or possibly south-west Wales. About two hours after sunset the Light will be seen rising from the horizon rather north of west, and leaning over to the south, stretching along the ecliptic past the Pleiades and passing above Orion. It may even be seen disappearing into the Milky Way, which will stretch in a great arc from north, overhead through west to the southern horizon.

It can be photographed; use an aperture of f/3.5 or better, and a short-focus lens, with a fast transparency film of ASA 100 or more. Set the camera facing due west, about 25° up in the sky; exposure 5 to 10 minutes, so that star trails will be short. Light pollution is always a problem; select as dark a site as you can.

It is always worth seeking out this faint, ethereal glow. There are few sights in the heavens that are more beautiful than the Zodiacal Light.

Millennium Comets

We have to admit that the 20th century was decidedly comet-barren. In 1910 the Daylight Comet shone forth, and so, shortly afterwards, did Halley's, which at that return was bright – in sharp contrast to the return of 1986, which was the most unfavourable for many centuries. After that, great comets were conspicuous only by their absence. Of course, there were several which were prominent naked-eye objects, including Arend–Roland, in 1957 (the comet which ushered in the *Sky at Night* programmes), Ikeya–Seki (briefly in 1965), Bennett (1970) and West (1976), but of these only Ikeya–Seki could be classed as being in the first rank. The main displays were postponed until very near the end of the century. Then we had first Hyakutake, in 1996, and then Hale–Bopp, in 1997.

On 30 January 1996 the Japanese amateur Yuji Hyakutake, using a pair of 25 × 150 binoculars, discovered an 11th-magnitude comet in Libra. A month earlier he had discovered another comet in the same region of the sky, but that first 'find' had caused no particular excitement; after all, dim comets are commonplace enough. But the second discovery, Comet C/1996 B2, was different. It was a long way away, but preliminary calculations showed that it would come very near the Earth in March, and would be in the far north of the sky. Unquestionably it would be very striking.

▼ **Comet Hyakutake –** *as photographed in 1996 by Kent Blackwell (Virginia Beach, USA). A particularly lovely green comet! It faded quickly during April.*

▲ **Comet Hale–Bopp –** *for many years. I took*
undoubtedly the best *this photograph in*
comet to pass our way *April 1997.*

It brightened quickly as it moved north, and developed a tail. Comet tails are of two kinds: gas (ion) and dust; they always point more or less away from the Sun, because the ion tails are repelled by the pressure of sunlight and the dust tails by particles in the solar wind. Hyakutake was expected to develop both, though it was not a 'sun-grazer', and would not approach the Sun closer than 0.229 of an astronomical unit (that is to say, around 34 million km [21 million miles], well within the orbit of Mercury). Perihelion was reached on 1 May. Earlier, on 24 March, it came within 15 million km (9.3 million miles) of the Earth – about 40 times the distance of the Moon. Moving quickly across the sky, it covered over 18 degrees per day.

When at its brightest the comet was near the north pole of the sky. I had my best view on 26 March, when the coma was in Ursa Minor and the tail extended through Coma Berenices as far as Virgo; earlier, I had been frustrated by cloudy skies. At maximum the magnitude was around −1, and there was a long, gossamer-like tail extending for 100 degrees. But the comet's main characteristic was its lovely greenish colour. It was active, though measures indicated that the nucleus was less than 3 km (2 miles) in diameter.

Hyakutake was, in fact, a very small comet, and became spectacular only because it came so close to us. It faded during April, and moved south; its glory was not prolonged, but it certainly qualified as a 'great' comet, and one of the most beautiful on record. I was very sorry to see it depart. I am unlikely to see it again; it will not return for about 15,000 years.

We dared not hope for a comparable comet before the end of the century, but on 22 July 1995 Alan Hale and Thomas Bopp, in the United States, independently discovered a comet which was by no means a difficult binocular object, but yet was 900 million km (560 million miles) from the Sun, way beyond the orbit of Jupiter. It looked as though it might become bright, and so it did. From Aquila it tracked slowly into Cygnus, and then into Andromeda; by autumn it reached naked-eye visibility, developing a brownish, curved dust tail and a long, delicate, blue ion tail. It passed Earth on 22 March at 1.315 astronomical units (about 196 million km [122 million miles]), and had become so striking that not even the most myopic observer could overlook it in a reasonably clear sky. Perihelion was reached on 1 April, at 0.914 astronomical units (137 million km [85 million miles]) from the Sun.

Hale–Bopp did not come anywhere near us, which was a great pity; if it had approached the Earth as closely as Hyakutake had done, it would have cast shadows. It was a giant by cometary standards, with a nucleus 40 km (25 miles) in diameter according to measurements made by the Hubble Space Telescope; it was therefore a great deal larger and more massive than Halley's Comet, while by comparison Hyakutake was miniscule. The nucleus became brighter than any star; the rotation period was given as 11.4 hours, and the nucleus developed a spiral structure. There was also a dim, yellowish sodium tail. Officially, the comet was catalogued as C/1995 O1.

Hale-Bopp remained a naked-eye object for months (easily a record), and even at the end of 2002 it was still within the range of moderate telescopes, though by then it had moved southwards into the region of the constellation of Mensa. Apparently it was last at perihelion 4200 years ago; it has been perturbed by the pull of Jupiter, and will be back in 2360 years' time. Its orbital inclination is over 89°, so that its path lies almost at right angles to that of the Earth. We look forward to welcoming it back at some during the year AD 4357.

Hale–Bopp will not be forgotten. It ranks among the really 'great' comets, and was a worthy prelude to the new millennium.

The Story of the Telescope

In April 1997 The Sky at Night *celebrated its 40th anniversary. For once we were allowed a 50-minute programme, to be broadcast at a reasonable hour in the evening; what could be a better choice than tracing the story of the telescope, from its humble beginnings through to the great instruments of today? The chapter presented here is a summary; the programme was in fact expanded into a book,* Eyes on the Universe, *published by Springer Verlag in 1997 and still in print at the time of writing.*

For thousands of years Man has studied the heavens, but it is only in the last few centuries that he has had any optical help. Our forebears had to depend upon the naked eye alone, and all in all it is amazing how much they managed to learn, but obviously they were limited.

As we have seen, the first telescopes may have been built by Leonard Digges around 1555, but there is no absolute proof, and the main story begins in the first decade of the 17th century, with the telescopes devised by Lippershey and turned skywards by pioneers such as Galileo. Looking back in history, it is probably fair to say that there have been just a few telescopes which have led to fundamental changes in our outlook. Everyone will have a personal list, but mine is as follows:

1. Galileo's first refractor, used astronomically from January 1610.
2. Newton's first reflector, presented to the Royal Society in 1671.
3. William Herschel's reflector, used to discoverer Uranus in 1781. I do not include his 49-inch, completed in 1787, because although it was the largest ever made up to that time, it really achieved very little.
4. Lord Rosse's 72-inch reflector at Birr Castle in Ireland, completed in 1845.
5. The 25-inch Newall refractor, made by Thomas Cooke in 1862. I include this not because it was used for fundamental work, but because it was the first of the great refractors.
6. The Mount Wilson 100-inch reflector, brought into use in 1917.
7. The Palomar 200-inch reflector, completed in 1948.
8. The Hubble Space Telescope, launched into orbit in 1990; it has a 94-inch mirror.
9. The first Keck reflector (Keck I), with its 387-inch segmented mirror, completed in 1991.
10. The VLT, or Very Large Telescope, at Cerro Parañal in Chile. It has four 8-metre (315-inch) mirrors working together. The first two mirrors, Antu and Kueyen, were operating by 1999, and all four by 2001.

I will say no more about the Digges telescope, because I have discussed it in Chapter 1, and even if it existed (as I am sure it did) we do not know what it looked like – or whether it was turned skywards. So we come first to Galileo's tiny 'optick tube', first used in earnest in January 1610. Galileo was not the first telescopic observer; some months earlier Thomas Harriot, one-time tutor to Sir Walter Raleigh, had produced a telescopic map of the Moon. But certainly Galileo's claim to being the first really systematic observer is unchallenged.

At that time the Church was still maintaining that the Earth must be the centre of the universe, with the Sun, Moon, planets and stars moving round it. Galileo thought otherwise; he supported the Sun-centred picture, but it was his telescopic work that led to definite proof. In particular, he found that the planet Venus shows a whole range of phases, from new to full, which on the old geocentric theory it could never do. He saw four satellites of Jupiter, showing that there was at least more than one centre of motion in the Solar System; he resolved the Milky Way into stars. Predictably, he was accused of heresy, brought to trial in Rome, and forced into a hollow and completely meaningless recantation, after which he was kept under virtual house arrest in his villa until he died in 1642. Amazingly, it was not until 1993 that the Catholic Church finally admitted that Galileo had been right all along. Nobody can accuse the Vatican of making hasty decisions!

▶ *Replica of Galileo's*
original telescope,
at Florence Museum.
I was allowed to hold it!

◄ **Newton's first reflector,** at the Royal Society; photograph taken in 1997.

Galileo's telescopes were of course refractors; the best of them magnified about 30 times. Unfortunately, there were serious problems. Light is a mixture of all wavelengths, and a lens refracts the different colours unequally, so that a bright object such as a star is seen to be surrounded by gaudy rings which may look lovely, but which are most unwelcome from the astronomer's point of view. One partial remedy was to make lenses of very long focal length, and 17th-century telescopes were almost incredibly unwieldy. Christiaan Huygens, probably the best observer of the time, made one telescope with a focal length of 150 ft; the small object-glass was fixed to a mast. Yet, with one of these 'aerial telescopes', Huygens was able to discover Titan, the largest of Saturn's satellites (1655), and also to recognize the true nature of Saturn's rings.

Later in the century the Paris Observatory was founded, and French king invited an Italian astronomer, G. D. Cassini, to take charge. Cassini did so – but when he arrived, he found that the Observatory had been designed for appearance rather than practicability, and awkward turrets and minarets obscured so much of the sky that Cassini was forced to take his telescopes into the garden and observe from there!

To overcome the 'false colour' problem, Isaac Newton developed a new type of telescope, the reflector. Instead of using a lens to collect the incoming light, he used a mirror, which reflects all colours equally, and in 1671 he presented the Royal Society with a telescope in which the light was collected by the main mirror, sent back up the tube on to a smaller flat mirror set at an angle of 45°, and thence into the side of the tube, where the eyepiece was placed. The Newtonian principle is still used. Earlier, James Gregory had planned a reflector in which the secondary mirror was concave, and the light was sent back to the eyepiece via a hole in the main speculum, but apparently Gregory never built a telescope of this kind, so that the priority is Newton's. Another variant is the Cassegrain, which again uses a hole in the main mirror, but where the secondary is convex instead of flat (as with the Newtonian) or concave (as with the Gregorian). Cassegrain telescopes are very much in vogue today.

The first British observatory was set up at Greenwich, in 1675, by express order of King Charles II. Britain has always been a sea-faring nation, and there had been many cases of ships losing their way because they were unable to determine their longitude. (Latitude was easy enough; one's latitude is always equal to the apparent altitude of the celestial pole above the horizon, and this point is marked within 1° by the Pole Star.) The best way of finding longitude was by measuring the apparent position of the Moon against the stars; this gave the local time, which could be compared with Greenwich time. Clearly this needed a good star catalogue, and the best available, compiled by Tycho Brahe between 1576 and 1596, was not accurate enough, because it had been made by naked-eye observation alone. At Greenwich, the first Astronomer Royal, John Flamsteed, compiled a better catalogue by using telescopic measurements – though it took him a long time, and was never used for its original purpose, because the 'lunar distance' method became obsolete when Harrison developed the marine chronometer.

Flamsteed had to provide his own telescopes, and when he died his widow reclaimed them; what happened to them we do not know. The next Astronomer Royal, Edmond Halley, had to begin all over again. Some of Halley's telescopes still survive, and are on display at the Old Royal Observatory in Greenwich Park, London.

Newton had seen no remedy for the false-colour problem, and for once he was wrong. In 1733 a wealthy amateur, Chester Moor Hall, partially solved it by making a compound object-glass; there were two components of different kinds of glass, whose errors tended to cancel each other out. The principle of the 'achromatic refractor' was followed up by John and Peter Dollond, who produced good, short-focal-length telescopes which were far better than the old aerial instruments, but the next step was taken in the 18th century by William Herschel, who began his career as a musician but who made and used reflecting telescopes which were by far the best of their time. With one of these – a reflector with a 6.2-inch

◄ *The Birr reflector –*
as I photographed in
January 1997, fully
restored and in good
working order!

mirror and a focal length of 7 ft – he discovered the planet Uranus, in 1781. In 1787 he built a giant reflector with a 49-inch mirror and a focal length of 40 ft. The mirror was made of speculum metal, an alloy of copper and tin. Despite its size, the telescope was never a real success – it was too cumbersome – but at least it had shown that large mirrors could be made.

In 1845 the third Earl of Rosse, an Irish nobleman, constructed a 72-inch reflector, and set it up at his estate in Birr Castle, which was by no means an ideal site but was the only one readily available. Lord Rosse mounted the telescope between two massive stone walls, so that it could swing for only a limited distance to either side of the meridian; it had no drive or finder, and the mirror was of course made of speculum metal. Restricted though it was, the 'Leviathan' was used to make the first observations of the spiral forms of the objects we now know to be galaxies. In 1909 the telescope was dismantled, but it has now been fully restored and brought back into use, though its main value is of course historical.

Within a few decades the 'Leviathan' had been overtaken by telescopes of more modern type; improvements in glass-making made it possible to construct large objectives, and although the false-colour nuisance can never be totally eliminated it can be drastically reduced. The first major refractor was

▼ *The Palomar*   *as I photographed it*
200-inch reflector,   *in 1990.*

made in England by Thomas Cooke; it had a 25-inch object-glass, and proved to be a great success (it is now at the Athens Observatory in Greece). Others followed before the end of the century, and for a while the reflecting telescopes

▼ **Pre-launch of the**   **Telescope,** *at Cape*
Hubble Space   *Canaveral, in 1990.*

were in eclipse. The largest refractor, at the Yerkes Observatory in the United States, was completed in 1897, and is still in regular use. It has a 40-inch object-glass, and is unlikely ever to be surpassed. There is a limit to the size of a useful lens; if it is too heavy it sags and distorts under its own weight, and becomes useless. A 49-inch was once made, and shown at the Paris Exposition of 1901, but it was a total failure. The future belonged to the reflector.

The American astronomer George Ellery Hale had master-minded the Yerkes telescope, but then persuaded friendly millionaires to finance the first modern-type, glass-mirror reflectors. At Mount Wilson, in California, Hale set up first a 60-inch and then, in 1917, a 100-inch, which was named the Hooker telescope in honour of John D. Hooker, the millionaire who had provided most of the funds for it. For many years the 100-inch was not only the world's largest telescope, but was in a class of its own, and in the 1920s Edwin Hubble used it to show that the spiral systems are in fact independent galaxies, millions of light-years away from us. The immense light-grasp of the 100-inch enabled him to identify Cepheid variables in the spirals. These convenient stars 'give away' their real luminosities, and hence their distances, by the way in which they fluctuate. Only the Hooker telescope was able to show them with sufficient clarity.

Still Hale was not satisfied, and he planned a 200-inch reflector. Again he obtained the necessary money, and the 200-inch was completed in 1948, though unfortunately Hale did not live to see it. The choice of site was important. The Earth's atmosphere is the main enemy of the astronomer, which is why most modern observatories are sited on mountain-tops; Palomar, where the 200-inch is situated, lies well above the worst of atmospheric haze and pollution.

Just as the Hooker reflector had been supreme, so this was also true of the Hale 200-inch; Walter Baade used it to show that there had been an error in the Cepheid scale, so that the universe is more than twice as large as had been believed (the Andromeda Spiral, for instance, is 2.2 million light-years from us; Hubble's value had been a mere 750,000 light-years).

Of course, photography had long since taken over from sheer visual observation; it is seldom that anyone now actually looks through a giant telescope. Now, however, photography is itself being superseded by electronic devices, which are much more sensitive. This means that telescopes such as the 200-inch are much more powerful than they used to be when used with the old-style photographic plates.

Until fairly recently all major telescopes were equatorially mounted. An altazimuth mounting means that there are two motions to be considered: east/west (azimuth) and north/south (altitude). Computers now have no difficulty in dealing with this, and the altazimuth mounting has taken over. The first giant telescope to be set up in this way was the 236-inch reflector built by the Russians in 1975; the optics and the site are unsatisfactory, but at least the mounting proved to be very effective. It is improbable that any future telescopes of large size will be equatorial.

There are obvious problems in making large mirrors, and various other patterns have been used. On Mauna Kea, in Hawaii, the largest instruments are the two Keck telescopes; each has a 387-inch mirror made up of 36 separate segments, joined together to form the correct optical curve. When working together the Kecks could, in theory, distinguish the headlights of a car separately over a range of 25,000 km (16,000 miles). Yet even since we presented our 40th anniversary programme, the Kecks have been surpassed. At Cerro Parañal, in the Atacama Desert of northern Chile, the VLT or Very Large Telescope is being brought into operation. It is in fact made up of four 8-metre telescopes working together. The eventual resolution will be a tiny fraction of a second of arc. The high-altitude site is almost ideal; there is almost no water vapour in the air – and rainfall occurs about once in a hundred years. The first two mirrors, named Antu and Kueyen, were in action before the end of 1999, and the other two, Melipal and Yepan, in 2001.

Yet all ground-based telescopes are handicapped by the atmosphere, and the only solution is to use space research methods. The Hubble Space Telescope, with its 94-inch mirror, was launched into orbit in 1990, and operating from above a height of 480 km (300 miles) it enjoys perfect seeing, so that although it is much smaller than some of the 'ground giants' it can in many ways outperform them. It can be regularly serviced by astronauts, as was last done in April 2002, and it is expected to continue operating for some years yet.

Less than four centuries separate Galileo's tiny 'optick tube' from the giant VLT and the orbital Hubble. No doubt progress will be maintained during the 21st century, and before too long we should be able to establish observatories on the surface of the Moon. The story of the telescope is far from over; indeed, it may only just be beginning.

When Stars Grow Old

What do we know about the life-stories of the stars? The answer is: 'A great deal.' We know how they are born, how they evolve, and how – in their various ways – they die. Many details remain to be clarified, but the general picture has emerged.

Normal stars are composed mainly of hydrogen, and in a star such as the Sun this hydrogen is 'burned' in the core; as the star grows old, this hydrogen is used up, and the star has to use other fuel, which makes it change in temperature, size and brightness. The 'burning' is actually nuclear fusion of hydrogen into helium, and the Sun will do this for most of its active life of around 10,000 million years. The energy is radiated from the core to the outer layers (the star's atmosphere), where convection takes over. We see the Sun simmering like a pan of water on the cooker, due to these convection cells, each about 960 km (600 miles) across. Yet from Earth the Sun looks round, smooth and constant. A major flare makes no obvious difference to the total brightness, so that the Sun cannot be classed as a variable star in this sense.

Our main tool in tracking a star's evolution is the HR or Hertzsprung–Russell Diagram (*see page 82*), which relates the temperature of the star to its luminosity compared with the Sun. The Diagram was worked out in the early years of the 20th century by Ejnar Hertzsprung and Henry Norris Russell, and is of the utmost value to astronomers.

Normal stars such as the Sun lie on a broad band across the Diagram, known as the Main Sequence, with hot, blue-white stars at the top left and cool red stars to the lower right. The colour sequence of spectral types (O B A F G K M) relates to the temperature of the star. The Sun lies on the Main Sequence. By stellar standards it is not very massive (a few stars have 100 times the Sun's mass) and it is in every way quite normal.

Above the Main Sequence, in the top right area, we have red giants and supergiants, which are large, old and cool. And at the bottom left we have white dwarfs, which are small and very ancient.

Most stars stay on the Main Sequence for most of their active careers, but when their hydrogen 'fuel' begins to run low they have to change. The energy created by the nuclear fusion causes the outer layers of the star to expand, whereas gravity acts in the opposite sense and tends to make them contract. As the hydrogen in the core is burned, the star moves up the Main Sequence, and its core becomes rich in helium. The star then moves off the Main Sequence. When the hydrogen in the core is finally exhausted, the outer layers of the atmosphere try to collapse; this makes them heat up, igniting their hydrogen, and the hydrogen in the layers around the core is then burned. The star expands to become a red giant, such as Aldebaran or Arcturus. Put Arcturus in the centre of the Solar System, and it would extend out halfway to the orbit of Mercury.

Stars of this kind are quite stable, and the phase can last for a long time. Red giants are cooler than the Sun, but 100 times more luminous. During its career the star will visit this part of the Diagram several times. If the mass is greater than that of the Sun – perhaps by a factor of 2 – the atmosphere will become unstable, and the star will become variable, as with Mira Ceti. Mira is the prototype long-period variable; its period is 331 days, and the magnitude range is from 2 to 9. Images from the Hubble Space Telescope show that the star is not spherical, but is shaped more like a rugby ball; this may be because Mira has a companion which is smaller, hotter and close-in, and this companion may pull on Mira's extended atmosphere and distort it. Though Mira is not much heavier than the Sun, its diameter is of the order of 320–530 million km (200–330 million miles), so that if it were central in the Solar System it would extend out to around the orbit of Mars.

Also in this area of the Diagram are the RV Tauri variables. They have shorter periods than the Mira stars, and are less regular. R Scuti is the brightest of them; it has a single period of 140 days. U Monocerotis has a more complicated cycle, with a period of 92 days and a longer cycle of 2320 days, which affects the overall fluctuations. There are only about 100 known RV Tauri variables in our Galaxy; they have about the same mass as the Sun, but have very tenuous atmospheres, so that a pulse in the inner, hotter layers may cause a shock wave in the outer layers, so amplifying the effect.

Perhaps the best-known of all variables is Betelgeux in Orion, which is larger than Mira and whose variations are much less regular. It is so large that surface details have been detected on it, by Richard Wilson, using the aperture synthesis technique on the William Herschel Telescope on La Palma. This is the first time that surface details on a star have been recorded with a ground-based telescope. The network of 27 radio telescopes (covering 35 km [22 miles]) in New Mexico, known as the Very Large Array, gives a

▼ *Mira Ceti,* as imaged by the Hubble Space Telescope in both visible and ultraviolet light.

Mira is oblong-shaped; the hook-like appendage may be due to the pull of its hot companion.

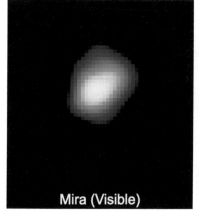

Mira (Visible)

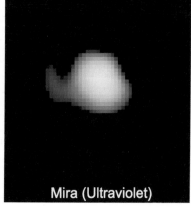

Mira (Ultraviolet)

different view of the atmosphere of Betelgeux. Jeremy Lim and his co-workers have traced the very cool gas-cloud which is irregular in shape, but in places extends out to a distance equal to that between the Sun and Saturn. Betelgeux shows convection cells, similar in type to those of the Sun, though Betelgeux has a few enormous cells rather than many smaller ones. Cool material such as dust can be completely lost from the star in this way.

There are many types of peculiar stars in the giant and supergiant regions of the HR Diagram. There are the R Coronae Borealis stars, which have enormous amounts of carbon in their atmospheres but very little hydrogen. They fade quickly when a cloud of carbon soot is expelled, and take time to recover when the soot is dissipated. We also have stars which have concentrations of one particular element on their surfaces. One such star is Sigma Orionis E. When we look at the pole about which it spins, we find a strong magnetic field, and this field causes concentrations of particular elements to form around the magnetic poles – helium round one pole and silicon round the other; this means that for part of the 1.2-day rotation period you see strong spectral lines due to helium, and at other times strong lines due to silicon. Other members of the group have different elements forced up to the surface by the magnetic field – or forced down, so that there appears to be a paucity of some particular element around the magnetic pole.

As the star burns hydrogen in the layers above its core, the core itself is slowly compressed. The 'helium flash' occurs when helium ignites in the core, and the core expands. It takes a normal star around 2000 million years to reach the flash point from the Main Sequence (that is, about 15% of the time on the Main Sequence). We may even be seeing one star, Sakurai's Object, undergoing the helium flash at the present time.

The explosion in the core as the new source of energy ignites changes the nature of the star, but the surrounding atmosphere (which is still burning hydrogen) damps the catastrophe, and the star survives, though some material must be lost. The star moves very quickly to the left of the giant area, on the 'horizontal branch', so called because as the star moves in the Diagram it changes in temperature, but not in luminosity. Lighter stars move further to the left, closer to the Main Sequence, and to get back to the giant branch they have to cross what is termed the instability strip, becoming RR Lyrae variables which show regular but quite small fluctuations. The pulses causing these variations come from deep inside the star, and so they can tell us a great deal about the structure of the star below its surface layer.

The pace is speeding up. It takes a star considerably less than 10 million years to move from the horizontal branch back to the giant area. Once it reaches the upper right, it moves again through the giant area, and becomes unstable and variable, with deep-seated pulsations. The star can loop out into the hotter area and then return once more to the giant area. When these loops occur high up the track, they result in Cepheid variables, so called because the prototype star is Delta Cephei in the far north of the sky. Cepheids are very regular, with periods of from a few days up to about 50 days. Their period of variability relates directly to their absolute brightness. This is so reliable that when Cepheids are found in outer galaxies, we can find out how far away these galaxies are. The Pole Star is a Cepheid, but the amplitude had been declining throughout the 20th century. At one point astronomers thought that it might stop fluctuating altogether, but it seems to have settled down to a small range of about 3/100th of a magnitude.

▼ **NGC 6543, the Cat's Eye Nebula (C6):** a bright planetary nebula, lying 3000 light-years away, between Zeta and Delta Draconis, imaged by the Hubble Space Telescope. The nebula is about 1000 years old and represents a dying star; it could even be a double-star system.

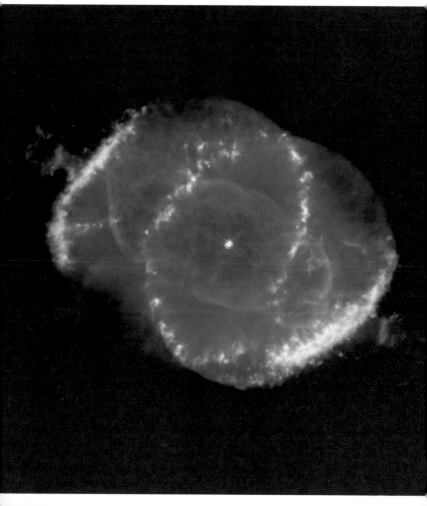

What happens after the giant phase of a star's lifetime? Mass-loss from a star with a mass about the same as that of the Sun now becomes important, as the star moves beyond the red-giant phase. The star can become a planetary nebula and then a white dwarf, with a mass usually about half that of the Sun. The mass-loss may be steady, or there may be one more violent ejection of material.

Planetary nebulae demonstrate the violent changes which a star must undergo before it becomes a white dwarf. The centre of the star tries to cool down, but the thin atmosphere acts in the manner of a blanket round a hot-water tank and keeps the heat trapped, so that a white dwarf takes a very long time to cool.

Many problems remain. For example, it may well be that the star FG Sagittae is in the process of turning into a planetary nebula, and the star ought therefore to be a white dwarf. However, the star has behaved so strangely that we are by no means sure. It brightened at the start of the 20th century, and is now starting to fade again. In 1880 the surface temperature was 45,000°C; it is now down to 6000°C, and the star has again become variable, changing into a red giant the size of the orbit of Mercury and increasing its radius by three times the radius of the Sun in each year. At one time during the 1970s it was cooling by 250 degrees each year, but it now seems to have changed its mind, and may not yet become a white dwarf at all.

Stars less massive than the Sun move quietly across the Diagram to the white dwarf area, where they shrink slowly and must eventually become cold, dead black dwarfs – though the universe may not yet be old enough for this to have had time to happen. On the other hand, stars which are much more massive than the Sun move across the Diagram at greater speed, and make extravagant excursions from red to blue and from blue to red. They are able to burn elements heavier than helium, such as carbon and silicon. A really massive star cannot lose enough mass to become a white dwarf, and so it explodes as a supernova – as Eta Carinae in the southern sky will do one day.

But that is another story.

Rings of Moons

I have always maintained that when seen through a telescope Saturn is the most beautiful object in the entire sky. Its glorious ring system is in a class of its own. Jupiter, Uranus and Neptune all have rings, but these pale compared with those of Saturn.

The Saturnian rings are made up of millions of small pieces of ice, whirling round the planet in the manner of dwarf moons. Of course, we see them at an angle; a bird's-eye view would show that they are circular. There are two bright rings, A and B, separated by a gap known as Cassini's Division in honour of its discoverer. Closer-in is the semi-transparent Ring C, or the Crêpe Ring, and there are a few more faint rings outside the main set.

We are not sure how the rings were formed. They may simply be debris left over, so to speak, when Saturn itself was formed; they may be the shattered remnants of an old icy satellite which wandered too close in and was disrupted. The Voyager probes which bypassed Saturn in 1980 and 1981 sent back superb views, and so has the Hubble Space Telescope much more recently; there are thousands of narrow ringlets and minor divisions. It looks to me like some sort of wave effect, due possibly to Saturn's family of satellites.

Nine satellites were known before the Voyager missions. (If you would like data about them, look at the Table on the facing page.) I can see eight of these with my 15-inch reflector at Selsey, and the only pre-Voyager satellite which is too faint for me is Phoebe.

The 'old' satellites go round Saturn at various distances in various periods. Mimas, at a mere 185,000 km (115,000 miles) from Saturn, has a period of

▼ **Saturn,** *as viewed by the Hubble Space Telescope on 1 December* 1994. *Note the white storm near the planet's equator.*

SATELLITES OF SATURN

Name	Distance from centre of Saturn (thousand km)	Orbital period (days)	Diameter (km)	Mean opposition magnitude
Pan	134	0.58	20	19
Atlas	138	0.60	36×34×28	18.0
Prometheus	139	0.61	150×90×70	15.8
Pandora	142	0.63	110×85×60	16.5
Janus	151	0.69	140×120×105	15.7
Epimetheus	151	0.69	200×180×150	14.5
Mimas	186	0.94	398	12.9
Enceladus	238	1.37	498	11.7
Tethys	295	1.89	1058	10.2
Telesto	295	1.89	30×26×16	18.5
Calypso	295	1.89	30×16×16	18.7
Dione	377	2.74	1120	10.4
Helene	377	2.74	32	18.4
Rhea	527	4.52	1528	9.7
Titan	1221	15.95	5150	8.3
Hyperion	1481	21.28	370×280×225	14.2
Iapetus	3561	79.33	1440	10.2–11.9
Phoebe	12,940	550.5 R	230×210	16.4

22½ hours; Iapetus, at over 3 million km (2 million miles), takes 79 days. And Phoebe, at over 12 million km (8 million miles), takes 550 days.

Titan is the giant of Saturn's family. It is larger than our Moon, and larger than the planet Mercury. Rhea, Iapetus, Dione and Tethys come next in size; the rest are much smaller.

Only Titan is really bright. Almost any telescope will show it, and so will good binoculars. A telescope of, say, 3 inches aperture will also show Rhea, Iapetus at its best, Dione and Tethys. The rest require larger telescopes, and the small inner satellites can be seen only from probes or (so far) with the Hubble Space Telescope. Let us now consider the satellites one by one; logically we ought to begin with Titan, but Titan is so exceptional that it may be better to leave it until last.

In 1671 Giovanni Cassini, an Italian astronomer, was called to Paris to direct the new Observatory there. He was an expert observer, and he used his telescopes to look at Saturn. Of course, he saw Titan, which had been known since 1656, and he also discovered a new satellite, Iapetus. (*En passant*, the satellites are in general named after the children of the god Saturn, who preceded Jupiter as ruler of Olympus.) Iapetus was soon found to have an orbital period of 79 days, but Cassini also noticed something very interesting. When Iapetus was west of Saturn, it was easy to see, and was brighter than the tenth magnitude, but when near eastern elongation it disappeared for several weeks.

In fact this is not true, but the magnitude does drop below 11, which is why Cassini lost sight of it. Eventually he realized this, and he had the true explanation. Iapetus has one hemisphere which is highly reflective, and another which is dark. When the satellite is west of Saturn, it is the bright hemisphere which faces us, while when Iapetus is east we see the darker side. This is understandable. Because of tidal effects, most satellites have captured or synchronous rotation. Our Moon goes round us in 27.3 days; it also rotates in 27.3 days, so that the same side is turned towards us all the time – and until the round-the-Moon flight of Russia's Lunik 3, in 1959, we had no direct knowledge of the far side. With Iapetus, the orbital period and the axial rotation period are equal at 79d 8h, and so the variations in magnitude are quite regular.

Yet why are the hemispheres different? It is purely a matter of colour; both are cratered, and show the same characteristics. We have here what I call the 'Zebra Problem'. Is a zebra a black animal with white stripes, or a white animal with black stripes? Is Iapetus bright with a dark stain, or dark with an icy layer? We can find out. By observing the movements of Iapetus, and the effects on other satellites, we can prove that the overall density of the globe is low, and that the make-up of Iapetus contains a great deal of ice. So it really is a bright globe with a dark stain.

▼ *Iapetus, the third largest of Saturn's satellites. This image was obtained by* *Voyager 1 on 22 August 1981, from a distance of 11 million km (680,000 miles).*

▶ *Saturn's satellite Mimas,* as viewed from Voyager 1 in August 1981. The large central crater is known as Herschel. The black spot at the top of the image is due to the camera, and is not a feature on Mimas itself.

Next, what exactly is the stain? We have to admit that we do not know. One suggestion is that it is due to material wafted on to Iapetus from the distant Phoebe, but this does not now seem likely; the colours of Iapetus and Phoebe do not match. It is more probable that the material has welled up from inside Iapetus. No other satellite shows this curious appearance, either in Saturn's system or in any other.

Of course, Iapetus is not massive enough to hold on to any atmosphere, and it is very cold indeed. But one day it may be reached, if only because it moves well outside the main part of the radiation zones surrounding Saturn. Also, from Iapetus an observer would have a good view of the rings, because the orbit is appreciably tilted, whereas the other satellites move more or less in the ring plane.

Cassini kept on observing. In 1672 he found another satellite, Rhea, much closer-in to Saturn, and with an orbital period of only 4½ days. It was about the same size as Iapetus, but was not variable. Voyager images show it to be a heavily-cratered globe, and clearly it has been badly battered in the past. The magnitude is about 10, so that a 3-inch refractor will show it easily.

Cassini found two more satellites in 1687: Tethys and Dione, both of about magnitude 10½. Tethys is quite unlike Iapetus or Rhea; it seems to be made up of almost pure ice. There are craters, and also a long trench, Ithaca Chasma, which runs halfway round the surface, from pole to pole. The escape velocity is no more than 0.4 km/s (0.25 miles/s), so that there can be no atmosphere. Dione, about the same size, is much denser and more massive, and the surface features are different; there are two contrasting hemispheres, one with strange wispy features, and the other with large, conventional craters. Naturally, the rotation period is synchronous with the

▲ **Rhea,** *as imaged by Voyager 1 in 1980 from a distance of 128,000 km* *(79,500 miles). Rhea is heavily cratered, with few really large formations.*

orbital period – 2d 18h – and the same face is always turned Saturnwards, so that there is no surprise in finding that the two hemispheres differ; after all, there are marked differences between the Earth-turned side and the far side of our own Moon.

Cassini found no more satellites, but in 1787 William Herschel added two more, Mimas and Enceladus. Both are small. Mimas is always so close to Saturn that it is not an easy telescopic object; its orbital period is less than a day. The surface is dominated by a huge crater, now named in honour of Herschel; it has a massive central peak. The impact which caused it must have put Mimas in danger of being smashed up completely. The rest of the surface is conventionally icy and cratered.

Enceladus is a puzzle. The diameter is just over 480 km (300 miles). There is no large crater, but wide areas of the surface are almost crater-free, and much of the surface looks young. Either no craters were ever formed in these areas, or else they have been erased, presumably by soft material (slushy ice?) swelling up from below. It could be that the process is going on even now, and that Enceladus is not inert. The escape velocity is low – no more than 0.19 km/s (0.12 miles/s) – and there is no question of there being any atmosphere, but Enceladus is certainly a curious place.

Next, in 1848, Hyperion was found, independently by W. Bond in America and William Lassell in England. It moves beyond Titan, at 1,480,000 km (920,000 miles), in a period of 21¼ days. It is small and faint, and it is not spherical; it is shaped rather like a hamburger, and has a darkish, cratered surface.

Hyperion is unusual in another way; it does not have synchronous rotation. The spin is 'chaotic', and Hyperion seems to be tumbling along in its orbit, so that the rotation period is not constant. All in all, it looks very much as though Hyperion is part of a larger body which has broken up, presumably by collision – but in this case, where is the other half? True, way back in 1904 the American astronomer W. H. Pickering reported the discovery of a new satellite moving between the orbits of Titan and Hyperion, and it was even given a name – Themis – but it was never confirmed, and it seems that what Pickering saw was an ordinary star.

Phoebe, the outermost satellite, was not well imaged by the Voyagers, so that we do not know much about its surface features, but it seems to be dark, reddish and cratered. It moves round Saturn in a retrograde direction, and is almost certainly an ex-asteroid which was captured by Saturn in the remote past. It may well have been an escapee from the Kuiper Belt.

Titan is in a class of its own. It has a thick atmosphere made up chiefly of nitrogen, but there is also a great deal of methane, so that from our point of view the atmosphere would be poisonous. The temperature is low; methane could exist either as a solid, a liquid or a gas. There may well be cliffs of solid methane, lakes or seas of liquid methane (or ethane), and a methane rain dripping down from the orange clouds in the nitrogen sky.

We may find out in 2004. On 15 October 1997 a new space-probe was launched: Cassini–Huygens. The main aim is to study Titan, though the other satellites will also come in for attention as well as Saturn itself. Cassini will enter a closed path round Saturn, and Huygens will parachute down on to Titan's surface. Unfortunately, it will not stay in touch for long after arrival; the orbiting Cassini will be its only link with 'home', and Cassini will pass quickly out of range. By the time it returns, the battery in Huygens will have died. So a journey of many years culminates in a tense period of 30 minutes at most.

Will Huygens come down on ice or rock, or will it splash into a chemical ocean? Time will tell. Watch the *Sky at Night* programme for November 2004!

The remaining satellites are all very small and close-in, and are beyond the range of ordinary telescopes, though the Hubble Space Telescope can show them. The tiny Pan actually moves inside the ring system, and may be responsible for Encke's Division in Ring A. Atlas moves close to the outer edge of Ring A, and is responsible for its sharp border; Ring F is stabilized by two 'shepherds', Prometheus and Pandora; Janus and Epimetheus are co-orbital, and are probably two parts of a larger disrupted body. New small outer satellites have been discovered recently, all of which are certainly captured asteroids and are a long way out. The grand total has now reached 30 plus.

What would we see if we could visit the main icy satellites? From most of them the rings would remain edgewise-on, and the best view would be had from Iapetus. This lies far in the future, but there can be no doubt that the satellites of Saturn are fascinating little worlds.

Caribbean Eclipse

There is no doubt in my mind that a total eclipse of the Sun is the grandest sight in all nature. As the last sliver of the brilliant solar disk disappears, the sky darkens and the corona flashes into view; the spectacle is breathtaking. The trouble is that as seen from any particular location on Earth, total eclipses do not happen very often, because the Moon's shadow is only just long enough to touch *terra firma*; the track of totality can never be more than 270 km (169 miles) wide, so that you have to be in exactly the right place at exactly the right time. From England, there will be no more totalities until 2090; the last two were in 1927 and 1999. (I saw neither. The 1927 track crossed Yorkshire; I was four years old, and lived in Bognor Regis. In 1999 I was in Falmouth, in Cornwall, under an umbrella which more or less sheltered me from the rain. Well, you can't win them all!)

According to Spode's Law – if things *can* be awkward, they *are* – totality tracks usually cross areas which are either well away from land, or are extremely difficult to get at. And, of course, there is always a chance that the sky will be cloudy at the critical moment. I am fortunate enough to have seen seven totalities, and three of these have been from aboard a ship. Eclipse-chasing on the water has the obvious advantage that if the weather prospects are poor, you can – within certain limits – move to a clearer area. This happened in 1995, when I was on board the cruise ship *Marco Polo* in the China Sea. Our Swedish captain manoeuvred the ship into the only cloud-free spot for many kilometres around.

For the eclipse of 26 February 1998 I was again scheduled to be afloat, this time on the *Stella Solaris*, which flies the Greek flag and has a Greek captain. My role was twofold. I am not a proper observer of the Sun – the Moon is my main interest – but I was due to give some lectures to the ship's passengers, and also to make a television broadcast for the *Sky at Night* programme during the eclipse itself.

One particularly enjoyable feature of an eclipse cruise is that there are so many congenial people around. On the *Stella Solaris* we had, as lecturers, Dr Edward Brooks of Boston College, the leading expert on 'eclipse weather'; George Keene, whose knowledge of eclipse photography is second to none; Dr Paul Knappenberger, Director of the Adler Planetarium in the USA; Dr Edwin Krupp, Director of the Griffith Observatory in Los Angeles, who had pioneered the science of archaeoastronomy; and Dr Ronald Parise, the only astronomer who was officially trained as an astronaut, and who had flown in 1990 aboard the Space Shuttle *Columbia* and in 1995 on the *Endeavour*. We also had the *Sky at Night* team: Pieter Morpurgo to produce, Mike Winser to take the pictures, and Doug Whittaker to look after the sound.

One very important person on the cruise was Dr Anthony Aveni, both in his capacity as an eminent astronomer and as the official timekeeper during the eclipse. This was a role I had filled myself during the eclipse of 1954, in Sweden, but Tony Aveni was much more efficient than I had been so long ago. Finally, there was Ted Pedas, who was the project co-ordinator and who had organized the entire expedition.

What did we expect to see? Well, the usual phenomena of totality: the Diamond Ring, the chromosphere, the corona, the prominences, and so on. The Sun was not long past the minimum of its 11-year cycle of activity, so we expected the corona to be more 'spiky' and less symmetrical than when sunspots are plentiful. Several planets would, we hoped, be on view; Venus certainly, Jupiter, Mars, Mercury and possibly Saturn. This depended upon how dark the sky would become, which is something that can never be reliably predicted – even by Ed Brooks.

The *Stella Solaris* carried several hundred passengers, most of whom were keenly interested in the eclipse – though I must add that one dear lady solemnly read a book throughout totality! There was a full series of lectures; of special importance were those given by George Keene, the photographic expert, because almost everyone was keen to take pictures, and the Sun is dangerous. Only during full eclipse is it safe to look at it direct through

▼ **Total solar eclipse –** *while aboard the*
an excellent image taken Stella Solaris *in*
by Chris Doherty in 1998, *the Caribbean Sea.*

binoculars or a telescope. If even a tiny portion of the bright surface remains on view, the greatest care is needed. Either project the image, or else make very sure that you are using the right types of filters. People tend to forget that a camera is a lens, so that unprotected viewing will result in eye damage at the best and permanent blindness at the worst. Luckily, everyone took George's warnings to heart, and there were no cases of 'spots in front of the eyes'.

I knew that I would be unable to take any proper pictures, because I could not take part in photography and do a television commentary at the same time. Luckily Chris Doherty, who was with me, could be relied upon to take excellent pictures. I handed my camera over to a fellow passenger who 'aimed and clicked' during totality and did, in fact, produce some highly creditable results.

Ed Brooks assured us that the weather would be kind, and, as usual, he was right. With typically skilled Greek seamanship Captain Panarios took us to precisely the right place; there were no clouds to be seen, and everything appeared to be going according to plan. Rehearsals took place on the 24th, and on the morning of 'eclipse day' equipment was set up all over the decks. The BBC team chose an excellent vantage point on what was known as the *Solaris* deck, with Chris Doherty a short distance away; also within range was Dudley Fuller, whose aim was to record the eclipse on video.

We were some way off the coast of Venezuela, well away from land; indeed, the track crossed only a narrow neck of Central America. It had started in the Pacific and ended in the Atlantic, so that the only land crossed, apart from Central America, consisted of a few Caribbean islands. (One of these was Montserrat, which had been devastated by its volcano; to be candid I was glad that we were not too close to it.) Totality was due in the early afternoon, and would last for only four minutes, so that everything had to be thoroughly rehearsed. Strange mistakes can be made in the excitement of the moment. I recalled that at one eclipse, seen from a ship off the coast of Africa, one enthusiastic astronomer took 40 photographs of the corona under ideal conditions – with his lens-hood in position the whole time . . . .

First contact came – a tiny notch in the edge of the Sun. Slowly it spread, until the light dimmed and the temperature began to fall. Final preparations were made. Mercifully the *Stella Solaris* was rock-steady; Captain Panorias had seen to that. The Moon's shadow raced over the sea; there was the flash of the Diamond Ring, together with what are called Baily's Beads, due to sunlight coming to us via valleys on the Moon's rough edge; and then came the corona.

It was without doubt the loveliest total eclipse in my experience. The corona was brilliant and structured, and there were two bright prominences. Nature seemed to go into a state of suspended animation; Tony Aveni broadcast the 'time' – otherwise the only other voice was mine, carrying out my commentary loudly enough to satisfy Doug Whittaker but, I hope, not loudly enough to disturb the viewers. Those four minutes seemed like four seconds. Then – again the Diamond Ring, more glorious than ever; the corona faded, the light flooded back over the sea, and in an instant Nature seemed to wake up as suddenly as it had gone to sleep. Instinctively there was a tremendous round of applause. The Sun – and Captain Panarios – had served us well.

Then came the aftermath. With the BBC team, I went round to see how various people had managed. Chris Doherty was highly delighted; his plan of campaign had worked perfectly. So was Dudley Fuller, whose video had, he thought, been successful (as indeed it was). George Keene had taken his usual splendid photographs, and all in all everyone seemed very happy. Someone had even seen those elusive features the shadow bands, and of course the planets, plus a few bright stars, had been obvious.

Astronomically, that was that; the cruise itself went on for nine days, taking us to Curaçao, Aruba, Jamaica and Cozumel in Texas before we disembarked to fly home. It was all great fun, and we put on what we hoped was an entertainment; Dudley Fuller is an expert jazz pianist, while I hope that I did not disgrace myself when playing the xylophone.

Yes, I thoroughly recommend eclipse cruising. And in my own case there was the added bonus that on 4 March, the day before we were scheduled to leave the *Stella Solaris*, I had my 75th birthday. To my surprise I was the guest of honour at a party on deck, complete with cake. I felt decidedly ancient, but I am sure that there is no better way to pass through this milestone than to celebrate it on a cruise ship in the Caribbean!

A Cold Look at Space

B odies in the sky send out radiations at all wavelengths, not only in visible light. Indeed, the visible range covers only a very small part of the total electromagnetic spectrum. Unfortunately, most of the longer and shorter wavelengths are absorbed by layers in the Earth's upper atmosphere, so that we are forced to use space-research methods.

Infrared studies are particularly important. In 1983 IRAS, the Infrared Astronomical Satellite, soared aloft and operated for the best part of a year, accomplishing an amazing amount of work. It discovered thousands of new infrared sources, obtained accurate positions for others, and provided researchers with a mass of data. It also detected clouds of cool material around several stars, including the brilliant Vega, and this rekindled interest in the possibility of other planetary systems.

On 18 November 1995 came the launch of a new satellite, ISO, the Infrared Space Observatory. It was put into a highly elliptical orbit, and soon proved to be a major success. One drawback was that its instruments had to be kept cool by the use of liquid helium – they had to remain only very slightly above absolute zero – and in time this helium boils away. ISO was intended to last for 18 months, but in fact it lasted for much longer than that, and did not cease operating until the spring of 1998.

ISO contributed new results in almost every branch of astronomy. For example, it made detailed observations of Jupiter at various wavelengths, which the Hubble Space Telescope cannot do. Each wavelength looked at a different depth in the Jovian atmosphere. These results can be compared with those of the Galileo entry probe, plus what we learned from the impact of Comet Shoemaker–Levy. At 3.3 microns, methane absorbs the radiation, so that Jupiter looks dark. At 5.7 microns there are 'hot spots' where ISO peers deep into the atmosphere, through dry anti-cyclonic regions of sinking gas. At 7.6 microns it is the stratosphere which is seen, and at 9.4 microns the cloudy zones which previously looked bright show up as dark masses. All these results enable us to build up a much more reliable picture of Jupiter's outer layers.

Then there was the beautiful comet Hale–Bopp, which was such an impressive sight in our skies for months during 1997. Unfortunately, ISO could not point anywhere near the Sun and so could not examine Hale–Bopp at its best, but images taken when the comet was still at a distance of 4.6 astronomical units (around 690 million km [430 million miles]) showed the dust streaming away from the nucleus. Carbon dioxide was detected as it was evaporated from the comet, but water, surprisingly, was not found. Water was identified later, when the comet had approached to a distance of 435 million km (270 million miles) from the Sun, and carbon monoxide was then seen as well. The comet was warming up, and it may be that the dust screened the water, preventing evaporation, for longer than had been expected.

However, ISO's main targets lay far beyond the Solar System. Vega was one prime objective. The dust ring round it is unusual, because a star as old as Vega ought by now to have lost its dust; possibly the remains indicate a 'failed' attempt to produce planets. In Vega's case, planets are not likely, because calculations by Dr Helen Walker and her associates show that the total mass of the dust-cloud is no more than half that of the Moon. Other stars – such as the southern Beta Pictoris – have dust-clouds which are more massive, and planets most certainly cannot be ruled out. It is interesting to note that one of our closest stellar neighbours – Epsilon Eridani, less than 11 light-years away – seems to have a dusty shell at a much lower temperature than those of Vega or Beta Pictoris. One planet certainly exists.

There is also the star IRC+10°216, which appears very dim because it is encircled by a large shell of dust. In the infrared, it glows brightly. It is a very old star, and it has been found that its atmosphere is made up chiefly of carbon monoxide and hydrogen cyanide – not a very pleasant mixture!

ISO also studied protostars. For instance, Lynds 1689 is a dark cloud in the constellation Ophiuchus. Derek Ward-Thompson has found a new star here, still appearing dark because it is in its earliest stages of formation; but though it is dark when imaged with an ordinary camera, it is different when examined with the longest wavelengths that ISO could manage. It was found to be a cloud of dust and gas just about to start collapsing and warming up. It was too cold to be detected by IRAS. The JCMT (James Clerk Maxwell Telescope on Mauna Kea, in Hawaii) could identify it at sub-millimetre wavelengths, but these data could not lead to an estimate of the precise temperature. The ISO observations showed that the temperature is $-270°C$, which is a mere 13 degrees above absolute zero. It has a long way to go before it starts to shine in the same way as the Sun.

Of special interest are the 'sooty stars', of which much the brightest example is R Coronae Borealis in the constellation of the Northern Crown. Normally R Coronae is on the fringe of naked-eye visibility, but at unpredictable intervals it fades abruptly, remaining dim for weeks or months

▶ *The Eagle Nebula (M16):* a composite image obtained from the Infrared Space Observatory (ISO). The blue colours reveal shorter infrared wavelengths, while the red colours show longer wavelengths.

before recovering. It has an enormous amount of carbon in its atmosphere, and its spectrum is very unusual indeed. The star itself consists mainly of helium; it is well advanced in its evolution, so that it has 'burned' its hydrogen to produce the helium. By volume, over 96% of R Coronae is made up of helium, whereas, by volume, our Sun is 91% hydrogen, with a much smaller amount of helium.

With R Coronae, what seems to happen is that large clouds of pure soot are formed at low levels; it is this which causes the fades. When the soot is blown away, the star below is uncovered, and the magnitude rises once more.

R Coronae is one of about 40 known stars of this kind. We do not know quite why they should have this peculiar composition, but there are one or two clues. The old IRAS maps showed very large, cool dust shells associated with some of the R Coronae stars; these were at a temperature of around −230°C (40 degrees above absolute zero), but were several light-years across. Another clue has been provided by a strange star discovered by the Japanese amateur astronomer Sakurai. He believed it to be a nova, but it is now thought that he saw the 'flash' as the helium ignited and the star turned into a red giant, over a period of only a few months. By now, Sakurai's Object is starting to show a spectrum very like that of R Coronae, so that apparently it has been 'caught in the act'.

Turn now to objects well beyond our Galaxy. Systems which appear dark to the Hubble Space Telescope glowed brightly for ISO, so that we could obtain a complementary view – which is particularly valuable in studying molecules and dust in the colder areas of the universe, where most ordinary telescopes can make out nothing at all. One ingenious technique with ISO was to switch on the sensitive infrared equipment when the satellite was moving from one target to another; this is known as the Serendipity Survey, because it picks up objects that had been unsuspected. A test scan in the Coma cluster of galaxies showed that when the detectors scanned from one galaxy to another, a third galaxy was often registered during the slew.

ISO came to the end of its career in 1998, but sorting out all its 27,000 observations to create an archive of data took several years. It is still in orbit, but all the remaining fuel has been vented, so that if another vehicle ever collides with it there will not be an explosion to litter space with yet more debris.

ESA has plans for a similar but larger vehicle, FIRST (Faint Images of the Radio Sky), which will work at longer wavelengths (85 to 600 microns). It will look at very cool material, and also search the cosmic background, following up the pioneer studies by COBE, the Cosmic Background Explorer. It will carry a 3-metre telescope, and should be launched in 2006; its planned lifetime is 4½ years. But well before this, in 2003, NASA will launch a new infrared satellite, SIRTF (Space Infrared Telescope Facility). There will also be SOFIA (Stratospheric Observatory for Infrared Astronomy), successor to the KAO (Kuiper Airborne Observatory), which will carry a 2.5-metre telescope in a Boeing 747 jet; it will fly in the high atmosphere and have the advantage that the engineers and astronomers can fly with it.

ISO will always be remembered. It was a real triumph, and achieved even more than its makers can have hoped of it.

The Sun Awakes

Our programme is called *The Sky at Night*, but now and then we have to deal with the sky by day and talk about the Sun, because, after all, the Sun is a star. It is a very ordinary star – astronomers even relegate it to the status of a yellow dwarf – but to us it is all-important. It is 150 million km (93 million miles) away, and is so large that you could drop a million Earths into it and still leave room to spare.

It is made up of incandescent gas, and to some extent it is variable. Every 11 years it is active, with many of the dark patches known as sunspots, with associated phenomena; when quiescent, the disk may be clear for many consecutive days. During the mid-1990s activity was at its lowest, and few major sunspots were seen.

Let us begin by discussing the structure of the Sun. The visible surface is termed the photosphere, and is a layer a few hundred kilometres thick, within which solar material goes from being completely opaque to virtually transparent; the layer from which visible-light emerges has a surface temperature of about 5550°C. Below comes the core, where energy is being produced in the form of high-energy photons at a temperature of about 15,000,000°C. Above the core is the radiative zone, through which energy is transported by radiation – the 'random walk' of photons; it takes a photon from 100,000 to 1 million years to travel from the core to the surface, and

▼ **Projecting the Sun:** the safest method to use when observing the Sun. Here, Ron Makins demonstrates how to project the Sun on to a screen, using a 3-inch telescope.

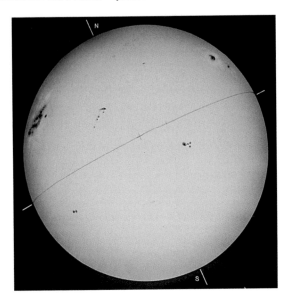

◀ **Large sunspot,** *as pictured by Paul Doherty on 17 March 1989.*

then a mere 8.6 minutes to cross space and reach the Earth. Above the radiative zone comes the convective zone, where energy is transported to the surface by convection; bubbles of gas rise, and there are circulating currents taking gas from deep down right up to the surface. This is shown by the granular structure of the photosphere, together with larger-scale supergranulation and giant cells.

Above the photosphere lies the chromosphere, a tenuous layer a few thousand kilometres thick, and outside this again comes the corona, the rarefied outer atmosphere seen with the naked eye only during a total solar eclipse.

The temperature decreases from the base of the photosphere (6150°C) to about 3900°C at the base of the chromosphere. Thereafter the temperature rises, gently at first, then very rapidly through the narrow transition zone which separates the chromosphere from the corona; in the corona the temperature rises to 1–2 million degrees Celsius. Since the laws of thermodynamics state that heat cannot flow from a cool source to a hotter one, we have to ask why the upper atmosphere has so high a temperature. It now seems that magnetic effects are responsible.

The solar wind, an outflow of plasma (mainly electrons and protons) escapes from the Sun, mainly through the low-density regions in the corona termed coronal holes. The solar wind carries about a million tons per day, and blows past the Earth at a speed of around 400 km/s (250 miles/s). It has a profound effect on the magnetic field and the magnetosphere of our world. The Earth behaves as though there were a bar magnet in its core, with lines of force entering at one pole and emerging at the other. But for the solar wind, the field would be symmetrical, but the effect of the wind is to squeeze the Earth's magnetic field inwards on the Sun-facing side, and draw it out into a long tail on the downstream side. The main border of the field is termed the magnetopause; here the solar wind is halted, producing what we call a bow shock.

Particles entering the upper atmosphere cause atoms and electrons to emit light; this produces the aurora. Short-wave X-rays and ultraviolet ionize the gas, and produce the ionosphere, which reflects radio waves; there is thus a direct link between the solar atmosphere, the solar wind, and the Earth.

Sunspots, relatively cool areas on the photosphere, usually appear in pairs or groups. Regions of concentrated magnetic fields are revealed by magnetograms. Spots are symptoms of underlying bipolar magnetic regions (adjacent areas of opposite magnetic polarity), formed where a twisted flux tube – that is to say, a bunch of concentrated field lines – emerges through the photosphere to form a region of an outward-directed or positive field; it then curves round in a loop and re-enters to form a region of inward-directed or negative field. This is why the leading and following spots of a group are of opposite polarity. Spots are cooler than the surrounding photosphere because the magnetic field inhibits the outward flow of energy.

Prominences are clouds of gas suspended in the solar atmosphere by magnetic forces; they are sometimes catapulted to heights of several thousands of miles, and may even be ejected from the Sun altogether. Flares are explosive releases of pent-up energy stored in tangled magnetic fields above complex sunspot groups. A flare can release up to 10^{25} joules (equivalent to 10,000 million one-megaton nuclear bombs) of energy in a matter of minutes; this is in the form of visible light, X-rays, all kinds of electromagnetic radiations, and energetic atomic particles, some of which are accelerated up to nearly half the speed of light. X-rays and energetic particles from flares strike the ionosphere and magnetic field of the Earth, as well as posing dangers for astronauts and (to a much lesser extent)

▼ **The solar cycle:** note the 'Maunder Minimum', a period between 1645 and 1715 when very few sunspots were observed, though records are incomplete. The vertical scale on the diagram is the Zürich number, calculated from the number of groups and the number of spots.

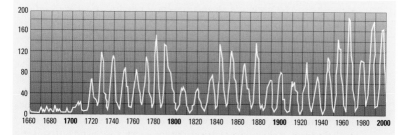

passengers in high-flying aircraft. They trigger disturbances in the Earth's magnetic field, setting up currents and causing compass needles to swing; there are power surges in electrical transmission lines, plus power failures and computer crashes.

The mean period of the solar cycle is of the order of 11 years, as is shown by the rise and fall in the numbers of sunspots. At maximum there are numerous groups. The rise to maximum takes 4–5 years, but the following fall to minimum takes 5–6 years. Successive maxima are not equally energetic.

The latitudes at which spots occur depend on the state of the cycle; this is termed Spörer's Law, since attention was first drawn to it in the 19th century by F. G. W. Spörer. The polarity pattern reverses at the end of a cycle, and all these effects indicate underlying changes in the solar magnetic field. The frequency and strength of eruptive prominences, flares and coronal mass ejections (CMEs) also increases and decreases according to the cycle. The shape and size of the corona is also affected, together with the extent to which blasts of particles and high-frequency radiation impinge upon the Earth's atmosphere and magnetosphere.

The Sun is being constantly monitored from ground level, and also by satellites and spacecraft. The Japanese Yokhoh X-ray satellite, launched in 1991, images X-ray emissions from the corona. The Ulysses spacecraft was launched in 1990, and used Jupiter's pull to throw it into a trajectory which takes it above the poles of the Sun – which can never be properly observed from Earth because we always see the Sun broadside-on. Ulysses found that a fast solar wind (at least 690 km/s [430 miles/s]) emerges from the coronal holes above the solar poles, and a slower wind (400 km/s [250 miles/s]) from above the equatorial regions. Ulysses has also provided a wealth of information about the solar wind in general, and about the solar and interplanetary magnetic fields.

Another NASA vehicle, TRACE (Transition Region and Coronal Explorer) was launched into Earth orbit on 1 April 1997 to study the high-temperature regions of the solar atmosphere at extreme ultraviolet wavelengths, which link fine-scale surface features with the changing structure of the solar atmosphere. With a resolution five times better than that of any previous solar satellite, it soon produced important results. For instance, it was the first to monitor a process termed magnetic reconnection. This occurs when oppositely-directed magnetic fields meet up, and reconnect to form new magnetic structures. When this happens, part of the energy tied up in the magnetic fields is released, and converted into other forms of energy – heat, radiation, streams of high-energy particles, and moving clouds of gas. Solar flares are believed to be powered by magnetic reconnection events; plasma is heated to tens of millions of degrees, with the consequent emission of X-rays. Other radiations follow, when streams of particles, accelerated to very high velocities, plough into the solar material. As the field lines snap into their new shapes, they hurl clouds of plasma outwards through the corona and into interplanetary space. For the first time, in May 1997, TRACE imaged a small-scale reconnection, when two adjacent loops of magnetic field came into contact.

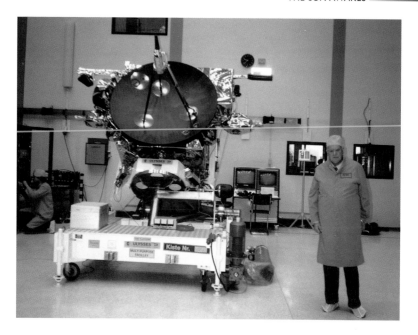

▲ **Ulysses,** the spacecraft launched to pass over the poles of the Sun – which can never be properly seen from Earth. I took this picture (time delay!) as Ulysses was being completed. It is still orbiting the Sun and will never return to Earth.

SOHO, the Solar and Heliospheric Observatory, was launched in 1995, and placed at a Lagrangian point of the Earth/Sun system – a stable position in which the spacecraft always remains between the Earth and the Sun, at 1,450,000 km (900,000 miles) upstream of the Earth. SOHO has an uninterrupted view of the Sun, and can give advance warning of solar particles heading our way. Britain is deeply involved in this mission; the coronal diagnostic spectrometer (CDS) was built and operated by the Rutherford Appleton Laboratory (RAL) in Oxfordshire.

SOHO has provided spectacular images of CMEs, including the major ejection of 7 April 1997, in which a vast bubble of plasma was sent hurtling towards the Earth; also the 6 November 1997 event. The solar wind instrument on SOHO gives information about the arrival of a typical mass ejection between 30 and 60 minutes before it arrives, and gives advance warning about the likely severity of the 'storm'. SOHO has also discovered several comets which have plunged into the Sun and been destroyed; it has discovered solar tornadoes, spiralling plumes of gas accelerating upwards from the chromosphere within polar coronal holes. These tornadoes may play an important role in contributing to the fast solar wind which streams outwards from the holes.

A SOHO team led by Dr Richard Harrison of RAL has also discovered what are termed flashers or 'blinkers', which erupt sporadically all over the Sun. There are about 3000 of them on the Sun at any one time. Blinkers may help to provide solutions to two of the key mysteries about the Sun: How is the solar wind ejected? And how is the solar atmosphere heated? Blinker explosions may be the sites of particle acceleration and plasma heating.

SOHO has cast doubt upon one of the suggested mechanisms for heating the corona, the transport of energy by means of magnetic waves. Some of the suggested waves have been observed, but they fade out before reaching the hottest part of the atmosphere. However, there is ample evidence to support the theory that a substantial proportion of the heating comes from ongoing reconnection events (resembling mini-flares) such as blinkers.

There are also sunquakes. SOHO has produced dramatic images of seismic waves generated by the blast of a solar flare, spreading out across the surface of the Sun like ripples from a splash in a pond. These waves can start out at around 40,000 km/h (25,000 mph), and by the time they fade from view they have accelerated up to about 400,000 km/h (250,000 mph) – and have travelled a distance equal to ten Earth diameters.

Helioseismology is a new science. The surface of the Sun is constantly vibrating, rather like the skin of a drum, because of the seismic waves which oscillate beneath its surface and in the deep interior. A pressure wave triggered by a disturbance at or near the Sun's surface will pick up speed as it heads downwards into the lower layers, and its direction of propagation will be bent, so that after penetrating to a maximum depth it returns to the surface, where it is reflected again. Disturbances which circumnavigate the Sun set up standing waves, and the overall vibrations are recorded by SOHO. We are in fact dealing with many thousands of different vibrational modes at a million points all across the Sun's surface.

Analyses of the various vibrational modes tell us a great deal about how the temperature, density and rate of rotation change with increasing depth below the surface, and at different latitudes above or below the solar equator. SOHO has charted streams of gas below the surface, and has plotted the flow of huge convection cells deep down into the convective zone; there is a sharp change in the rate of rotation at the boundary between the convective and radiative zones. Ongoing analyses may eventually allow us to solve some of the major problems – such as why the Sun's core appears to be cooler than theory predicts.

SOHO has performed well. It began its observations near solar minimum; it lasted through the peak of the next maximum in 2001, and we must await the results of further research. Nearby though it is, there is still a great deal about the Sun that we do not understand.

The Flying Horse

It has been said that the evening sky in autumn is less interesting than at any other time in the year. Well, it is true that the Summer Triangle is past its best, and that Orion does not rise until the early hours, but there is still plenty to be seen – quite apart from any planets that happen to be on view.

The main autumn constellation is Pegasus. Its four chief stars are arranged in a square. In mythology, Pegasus was a flying horse which carried the hero Bellerophon in quest of the Chimaera, a particularly nasty fire-breathing monster. (Bellerophon later came to an untimely end, but that was not Pegasus' fault!)

Following a system introduced as long ago as 1603 by the German amateur astronomer Johann Bayer, each star is given a Greek letter, from Alpha through to Omega, so that here we have Alpha, Beta and Gamma Pegasi. We used to have Delta, but for some curious reason Delta Pegasi has been given a free transfer to the neighbouring constellation of Andromeda, and has become Alpha Andromedae. I have never seen the logic behind this; the star so clearly belongs to the Square, whereas Andromeda has no definite pattern at all. Mythologically, Andromeda was a princess, but in the sky appears merely as a line of brightish stars.

Some stars have individual names, mainly Arabic. Alpha Andromedae (née Delta Pegasi) is Alpheratz; Alpha Pegasi is Markab, Beta is Scheat and Gamma is Algenib. In fact, these names are not much used nowadays.

Come now to magnitude, which is a star's apparent brilliancy; the lower the magnitude, the brighter the star. In the Square, Alpheratz is of magnitude 2.1, Markab 2.5, Algenib 2.8 and Scheat rather variable (I may as well use the proper names for the moment). This means that Alpheratz is the brightest of the four.

However, this does not mean that Alpheratz is the most luminous, because the stars are at different distances from us. A star may look brilliant because it is relatively near (as with Sirius), because it is really very powerful (as with Rigel), or a combination of both. Distances are measured in light-years; one light-year is equivalent to about 9.46×10^{12} km – or 9.46 million million million km (5.8 million million million miles). Here are the data for the four stars in the Square:

THE SQUARE OF PEGASUS				
Star	Magnitude	Distance (light-years)	Luminosity, Sun-1	Colour
Alpheratz	2.1	72	96	White
Markab	2.5	100	60	White
Scheat	2.4 to 2.8	176	310	Orange
Algenib	2.8	490	1320	Bluish-white

Algenib, then, is decidedly in the background, and from a different vantage point in the Galaxy there would be no semblance of a Square.

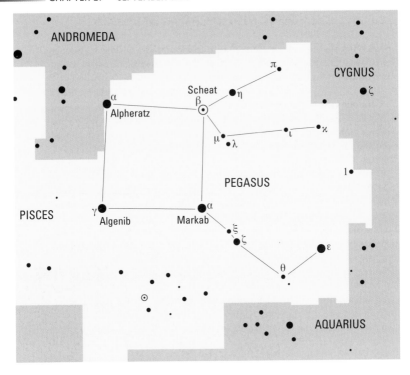

▲ *The Square of*
Pegasus.

Algenib is much further away from Alpheratz than we are; the four stars in the Square have absolutely no real connection with each other.

The stars are of different colours because their surface temperatures are different. Scheat is much the coolest of the four; its surface temperature is no more than 3400 degrees, while the temperatures of the other stars exceed 10,000 degrees. Look at the four one after the other, even with the naked eye, and you will notice the difference; binoculars bring out Scheat's warm orange hue very clearly.

Moreover, Scheat is variable. Sometimes it is brighter than Markab, sometimes fainter. It swells and shrinks, and there is a rough period of 38 days, so that a light-curve can be drawn; the current magnitude can be estimated by comparing Scheat with the other stars, which are constant in brightness. Scheat is an old star, well advanced in its evolution, so that it has become unstable. It is also very large; it ranks as an orange giant.

One point of minor interest. Normally, on a clear night you can see stars down to magnitude 6; fainter than that, you need optical aid. How many naked-eye stars can you see inside the Square of Pegasus? Count them, and you may well be surprised.

There is one other brightish star in Pegasus, well away from the Square. This is Epsilon Pegasi or Enif, magnitude 2.4, so that it is actually the brightest star in the Horse unless you include Alpheratz. It is decidedly orange, and it is very powerful; it could match 5000 Suns, but it is 500 light-years away. This means that we now see it as it used to be 500 years ago, when Henry VII was king of England. Once we look beyond the Solar System, our view of the universe is bound to be very out of date.

Not far from Enif in the sky there is a very interesting object: a globular cluster, known as M15 because it was the 15th object in a famous catalogue of clusters and nebulae drawn up in 1781 by the French astronomer Charles Messier. To find it, take a line from Theta Pegasi or Biham (magnitude 3.5), pass it through Enif, and go on until you find a dimly luminous smudge; this is M15. It is too faint to be seen with the naked eye, but binoculars will show it. It is a vast, symmetrical system of stars – hundreds of thousands of them. It is a long way off, and lies at a distance of 49,000 light-years.

Over 100 globular clusters are known in our Galaxy. They lie round the edges of the main system; the Galaxy is flattened (I have often compared

▶ *M15 (NGC 7078),*
as imaged by the Hubble
Space Telescope. Located
in the constellation of
Pegasus, M15 is densely
packed globular star
cluster, filled with stars
that are about 12,000
million years old,
compared to our
Sun which is a mere
4500 million years old!

its shape with that of two fried eggs clapped together back to back) and the globulars make up a kind of outer framework. Most of them lie in the southern part of the sky, but M15 is well north of the celestial equator.

Near the centre of a globular cluster, the stars are more crowded together than they are in our part of the Galaxy. If we lived on a planet moving round a star inside such a cluster, the night sky would be glorious; there would be many stars bright enough to cast shadows, and many of them would be old orange or red giants, because globular clusters are very ancient systems. Yet even in the central regions the stars are too widely spaced for collisions to occur. A direct meeting between two stars is vanishingly rare.

Turn next to the areas near Pegasus. As we have seen, Andromeda is marked by a chain of fairly bright stars. Not far from the orange Mirach (Beta Andromedae) there is a tiny blur which was numbered 31 in Messier's catalogue. It is not a globular cluster, but an independent galaxy; it is over 2 million light-years away, and is larger than our Galaxy. It is spiral, though it lies at a narrow angle to us and the full beauty of the spiral is lost. Also in the constellation is Almaak or Gamma Andromedae, a lovely double star with one component much brighter than the other.

Go back to Pegasus, and use Scheat and Markab as pointers. After passing through a dim area, this line leads on to Fomalhaut in the constellation of Piscis Australis, the Southern Fish. Fomalhaut is bright; its magnitude is 1.3, and it is the southernmost of the first-magnitude stars to be visible from Britain. Even from southern England it is always low down, and from northern Scotland it barely rises at all.

Fomalhaut is a near neighbour, only 22 light-years away and a mere 13 times as luminous as the Sun, so that it is very puny when compared with, say, Enif. However, it is of special interest to us because it is one of the stars known to be associated with cool, possibly planet-forming material. I am not claiming that there is a system of planets moving round Fomalhaut, but certainly the possibility cannot be ruled out. It is the only bright star in the Southern Fish, which is otherwise unremarkable. Do not confuse Fomalhaut with Beta Ceti (Diphda) which lies roughly in line with Alpheratz and Algenib. Diphda is a full magnitude fainter than Fomalhaut, and is much higher up.

So even though we still lack Orion, there is plenty of interest in and near Pegasus. Next time you see a clear autumn sky, I suggest that you go outdoors and strike up an acquaintance with the Flying Horse.

— *The Royal Greenwich Observatory* —

On 31 October 1998, Britain's flagship observatory – the Royal Greenwich Observatory – ceased to exist. The Government closed it down, to save money. We presented the programme about the RGO on 16 November 1998, very soon after the closure. With me was Dr Jasper Wall, the last Director of the RGO, and this article is based upon what he said. My own comments are added at the end. As you will gather, my opinions about the destruction of the RGO are very definite.

It was founded by Royal Warrant in June 1675, by order of King Charles II. Christopher Wren was granted £500 to design it. It was Britain's first official observatory, but its original purpose was navigational; sailors out at sea needed to find their longitude (latitude was easy enough), and this meant using a very accurate star catalogue. The Reverend John Flamsteed, the first Astronomer Royal, was charged with producing such a catalogue – and he did so, though it took him a long time. The RGO had started its career.

After Flamsteed came Edmond Halley, who carried out an amazing amount of work. In particular, he refined the movements of the Moon. Yet, ironically, developments in the making of clocks usable at sea meant that the Greenwich work was never used in quite the way originally intended.

The problem of longitude-finding can be solved if you carry Greenwich time with you. The standard pendulum clock of the age was useless on a

▼ *The Old Royal Observatory, in* Greenwich, London – now a museum.

▲ **Herstmonceux** *headquarters of the Royal*
Castle – *once the* *Greenwich Observatory.*

rolling ship, and so the Admiralty offered a prize of £20,000 for a clock that would work under very exacting conditions. The prize, equivalent to about £1 million today, was won by John Harrison in 1759, with the famous Harrison 4 (H4), the fourth in a line of clocks which took Harrison over a quarter of a century to develop. Harrison's clock also had to be copied – and it was, by Larcum Kendall. After a long battle with the Admiralty, Harrison did eventually receive his prize.

H4 began the science of marine chronometers, and as late as the 1960s the RGO had a chronometer department which was the official calibrator for all naval timekeepers.

Yet by the time Harrison had perfected his chronometer, the situation had changed. It has been suggested – perhaps unfairly – that the then Astronomer Royal, Nevil Maskelyne, deliberately held up justice for Harrison. In any case, it was Maskelyne who produced the *Nautical Almanac*, which gave precise positions of the Sun, Moon and planets throughout the year. The Nautical Almanac Office, founded by Maskelyne, has continued to this day, and produces not only the *Almanac* itself but also the *Astronomical Ephemeris*.

Between Halley and Maskelyne came another distinguished Astronomer Royal, James Bradley, who used the apparent changing positions of the stars to give practical proof of the Earth's movement round the Sun. Bradley also demonstrated the 'rocking' of the Earth in response to the gravitational pull of the Moon, exactly as had been predicted by Newton.

During the 19th century the long-serving Astronomer Royal was Sir George Biddell Airy, who set up the first major telescopes at Greenwich, and was also responsible for making the Observatory the timekeeping centre of the world. Airy was a remarkable individual – essentially chief government scientist and research councillor combined. He was consulted about every technical and scientific problem, and kept meticulous records, carefully annotated and bound, even including his laundry bills! His archival collection is a treasure for historians of science, and indeed for the Victorian Age. Of his telescopes, the Airy Transit Circle is still in working order, while the Northumberland Telescope has been taken to Cambridge.

It is a pity that Airy was involved in controversy over the discovery of Neptune, but this was in fact a minor blemish. It was in 1884 that the Greenwich Meridian was officially adopted worldwide as the zero for longitude. By then Airy had retired, but the credit was his.

In the 20th century Greenwich became unsuitable as a site for astronomical observation – London had spread! – and in 1957 the RGO was transferred to the clearer skies of Herstmonceux in Sussex. The old Observatory became a museum, and it still is.

At Herstmonceux, under Sir Harold Spencer Jones and then Sir Richard Woolley, the 98-inch Isaac Newton Telescope (INT) was set up. For political reasons the telescope had to be sited in Britain, but Herstmonceux, overlooking the misty Pevensey Marshes and the encroaching lights of Eastbourne, was far from ideal. A better site was needed, and was found on La Palma, the most westerly of the Canary Islands. The RGO developed an observatory atop an extinct volcano, the Roque de los Muchachos. The INT was moved there, and was joined by a 1-metre

▼ *The 'new'*
Royal Greenwich
Observatory, *at*

Cambridge, photographed in 1995 – now, sadly, destroyed.

(39-inch) telescope, the Jacobus Kapteyn reflector, and the Carlsberg Transit Circle, undoubtedly the best of its kind anywhere in the world.

The RGO at Herstmonceux remained the headquarters; moreover, it had its unique library, its priceless plate collection and its educational facilities. Nevertheless, in the 1980s it was decided, against the wishes of virtually all astronomers – to close Herstmonceux and transfer the RGO to a purpose-built office at Cambridge. The Herstmonceux telescopes were simply abandoned.

The William Herschel Telescope (WHT), at La Palma, came into operation in 1987; it and the Isaac Newton Telescope were still controlled by the RGO. The WHT is a landmark telescope, and has features which all future ground-based telescopes will surely follow. The mounting is altazimuth rather than equatorial; this is much more compact, with the bearings much easier to design. The building is separated from the telescope enclosure, so that no heat from the building can rise into the light-path to blur the images which the telescope forms so beautifully.

The telescope is equipped with the most modern technology. For example, there is the multiple-object spectrograph, with which the telescope uses optical fibres to take up to 150 spectra simultaneously – say, of the stars in a globular cluster or in a cluster of galaxies.

There is excellent response in the ultraviolet, and this has been used by Max Pettini to identify galaxies at vast distances. These will have very high red shifts. Pettini's method was to take images of the same field through several filters; faint, fuzzy objects seen at red and green wavelengths but not in ultraviolet could be assumed to be very remote galaxies. With high red shift, the ultraviolet is shifted into the visible range, so that the filter sees nothing at all. These are the galaxies which 'drop out' in the ultraviolet.

From this we can find out just how the galaxies are distributed in space. The surprising result is that they are not distributed smoothly, but in great concentrations or 'walls'. This seriously challenges the picture of galaxies assembling themselves gently by means of gravity, and then clustering together progressively as the universe ages. Such apparently well-developed structure during the early history of the universe is therefore inconsistent.

Next in the RGO plan came Gemini – and here the RGO was awarded contracts worth £9 million towards building the twin 8-metre telescopes, Gemini North, on Mauna Kea in Hawaii, and Gemini South, in the Chilean Andes. Following on the success in designing the support for the 4.2-metre (165-inch) mirror of the WHT, the RGO designed the mounts for the Gemini mirrors. These mirrors are very thin, so that mounting them and holding them in place is rather like supporting a gigantic window-pane. The support has over 200 computer-controlled pneumatic pumps, and there is a huge airbag beneath the mirror to help in supporting the load.

Every telescope mirror must be re-coated perhaps once a year. Conventionally, you do the 'mirror silvering' in a very large vacuum tank in which you explode a bar of silver or aluminium with a pulse of electricity. (The pulse for the WHT dims the lights in La Palma; the vacuum tank has to be truly enormous to accommodate the mirror.) Such techniques can hardly be used for 8-metre mirrors atop 4200-metre (14,000-ft) mountains, so the RGO developed a 'sputtering technique', using a vacuum tank not much bigger than the mirror. In this tank there is a single radial track on which a 'mirror-painter' is mounted. This is a high-voltage tube which evaporates aluminium in a streak about a metre long. To coat the mirror, this mirror-painter is moved along the rail while the mirror is turned slowly beneath it.

There are also other new methods. Modern telescopes must have provisions for these techniques built in from the start, and the Gemini telescopes were designed accordingly. The main problem is our atmosphere, which is unsteady; heat bubbles in it blur the image. Using bright stars near the field of view, or even creating 'fake' stars by means of a laser, it is now possible to find how the atmosphere has bent the wavefronts coming to the telescope. By using a distortable mirror which compensates for these effects, it is possible to reconstruct the image as it would be if seen from above the atmosphere. This is termed 'adaptive optics'.

We have entered the 'electronic age', and the RGO has been in the forefront. CCDs (charge-coupled devices) are all-important. For the INT, the RGO built a wide-field camera by putting four huge CCDs together in a mosaic arrangement. The CCDs cover an area of about 4×4 inches; there are around 32 million pixels involved, and a large area of the sky can be mapped with each exposure. This camera turns the INT into the ideal survey instrument for the Gemini telescopes.

▶ **Official opening of the 'new' RGO,** Cambridge, in 1988. Facing the camera to my right is Professor Alec Boksenberg, then Director of the RGO; to my left, kneeling, is Robert Jackson, MP, then Minister for Science. Within ten years, the Government had destroyed the RGO. (Photograph courtesy Rutherford Appleton Laboratory, Oxfordshire.)

Quite apart from all this, the RGO has been an invaluable meeting centre. There have been 40 years of summer schools, where second- and third-year undergraduates came to spend a couple of months at the Observatory to gain experience. At the last count, nearly half Britain's astronomers had attended the school (there have also been several marriages). There have been annual Herstmonceux conferences, international gatherings on specialized topics, and much else. The RGO has also played a major role in astronomical education.

Now it is over. Our great Observatory has passed into history. It will never be forgotten; sadly, it can never be restored.

This was more or less what Jasper Wall said during our programme. The comments which follow are my own, and I take full responsibility for them.

Looking back far enough, it may be fair to say that the rot really started in 1971 when the post of Astronomer Royal was split from that of Director of the RGO. However, the major crisis came with the shift from Herstmonceux to Cambridge. I was involved, since I was asked to convene a meeting to discuss the whole matter. This was held on 6 June 1986; at my request, Professor P. A. Wayman, Director of the Dunsink Observatory in Ireland, took the Chair. Not one voice was raised in support of the move, and two of the main speakers against it were from the Cambridge observatory.

However, the move went ahead. It was stressed that the future of the RGO at Cambridge was secure, and I quote from a letter written to me on 7 July 1986 by the Prime Minister, Mrs Thatcher: 'All of the present RGO activities will move to Cambridge apart from the Equatorial Group of telescopes and the Exhibition Centre. Thus the Observatory will retain its independence and integrity, and there can be no question of the loss of the RGO as a national observatory.' The same wording was used by Professor Mitchell, then Chairman of the Science and Engineering Research Council, on 19 June. Frankly, I was convinced that this would not work out, and that the RGO would be quietly merged with the Astronomical Institute at Cambridge, but even I did not then think that the RGO would be destroyed.

What have we lost? (1) The RGO as an administrative headquarters. (2) The expertise of the RGO team. (3) The steady stream of important papers. (4) Instrument development. (5) Educational facilities. (6) The Library, now dispersed. (7) The plate collection, now stored somewhere in London and unavailable for use. (8) Herstmonceux as a conference centre. (9) Heritage.

Gains? So far as I can see, nil. Closing the RGO cost around £8 million, but this money will have to be spent on compensatory projects elsewhere, so that in the end there is no saving at all. And it is worth noting that the money spent on the huge, useless Millennium Dome at Greenwich would have financed the RGO well into the 22nd century. All in all, the closure of the RGO will go down as one of the worst pieces of scientific vandalism in modern times.

— *Nocturnals: Timekeeping by the Stars* —

Timekeeping by the stars is a very old science. Nowadays, of course, we have atomic clocks which are more accurate than the Earth itself, but things were very different in Renaissance times. Various instruments were in use, and one of these, for telling the time during night, was the nocturnal.

It seems that nocturnals were first made during the early 16th century, and the basic design has changed little since then; it is quite easy to make a nocturnal for oneself. In an age when clocks were expensive and unreliable, and the tinder box was the only method of producing light, the nocturnal made it possible to find the time at night without the need to strike flints or light candles. Nocturnals must have been particularly useful to soldiers, sailors, travellers, and all people whose occupations prevented their access to regular fixed clocks. Moreover, timekeeping and astronomy are inextricably linked, and the use of a nocturnal is one of the most direct ways to use the apparent motion of the stars to tell the time.

The sky seems to turn from east to west because of the rotation of the Earth. Northwards, the axis points to a point called the north celestial pole. By sheer luck, this is marked to within one degree by a brightish star, Polaris in Ursa Minor (the Little Bear). You can find Polaris easily by using the two Pointers in the Great Bear or Plough (Big Dipper), Merak and Dubhe (officially catalogued as Beta and Alpha Ursae Majoris).

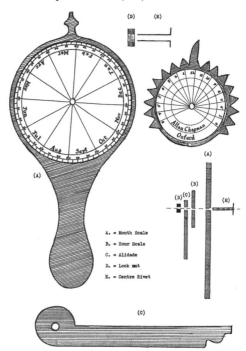

A. = Month Scale
B. = Hour Scale
C. = Alidade
D. = Lock nut
E. = Centre Rivet

▶ **Components of the nocturnal,** *showing the large hour plate, held upright in the observer's hand. Upon this plate is placed the smaller, circular toothed dial which carries the night hours, and the alidade, or pointer. All are secured by a hollow brass rivet.*

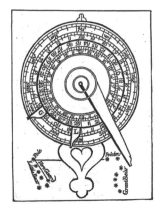

Because it is so near the pole, Polaris seems to remain almost still, with the other stars moving round it in a period of 24 hours. (Take a time-exposure during a starlit night, and you will find that the stars are drawn out into trails.) Because Ursa Major is not far from the pole, it never drops below the horizon as seen from Britain, and is circumpolar; whenever the sky is dark and clear, it is always on view. A nocturnal depends on using the Pointers as a celestial clock-hand.

The instrument itself is quite simple. The main plate carries a scale of 12 months, divided down into five-day intervals. The exact place from which this scale begins is calculated astronomically to suit a given epoch or cycle of years, and is governed by the precession of the equinoxes. As the Earth spins, the effects of the Sun and Moon cause the axis to turn slightly – rather like a boy's gyroscope which is starting to topple. But while a gyroscope 'precesses' in a few seconds, the Earth's axis takes 25,000 years. This means that the position of the main scale on a nocturnal does not need to be changed over a period of many lifetimes. Eventually, of course, it will need adjusting. When the Egyptian pyramids were built, the pole lay near the star Thuban, in the constellation of the Dragon; in 12,000 years' time the place of honour will be more or less marked by the brilliant blue Vega.

▲ *Engraving of a 17th-century nocturnal. Its dials could be used to find the time from both the Great Bear and Little Bear (Ursa Major and Ursa Minor). Note the notches marked 'G' and 'L' for use with whichever Bear constellation one was using.*

The arrangement of a nocturnal is shown in the diagram on the previous page. A plate serrated into 18 teeth is mounted above the month scale. This

▼ *To tell the time with a nocturnal, first set the 'midnight' pointer to the current date. Then hold it at arm's length and look at the Pole Star through the central rivet hole. Next, adjust the alidade until it is aligned with 'The Pointers' stars in the Great Bear. One can then read off the time at the point where the alidade crosses an hour notch.*

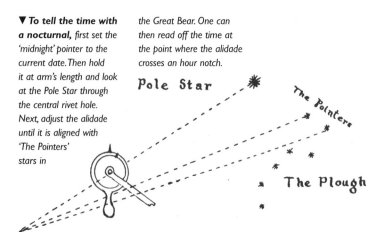

plate represents the 24 hours of the day, although since the nocturnal is intended to work only at night the plate is divided into 18 hours, to cater for the maximum hours of winter darkness – from 4 pm to 8 am. Each hour is indicated by a wooden tooth. The tooth representing midnight is longer and more pronounced than the others. The scale is marked by teeth, so that the time can be told in the dark using touch alone – a precursor to braille, if you like.

Lastly, there is the tail or alidade, mounted concentrically to both the month and hour dials. The upper edge of the alidade points exactly to the centre of the hollow rivet around which all the parts rotate.

To make an observation, first set the longer 'midnight' tooth on the serrated hour scale to the appropriate day of the year, and wedge it fast with a bit of card. Then, after dark, simply hold the nocturnal vertically and look at the Pole Star through the hollow rivet in the centre of the instrument. Once the Pole Star has been found, rotate the pointer, or alidade, until the Pointers in the Great Bear appear to rest upon its edge. The position of the alidade in relation to the toothed hour plate will give you the time.

Obviously the result cannot be very precise by modern standards, but, with practice, one can make a nocturnal give the time to 10 or 15 minutes.

Of course, all this applies only to the Earth's northern hemisphere, and in particular to regions from which the Pointers are circumpolar. From any latitude south of 40°N, the Pointers will set for part of each 24 hours. And from anywhere south of the equator, Polaris remains below the horizon. Unfortunately, there is no bright south polar star; the whole area appears very barren, and the star closest to the south pole, Sigma Octantis, is only just visible with the naked eye. Neither are there any southern equivalents of the Pointers; Beta Hydri, the nearest bright star to the pole, is more than 12 degrees away. There will be no respectable south pole star until about AD 5000, when the site will be fairly well marked by Omega Carinae, magnitude 3.8.

It would be absurd to claim that nocturnals are of any scientific value today, but it is still fascinating to make one, and to see how our forebears worked out time during the night.

▶ **Drawing taken from**
a circa 1600 painting of a
man using a nocturnal.

—— *Is There Anybody Out There?* ——

Of all the questions which have been asked over the ages, it is probable that 'Are there intelligent beings beyond the Earth?' is the question which we would most like to answer. Unfortunately, it attracts cranks rather in the way that an open jamjar attracts wasps, and we have to cope with astrologers, UFO enthusiasts, alien abductee stories, creationists and their kind. But putting aside all this sort of nonsense, can we make a proper scientific evaluation of the possibilities?

Come first to the Drake Equation, devised by Frank Drake in 1961 as a way to focus on the factors which might lead us to a rational estimate. The equation is as follows:

$$N = N^\star \ f_p \ n_e \ f_l \ f_i \ f_c \ f_L$$

N = the required answer.
$N^\star$ = the number of stars in our Galaxy.
(Around 100,000 million.)
f_p = the fraction of stars with planetary families.
(Perhaps 20–50%.)
n_e = the number of planets per star capable of supporting life.
(Perhaps 1–5%.)
f_l = the fraction of planets in n_e on which life appears.
(Estimates range from 100% down to 0.)
f_i = the fraction of f_l on which intelligent life evolves.
(Again, estimates from 100% down to 0.)
f_c = the fraction of f_l which can communicate.
(Perhaps 10–20%.)
f_L = the fraction of a planet's life for which a civilization survives.
(Who knows?)

Taking all these factors into account, it does seem that there must be a great many advanced civilizations, but of course there are other considerations to be borne in mind.

A star has to remain stable long enough and emit a reasonably constant amount of heat to enable life to survive. Round each star there must be an 'ecosphere', where the temperature on an orbiting planet would be neither too high nor too low, assuming the planet to be suitable in other respects. It seems, therefore, that stars of the same kind as the Sun are particularly promising candidates as planetary centres.

Extra-solar planets have been discovered in recent years – it seems that around 1 in 10 or 1 in 20 suitable stars may have orbiting planets. However, most of the planets found so far are much more like Jupiter than like the Earth, and, moreover, are strangely close to their parent stars. We can only hope that a reasonable percentage of stars will have at least one planet in the local ecosphere, where water could exist on the surface. It is significant that life can appear in what might be thought to be most improbable places – as, for instance, the hydrothermal vents and 'black smokers' at the bottoms of our own oceans.

Life as we know it on Earth is made up of the most common elements in the universe, and is based upon carbon. It is logical to assume that other life-forms on other words will be built up from the same building blocks. The general view today is that conditions suitable for simple life-forms to evolve will be present in myriads of places within our Galaxy (and no doubt in other galaxies also), and that given the right conditions life is almost certain to appear. However, on Earth it took at least 3000 million years for complex life-forms to evolve, finally leading to you and me. How often will we find other intelligent civilizations able to consider trying to contact other races, light-years away from them? This is something which we do not know.

▼ **The 100-m Green Bank Radio Telescope:** *in operation since August 2000, this very large telescope is studying* *radio waves coming from far-off galaxies, as well as pulsars, planets and comets, and even the early universe.*

▲ *M13 – a globular cluster in Hercules. A message was sent to it* *in 1974, but we cannot expect to receive a reply yet awhile!*

The obvious way to attempt to establish the existence of other civilizations is to use radio methods, as was first tried as long ago as 1961 by Frank Drake's team at Green Bank, in the United States. The target stars were Tau Ceti and Epsilon Eridani, which are the two nearest stars reasonably similar to the Sun; they are around 11 light-years away. One signal was soon detected, and caused a flurry of excitement, but, alas, turned out to be due to a U2 spy plane, then still on the secret list. Many searches have been made since then, so far without success, though it is worth noting that Epsilon Eridani does appear to be accompanied by a planet, plus a cloud of cool, possibly planet-forming material. SETI (the Search for Extra-terrestrial Intelligence) is now being energetically followed up, and several full-scale programmes are under way.

We cannot fix upon any definite frequency at which to search, but we can at least decide which we would ourselves choose if we were trying to send a signal to be picked up by others. The most promising region lies between the frequencies used by mobile phones and those used by satellite TV. Within this band there are two fundamental frequencies – that of hydrogen, the most common element in the universe, and the hydroxyl radical OH. Together these make up water, so we call the range the 'cosmic water-hole'. Just as animals meet at water-holes in the jungle, so we suspect that other civilizations would use this part of the radio band to communicate with us.

Yet it is a very wide band, and if we tried to search it using a single radio receiver scanning across the dial it would take an impossibly long time. Therefore, we use a 56-million channel receiver – taking 90 minutes to scan each stellar system as it shifts across the whole band.

Next, we must ask ourselves what types of signal would we hope to receive. The probable answer must be 'something along the lines of the Morse code', because very simple signals are the easiest to pick up across vast distances. It would certainly be possible to transmit an intelligible message in this way.

In 1974 the 100-ft Arecibo radio telescope was used to send a simple message to the globular star cluster M13, in Hercules. It took three minutes to send, and will arrive in 25,000 years' time. If a reply is sent back immediately, we may expect it around the year AD 50,000, which admittedly is rather a long time to wait. Pictures and plaques carried on the Pioneer and Voyager spacecraft, which are now well on their way out of the Solar System, should be of great interest to any alien civilization which happens to find them, but we have to admit the chances of their being found are very low.

The main programme at the present time is Phoenix, in which the 250-ft Lovell radio telescope at Jodrell Bank, Cheshire, is involved, together with the 1000-ft radio telescope at Arecibo in Puerto Rico. Suppose that a signal from an unidentified transmitter is received at Arecibo; how can we be sure that it is not due to a transmitter on Earth or on a satellite? It will also be received at Jodrell Bank, but because the Earth is rotating the Doppler effect means that the frequency will be very slightly different. This will show that the signal really is extraterrestrial, and comes from afar.

To test this system we make use of the Pioneer 10 spacecraft, which bypassed Jupiter in December 1973 and is now leaving the Solar System permanently; by now it is nearly 11,300 million km (7000 million miles) away, well beyond the orbit of Pluto. It is still transmitting a 10-watt signal – just ten times as powerful as a mobile phone. We observe this signal during each observing session to prove that the system is fully operational. Pioneer 10 still has an important role to play, even though its main task was completed more than a quarter of a century ago.

It will take years to observe the nearest thousand solar-type stars, but there is a problem due to the increased use of satellite communications for mobile phones and access to the internet; these transmissions are steadily encroaching upon the band which astronomers would like kept clear. It is rather like a curtain being drawn across a window. Some day we may even be forced to make SETI observations from the far side of the Moon, which will be completely radio-quiet.

If we are optimistic in our predictions about the number of intelligent civilizations in the Galaxy, then we ought to have a good chance of detecting an extraterrestrial signal in the foreseeable future. This would surely be the most dramatic discovery of all time. On the other hand, if it transpires that civilizations seldom reach our technological level, or that they self-destruct when they have reached a certain stage, we might even be the only communicative civilization in the Galaxy. Time will tell. Meanwhile, our message is: 'Come in, ET; we're waiting to hear from you!'

Maverick Asteroids

The asteroids, or minor planets, are small worlds; only one of them – Ceres – is as much as 800 km (500 miles) in diameter, and only one – Vesta – is ever visible with the naked eye. Most of them move round the Sun in orbits between those of Mars and Jupiter, but there are some which depart from the main swarm. In the far reaches of the Solar System we have the groups known as Centaurs and Trans-Neptunians. Much closer-in there are the NEAs or NEOs (Near Earth Asteroids/Objects), and it is these which occasionally make headline news – to say nothing of the 'disaster films' such as *Armageddon* that have been produced in recent years.

The first asteroid to be discovered was Ceres, in 1801. This was followed by the discoveries of Pallas in 1802, Juno in 1804 and Vesta in 1807. Nowadays, the Hubble Space Telescope has been able to show surface details on Ceres and Vesta, but in ordinary telescopes they appear as mere specks of light, betraying their nature only by their movements against the starry background.

From 1845 onwards the numbers of known asteroids increased dramatically. One irritated German astronomer even referred to them as 'vermin of the skies', because they left trails across plates exposed for quite different reasons. By 1868, 100 asteroids were known. By 1921 this number had

▼ **Asteroid Ida,** with its tiny satellite Dactyl. This image was taken on 28 August 1993 by the *Galileo spacecraft, from a range of 10,870 km (6755 miles). Ida is 56 km (35 miles) long.*

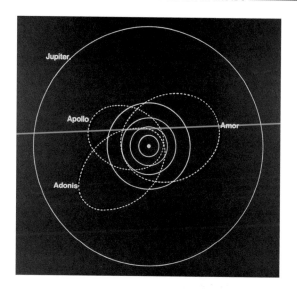

► **Orbits of three asteroids:** *Amor, Adonis and Apollo. The diagram shows how the paths of the asteroids cross the orbital paths of the inner planets in the Solar System.*

increased to 1000; by 1946, to 2000; and by 1985, to 3000. But as soon as astronomers began to use sensitive CCDs on their telescopes it became clear that the true numbers were much greater than anyone had expected.

By 2002 the number of known asteroids had grown to over 50,000. Of these, over 20,000 had well-known orbits and had received official numbers; the remainder needed further observation before we could be sure that we do not lose track of them – something which is only too easy to do.

Amateurs can, and do, discover asteroids. When a new one is sighted, three nights of measurement over a ten-day arc are needed. If there is no match with a known object, a temporary designation is issued by the International Astronomical Union. Half a dozen measurements over a 30–60 day arc will be enough to find the asteroid 'next time round'. Four oppositions are required to get the asteroid numbered; this may take from four to ten years. One English amateur, Brian Manning, now has 11 numbered asteroids to his credit. Names suggested by the discoverers are submitted to the IAU, and are almost always ratified. Manning named his first discovery (Asteroid 7239) 'Mobberley', after Martin Mobberley, who joined me in this programme. ('My' asteroid is 2601; it was discovered by Dr Edward Bowell from the Lowell Observatory in Arizona.)

Various asteroids have now been imaged from spacecraft, notably Gaspra, Ida and Mathilde. Ida proved to be attended by a tiny satellite (Dactyl), while Mathilde was porous and very black. But it is the NEAs which are of immediate concern to us.

They are small; most have diameters of a kilometre or two or even less, and the largest, Ganymed, is about 40 km (25 miles) across. Two new telescopes have been brought into use to look for NEAs: Spacewatch, and Linear (the latter was originally commissioned by the US Air Force to search for enemy satellites). Both have had remarkable success. Spacewatch, a 36-inch reflector, is run by the University of Arizona, and detects one NEA for every 900 asteroids discovered. The larger Linear telescope discovered 16,000 new asteroids during its first two years of operation (1997–8). But amateurs must not be forgotten; they too identify NEAs. For example, the American amateur Roy Tucker has found three.

NEAs are divided into several groups:

1. **Apollo class.**
These asteroids cross the orbit of Mars, but not that of the Earth.

2. **Amor class.**
These cross the orbits of both Mars and the Earth, so that they can come close to us. For example, on 29 September 2004, Asteroid 4179 (Toutatis) will pass the Earth at 1.5 million km (less than 1 million miles); it is a double body, either hour-glass shaped or else consisting of two components in contact – one of them is 4 km (2½ miles) across, the other only 2.5 km (1½ miles) across. Not that Toutatis is the holder of the 'approach record'; one tiny asteroid, not yet named, sped by at a mere 96,000 km (60,000 miles) in 1994.

3. **Aten class.**
These cross the Earth's orbit, and their mean distances from the Sun are less than that of the Earth. Only a few are known; the largest, 2100 Ra-Shalom, has a diameter of 1½ miles. There is one asteroid suspected to have a path lying wholly inside that of the Earth, but it has not yet been sufficiently well observed for us to decide whether this is correct or not.

What are the chances of our world being hit by an asteroid large enough to cause severe damage? The chances are slight, but they are not nil. There is a theory, widely accepted though unproved, that this did happen some 65 million years ago; a massive impactor struck the Earth at the site of Chixulub, off Central America, and threw up so much dust and debris that for a while the Sun was blotted out and the entire climate was changed – with disastrous results for the dinosaurs, which had been supreme for so long. Certainly, we know of many impact craters, such as the Meteor Crater in Arizona (it really should be 'Meteor*ite*' Crater), and Wolf Creek in Australia. And the Moon, of course, is covered with impact craters.

The official Minor Planet Centre, based at Harvard in the United States, has coined the term PHAs (Potentially Hazardous Asteroids) for objects which are more than 200 metres (650 ft) across and may come within 8 million km (5 million miles) of the Earth in the next two centuries. (Rather disturbingly, the third PHA to be discovered, Hermes in 1937, has been lost; it is less than a kilometre [half a mile] across. Hermes is the only named asteroid not to have been allotted a number, because all track of it has been lost and it is unlikely to be recovered.)

▲ *Wolf Creek impact crater, Australia.* *I took this photograph from an aircraft in 1993.*

If we were struck by an asteroid a few hundred metres across, the results would indeed be dire. It is most improbable, because the Earth is a small target in a large region of space, but one never knows, and it is only sensible to try to keep a watch on all objects of this kind – just in case. If one NEA is seen to be approaching us on a collision course, it might be possible to divert it by using a nuclear missile, but this would be dependent upon our having sufficient warning, and it is true that some NEAs are found only when they have passed their point of closest approach. Professional astronomers are doing their best, notably with the Spacewatch and Linear telescopes, but – of course! – shortage of funds is a major problem. By now almost 50,000 asteroids in all have been recorded; there may well be hundreds of thousands of as yet undiscovered asteroids in the main zone between the paths of Mars and Jupiter, and there may be several thousands of NEAs more than 1.6 km (1 mile) across.

All we can hope is that if a major impact does happen, we will cope with the situation better than the dinosaurs did. But certainly these maverick asteroids represent a threat that we would be very unwise to ignore.

Onwards to Mars

If asked to name the most interesting planet in the Solar System, most people would probably reply: 'Mars.' The reason is clear enough. Mars is less unlike the Earth than any other planet, and there is a distinct chance that life, of a kind, may exist there.

Mars is a small world, only 6800 km (4200 miles) in diameter and with a mass 1/10th that of the Earth; its weak pull means that it has lost a great deal of the atmosphere it must once have had, though a considerable amount still remains. The ground pressure is, however, below 10 millibars everywhere, and the main constituent is carbon dioxide; also the temperature is low, so that we could not survive there except under highly artificial conditions. The Martian year is equal to 687 Earth days. This is equivalent to 669 Mars days or 'sols', because the rotation period of Mars is longer than ours: 24 hours 37 minutes.

At its closest Mars may come within 56 million km (35 million miles) of us, and a small telescope will then show the main surface features; the dark areas, the ochre tracts still called 'deserts', and the white polar ice-caps which wax and wane with the Martian seasons. The deserts are composed of reddish minerals; Mars is a 'rusty' place. The dark areas, once regarded as seas, are now known to be regions where the red, dusty stuff has been blown away by winds in the tenuous atmosphere, exposing the darker material below.

The first telescopic sketch of Mars to show recognizable detail was made by Christiaan Huygens in 1659; it shows the V-shaped Syrtis Major, the most prominent dark feature on Mars. Later drawings showed extra detail. Then, in 1877, G. V. Schiaparelli, using a fine 9-inch refractor from Milan, made a new series of observations, and introduced the system of nomenclature which we still use, admittedly in modified form. It was Schiaparelli who drew the linear features which he called *canali* (channels). He was unsure of their nature, but Percival Lowell, who in 1895 set up a major observatory at Flagstaff in Arizona mainly to study Mars with a fine 24-inch refractor, believed the canals to be artificial waterways. Alas, we now know that the canals do not exist; they were due to tricks of the eye.

All our ideas about Mars were revolutionized in the 1960s and 1970s. The Mariner probes flew past the planet, and in 1971 Mariner 9 entered a closed orbit and sent back superb pictures of the craters, valleys and huge volcanoes; next, the Viking spacecraft made controlled landings, and sent back data direct from the surface.

Mars is essentially a bitterly cold, cratered wasteland. Winds are important. Fields of dunes surround the polar regions, where the winds transport cool air round the ice-caps. Patches of ground around craters and other obstacles at lower latitudes are swept clear of surface debris by both local and global winds, producing 'windstreaks'. When Mars is near perihelion, the winds there raise huge quantities of dust from the deserts, producing dust-storms which may blot out all the surface features; for example, in 1971 I was using the Innes 27-inch refractor at Johannesburg under excellent conditions, but could see virtually no detail at all for several consecutive weeks. Moreover, with the changing seasons the polar caps alternately freeze and thaw, either removing or adding volatiles in the atmosphere.

There is no doubt that in the past Mars was very active geologically. (This should really be 'areologically'; the Greek name for the war-god was Ares.) The fact that this activity waned more quickly than the Earth's is due to its lesser mass; it lost much of its internal heat much more rapidly. Thus, the huge volcanoes and their extensive lava-fields may have ceased to erupt around 100 million years ago, well before the dinosaurs died out on Earth. However, we can be sure that the volcanoes were active over a very long period.

When we look at a global map of the planet, we find that the northern hemisphere is around 2 km (1¼ miles) lower than the cratered uplands to the south. The northern hemisphere is much smoother than the southern, and clearly represents a younger landscape. The boundary between the two hemispheres has been christened the 'line of dichotomy', and is a very significant feature.

It seems that in the past there must have been surface water on Mars – even though liquid water could not exist there now, because the atmospheric

▼ **The rocky surface of Mars,** *from Viking 2, 1976.*   *The lander's footpad is at bottom right in the image.*

pressure is too low. There are obvious channels both on the northern plains and in the highland regions adjacent to the line of dichotomy, and this indicates that there may have been oceans or at least lakes. A particularly extensive system of channels has been found draining into the Chryse basin, the site of the first Viking lander, and there are indications of water flow, leaving tear-drop islands and scour marks along the channel floors. At the channel mouths in the northern plains, banks of smooth-surface debris can be seen very clearly. Wherever sediment was dumped on to the plains at the channel mouths it seems to have been levelled off, as though it were once a body of standing water. So what has happened to the water which must once have been present?

There is only one possible place where it can have gone: into the fractures and pores within the sub-surface rocks and the regolith. We know that much of the ancient crust was severely battered by meteoroids and became highly fractured, both by the impacts and by doming of the crust due to heat from below.

All the evidence indicates that there have been major climatic variations on Mars over a time-scale of millions of years – much more marked than on Earth, where the situation has not altered fundamentally since the days of the dinosaurs. There are several possibilities:

(1) *The changing tilt of the Martian axis* – The Earth's axis is tilted to the orbital plane by 23½ degrees; the inclination of Mars is a fraction under 24 degrees – practically the same. We know that the direction of the Earth's axis changes slightly, because of precession, and describes a small circle in

▼ **The Sojourner rover,** surface during the Mars
exploring the Martian Pathfinder mission in 1997

the sky, so that in 12,000 years' time Vega will be the north pole star. The tilt of Mars' axis alters more than ours. On both Earth and Mars southern summer occurs when the planet is closest to the Sun, so that the southern summers are shorter but hotter than those in the north, while the southern winters are longer and colder. On Earth this is not noticeable, because our orbit is nearly circular, but for Mars it is very noticeable indeed. The distance from the Sun ranges between over 240 million km (150 million miles) to less than 210 million km (130 million miles) over a Martian year. This shows up in the behaviour of the polar caps; the southern cap becomes larger than the northern one ever does, but it can also become smaller, and this has a great deal to do with past climatic changes.

The obliquity ranges between 14.9 degrees and 35.5 degrees, over a period of 120,000 years. When the angle is high, it approximately doubles the amount of solar radiation at the poles. This means that only a much reduced volume of volatiles can be stored in the polar caps at these times, and the laminated deposits found in polar canyons strongly suggest repeated changes in conditions.

(2) *Vulcanism* – In this theory Mars goes through periods of strong volcanic activity, with gases and water vapour sent out through vents and causing a temporary thickening and moistening of the atmosphere.

Certainly, there have been long periods of vulcanism. We believe that the first of these periods released the first Martian atmosphere, and generated the primordial crust. Vast volumes of basaltic lava were emitted from fissures in the thin, primitive crust. Later, around 3000 million years ago, shield volcanoes began to grow in the region of Tharsis, around Elysium, and in the southern hemisphere, particularly around the Hellas impact basin; subsequently, about 15 massive shields developed, emitting huge volumes of gases and molten basaltic lava. When vulcanism was at its peaks of activity, two contrasting effects would have been evident. As the magma rose into the upper crust, so the rocks became warmed, domed and fractured. This would have opened pores which would allow the downward percolation of any volatiles existing at or above the surface. If there had been any volatiles already locked up as ice, then much of this ice would have melted at the same time. Certainly, the near-surface temperatures over much of Mars would have risen for long periods over huge hot spots in the mantle below. The opposing effect results from the emission of ash and dust, and the formation of aerosols in the Martian atmosphere. From recent experiences on Earth (the eruptions of Mount St Helens, El Chichón and Pinatubo, for example) we know that this can lead to the lowering of global temperature over short periods.

(3) *Changes in the shape of the Martian orbit* – We know that the orbit alters considerably over the years. First, the perihelion of the orbit precesses with a 72,000-year period, and this affects which point on the planet's surface points towards the Sun when at its closest. This, combined with the obliquity changes, produces a cycle of 51,000 years over which the maximum radiation at the poles changes.

The orbital eccentricity shows two variations, the major one with a period of 2 million years. During this time the eccentricity ranges between 0.14 and 0.01. At the poles this has only a 1% effect on the solar radiation received, but this rises to 30% at the subsolar point. It has been calculated that polar temperatures resulting from the eccentricity and obliquity changes could, given a sufficient reservoir of carbon dioxide at the poles, cause a range in atmospheric pressure of between 0.3 and 30 millibars – a factor of 100!

(4) *Changes in the output of the Sun* – Can these cause ice ages and climatic variations on Mars? After all, our present Sun is very stable and well behaved, but early in its history this was not so, and the output of heat varied considerably. If Mars were once more friendly than it is now, could life have appeared there?

The Viking images show that open oceans, or at least large lakes, once existed at any rate in the northern hemisphere. Whether or not these existed under a cover of ice is unclear. Possibly these areas of open water existed only during very early stages in the planet's history. Since life on Earth began in the oceans around 3850 million years ago, then despite Mars being a cooler world there is every reason to suppose that primitive organisms may have evolved there as well. Algae and bacteria come to mind. Recent claims that meteorites found in Antarctica come from Mars, and contain signs of Martian life, are at best decidedly premature!

The latest probes have met with mixed fortunes. Pathfinder landed successfully on Mars on 4 July 1997, and carried a small rover, Sojourner, which was able to move around and analyze the rocks. The area chosen was the floor of a huge flood channel, Ares Vallis, in Chryse Planitia; it was reasoned – correctly – that a raging torrent would have swept down a wide range of boulders and fine-grained material from the ancient cratered uplands, so that the area should be a good 'grab site'. Sojourner performed excellently, and the former existence of open water seems no longer in doubt. Unfortunately, the probes of late 1999 were less favoured. The orbiting Global Surveyor worked well, but the Climate Orbiter was lost because of the two teams controlling it, one used imperial measurements and the other used metric (how this can have been allowed to happen passes all comprehension). The Mars Polar Lander probably came down in the planned position, but nothing was heard from it after arrival, so that presumably it landed at an angle and was unable to transmit. The 2001 Mars Odyssey was launched on 7 April 2001 and reached Mars on 24 October 2001. This probe is carrying scientific experiments designed to improve our understanding of the climate and geological history of the planet.

Will Mars change much in the centuries ahead? There seems no reason why it should. Despite all the precessional and orbital effects having been operative over the past 4750 million years, there has apparently been only one period of enhanced atmospheric density, higher temperature and surface water. If our crater-counting techniques are valid, this occurred at least 3000 million years ago. If major changes are to occur again, then

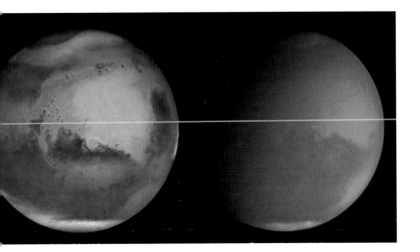

▲ **A Martian dust storm,** as viewed by the Hubble Space Telescope in 2001. The left-hand image shows the onset of smaller dust storms in late June; the right-hand image, taken a few months later in early September, shows the effects of a fully-developed global dust storm, obscuring the surface features of the planet.

they should have done so many more times during Martian history; but there is no evidence of this.

Finally, what about future Martian bases? Will they have to be underground, or will the present Martian atmosphere prove to be adequate as a screen against harmful radiations? We must also consider volcanic eruptions and meteoritic impacts.

The geological changes are few. Violent dust storms are features of the climate, at perihelion in particular, and it is true that these could pose some problems for both astronauts and instruments, but not with fatal effects. Eruptions and severe Marsquakes are unlikely. There would be some risk from unwanted and dangerous radiations from space (cosmic rays, X-rays and ultraviolet), but technology ought to be able to cope. Food and water do not pose severe tests for our ingenuity if a long-term base is to be supported. The major dangers may well come from human error and miscalculation.

We must wait and see, but surely we may hope for a proper Martian Base in the early part of the 21st century. The first man on Mars may already have been born.

Black Holes

O f all the objects in the universe, black holes are surely the most bizarre. We cannot see them, because they emit no radiation at all, but by now we are virtually certain that they do exist. A black hole is a region of space within which gravity is so powerful that nothing – not even light – can escape into the outside universe.

The term 'black hole' was coined in 1967 by Archibald Wheeler, but in a way the concept has been around since the late 18th century, due to the work of John Michel and Pierre-Simon de Laplace. It depends upon the idea of escape velocity – a mere 11 km/s (7 miles/s) in the case of the Earth; if a body is sufficiently massive, the escape velocity could reach the speed of light (300,000 km/s [186,000 miles/s]), and the body would be invisible, though its gravitational effects would still be marked.

Modern ideas are derived from Einstein's General Theory of Relativity. Matter produces a curvature in space in its neighbourhood. Einstein's equations solved for a spherical body of matter, by Karl Schwarzschild in 1916, showed that if a given quantity of mass is compressed inside a

▼ **Black holes:** some astronomers believe there is a massive spinning black hole at the centre of the distant galaxy MCG-6-30-15. This artist's illustration of a black hole surrounded by an accretion disk is based on observations taken with the XMM-Newton satellite in X-ray light.

particular radius, nothing will be able to escape. Fittingly, this critical radius is always known as the Schwarzschild radius. For the Sun, it is about 3 km (1.9 miles); for a star ten times as massive as the Sun, it is about 30 km (18½ miles); for the Earth, it is less than 1 cm (no more than one-third of an inch). This means that to turn our world into a black hole, you would have to squeeze it down to the size of a marble.

No natural process can turn the Sun or the Earth into a black hole, but with high-mass stars the situation is different. A solar-mass star will end its career as a white dwarf; a more massive star will explode as a supernova and then become a neutron star, but will not produce a black hole. For a star whose original mass was from 10–30 times that of the Sun, the maximum mass for the resulting neutron star can be no more than 3 solar masses. The rest of the material will have been hurled away into space.

Most stars lose a high proportion of their mass near the end of their careers, but if the core of a very high-mass star is more than three times the mass of the Sun when it finally runs out of nuclear fuel, it collapses without limit; no known force or pressure can halt the shrinkage. As it continues to collapse, and its surface gravity increases, light finds it harder and harder to escape. When the Schwarzschild radius is reached, light can no longer escape at all, and the star disappears from view; a black hole has been created. The matter contained inside the black hole continues to collapse, until it has been compressed into a point of infinite density, known as a singularity.

Therefore, a black hole consists of a central singularity, where matter is infinitely compressed and gravitational forces are infinitely strong, surrounded by a region with a radius equal to the Schwarzschild radius, within which nothing can break free. The boundary of the black hole is called the event horizon, because we can know nothing directly about what is happening inside it. A photon of light emitted inside the boundary would fall straight into the central singularity; a photon emitted from just outside the boundary would escape, provided that it were moving directly away from the black hole; a photon emitted on the event horizon itself would hover there for ever – rather in the manner of a man who is running up a downwards-moving escalator at precisely the same rate.

Once a black hole has been formed, its gravitational influence persists. This means that matter or radiation passing too close to the event horizon will be dragged in, and will fall into the central singularity. This would be rather unfortunate for any astronaut who happened to be caught. A tidal force arises wherever the force of gravity varies in strength across a distance, so that if an astronaut were to fall into a black hole feet first, he would find that his feet were subject to a much stronger force than his head. His feet would also accelerate downwards at a greater speed, and the luckless space-traveller would be stretched – rather as if he were to hang from a bridge with the entire population of a major city swinging from his ankles. Of course, he would promptly be torn to shreds. This is often termed 'spaghettification'!

There are also weird time effects. According to Einstein, time passes more slowly in a strong gravitational field than it does where gravity is weak – and we know that this is true, because it has been experimentally confirmed. Suppose that an observer at a safe distance were to keep a careful check on an identical clock carried by an infalling astronaut. At first the two clocks would agree, but as the astronaut approached closer and closer to the event horizon, the two clocks would start to differ. To the infalling astronaut, time would seem to pass at a normal rate, but the distant observer would conclude that the astronaut's clock was running slower and slower. When the traveller arrived at the event horizon, the observer would conclude that time had stopped, and that the astronaut would remain suspended for ever on the event horizon. Yet the astronaut would be crushed out of existence, and would reach the central singularity about 1/10,000th of a second after crossing the event horizon.

Bizarre though it may seem, both points of view are equally valid in their own frames of reference. Although the distant observer might argue that the traveller never crossed the event horizon, the only way that he could check would be to go himself on a journey to the black hole – something which he might well be rather reluctant to do, because he would find that he too would fall inwards and meet the same fate.

In any case, a collapsing star will vanish as it approaches its Schwarzschild radius because of a related effect: gravitational red shift. Light climbing out of a strong gravitational field loses energy, and its wavelength is increased. The closer the star's surface gets to its Schwarzschild radius, the greater its red shift. If the infalling astronaut were shining a blue laser towards the distant observer, the observer would see the laser change from blue to green, yellow, orange, red, dull red and then out of the visible range altogether. Close to the event horizon the effect is very great, and at the actual event horizon it is infinitely strong. Moreover, the distance between the penultimate and the final wave-crest reaching the observer would also become infinitely great, while the energy carried by the wave would sink to zero. Obviously, the star and the astronaut would vanish as effectively as the hunter of the Snark!

Next, consider a rotating black hole, as first described by the New Zealand physicist Roy Kerr. One curious feature is that the event horizon is surrounded by a flattened region called the ergosphere. Nothing inside the ergosphere can remain still, because the rotation of the black hole drags space around with it. In principle, if a particle were to enter the ergosphere and then split into two parts, one of which fell into the event horizon, the other could escape with more energy than the incoming particle originally possessed – rather in the manner of a man leaping on to a spinning roundabout and then jumping off again. Potentially, rotating black holes could be powerful energy sources.

An isolated black hole obviously cannot be seen against the background of space, but if there are neighbouring bodies these will be affected by the black hole's gravitational pull. For example, many stars are members of binary systems. If a binary consists of an ordinary star and a black hole, what we will see will be a visible star moving round an invisible companion. Knowing the orbital period and the separation of the two,

▲ **Centaurus A
(NGC 5128)** – an
X-ray image of this active

*elliptical galaxy, taken
by the Chandra X-ray
Observatory in 2001.*

we can then calculate their combined mass, as with an ordinary binary in which both components are visible. The black hole component cannot be seen, but we can deduce its mass if we can first find the mass of the visible star, which we can generally do from the nature of its spectrum. If the invisible body turns out to have a mass greater than three times that of the Sun, then a black hole has to be inferred.

If an ordinary star and a black hole form a close binary system, the gravitational pull of the black hole will distort the visible star into the shape of an egg. Gas will stream away from the 'point' of the egg towards the black hole. Because of the rotation, this gas will go into orbit round the black hole, producing an accretion disk, rather than falling straight into the hole. The infalling gas will reach a very high speed, and will carry a great deal of energy, so that it will be heated to a temperature of millions of degrees and will emit X-rays. Hot spots form where the stream of gas ploughs into the accretion disk, so that the X-ray output fluctuates rapidly as the disk rotates. Therefore, a black hole secreting matter from a companion star can be a powerful and variable X-ray source.

The first object of this kind to be discovered was Cygnus X-1, an X-ray source in the constellation of the Swan, in 1972. It consists of a bright blue supergiant star with about 25 times the mass of the Sun, revolving round an invisible companion in a period of 5.6 days. The mass of the unseen companion is thought to be between 10 and 15 times that of the Sun, which makes it a good black hole candidate. Other examples are known – including two in the Large Cloud of Magellan, 169,000 light-years away from us.

When the mass of the visible star is much greater than that of the companion, it is none too easy to obtain a reliable value for the companion's mass. Any errors in estimating the mass of the visible star have a marked effect on the calculated mass of the companion. The situation is much easier when the binary consists of a low-mass star, comparable to the Sun, and a high-mass companion. There, the visible star revolves round the unseen companion rather as a planet moves round the Sun, and its velocity gives a reliable clue which can be used to calculate a minimum mass for the dark body.

Much the best stellar-mass black hole candidates are X-ray transients or X-ray novae, which from time to time flare up in X-ray brightness by a factor of at least a million; over a few months they fade back to their original state. In sources of this kind, matter flowing from the visible star piles up on the accretion disk until a major outburst occurs. Subsequently, the accretion disk fades sufficiently to unveil the low-mass star, which can then be studied in detail and its spectral class, mass and orbital velocity determined. This in turn leads to a good estimate of the mass of the invisible object, as with V404 Cygni, an X-ray nova consisting of a star of 0.7 solar masses and a black hole candidate 12 times as massive as the Sun. A particularly good candidate is Nova Scorpii 1994, where the sources undergo partial eclipses when star and accretion disk pass in front of each other. We can be sure that the system is nearly edgewise-on to our line of sight, so that the measured speed of the visible star is very close to its actual orbital speed – leading to a really precise value for the mass of the unseen companion, seven times that of the Sun. In all there are about two dozen cases of X-ray transients in which the dark companions are almost certainly black holes.

There is compelling evidence that supermassive black holes, with masses of millions, hundreds of millions, or thousands of millions of solar masses exist in the central cores of active galaxies, which radiate strongly over a much wider range of wavelengths than happens with ordinary galaxies. A typical active galaxy has an extremely bright, compact central core, called an active galactic nucleus (AGN), which varies markedly in brightness over a short period. The rapid variability shows that the energy source must be very compact indeed, in some cases less than a light-day, roughly the size of the Solar System.

With some galaxies, notably the giant elliptical M87 in the Virgo cluster (distance approximately 60 million light-years), jets are sent out from the nucleus. With Centaurus A, two giant lobes of radio-emitting material lie outside the visible galaxy, and detailed photographs show narrow jets of material surging out of the AGN towards the distant lobes – suggesting that the lobes themselves are clouds of particles previously ejected from the

AGN. According to the 'unified model' theory for AGNs, each one contains a supermassive black hole surrounded by hot accretions of infalling gas, which are in turn surrounded by a torus of dust-laden gas. Jets of high-energy particles moving at large fractions of the speed of light are expelled perpendicular to the accretion disk, probably along the direction of the axis of rotation of the spinning black hole. The orientation of the torus and jets perpendicular to the observer's line of sight determine which type of active galaxy is seen. By measuring the Doppler effects in the spectra of stars and gas-clouds near the centres of the galaxies, their orbital velocities can be found – and hence their masses. For example, Hubble Space Telescope images and spectra of the centre of the huge elliptical galaxy M87 indicate the presence of a compact disk of material revolving round a compact invisible object. Doppler measurements of the approaching and receding sides of the disk show that it is rotating at around 740 km/s (460 miles/s). This means that a 2.4-thousand-million solar-mass object must be contained within 20 light-years of the centre. It can hardly be anything but a black hole.

Several other galaxies have similarly been found to contain flattened central disks. Centaurus A is one; this is an active galaxy which may be the result of a collision and merger between an elliptical system and a dust-laden spiral. And the galaxy NGC 7052 seems to have a dusty disk, about 3700 light-years in diameter, masking a black hole which has 300 million times the mass of the Sun.

Another interesting system is the galaxy M106, a spiral in Ursa Major. If a supermassive black hole lies at the centre of a galaxy, then stars and gas-clouds close to the centre should revolve faster than those further out – and this is precisely what happens. The black hole in M106 seems to be about 36 million times as massive as the Sun.

Black holes formed from collapsing stars may be rather uncommon, because only a small proportion of stars can have sufficient initial mass. But with galaxies, the situation is different, and they may indeed contain black holes of at least a few million solar masses. Many of these may now be quiescent, but can always become active again if clouds of gas, or disrupted stars, fall into their event horizons. And there can be no doubt that black holes must be very plentiful in the universe.

At least it is reassuring to know that our Sun cannot possibly produce a black hole. It will die much more sedately, and it will not change dramatically for at least 1000 million years yet. This is fortunate for us – to be engulfed by a black hole would not be an inviting prospect!

Fireworks from Space

Meteors are cometary debris, and are in general no larger than grains of sand. If a meteor dashes into the Earth's upper air, it is heated by friction and burns away, producing the luminous streak that we call a shooting-star. Meteors are quite harmless, because they burn out at a height of about 64 km (40 miles) above sea-level, and end their headlong plunge in the form of ultra-fine dust. (Meteorites, which are much larger, come from the asteroid belt, and are not related to either comets or shooting-stars.) What we see, of course, is not the tiny particle itself, but the effects which it produces in the atmosphere just before it is destroyed.

Because all the meteors from a particular comet are moving in parallel paths, perspective will make the meteors of the shower seem to radiate from one definite point in the sky, known as the radiant – just as the parallel lanes of a motorway will seem to diverge from a point near the horizon.

There are many annual showers, but the November Leonids, so called because the radiant lies in the constellation of Leo (the Lion) are of special interest. Some Leonids are seen every year between about 14–20 November, but every 33 years there is much greater activity. These meteor 'storms' are normally linked to the return to perihelion of the parent comet, Tempel–Tuttle. (The comet is so named because it was discovered by the German astronomer Wilhelm Tempel, and independently by the American observer Horace Tuttle.) At these times we may expect to plough through

▼ **'Road radiant'** – the parallel lanes seem to come from a point at the horizon. I took this photograph in Alaska in 1998.

the densest part of the trail left by the comet. In other years, the Leonids are decidedly sparse.

The first Leonid storm to be carefully documented was that of 1799, seen from South America by the German explorer Alexander von Humboldt and his French companion, Aimé Bonpland. In the early morning of 12 November they saw many thousands of meteors over a four-hour period. This extraordinary display was also described by an American government official, Andrew Ellicott, who saw it from a ship off the coast of Florida. There is no doubt that it was visible from Greenland in the north as far south as the equator.

In 1833 there was another Leonid storm; it was this which really marked the start of meteor science as we know it today. It caused great alarm among the uneducated and superstitious people of the time, who believed that the end of the world was nigh! It took place in the early morning of 13 November, and was best seen from the eastern parts of North and South America. The best scientific observations were made by two American professors, Denison Olmsted and Alexander Twining, who collected as many reports as they could; this was the first time that the radiant of a shower had been accurately pinpointed. It lies within the 'Sickle' of Leo, the curved line of stars making up the lion's head.

Around this time there was considerable interest in looking for records of great meteor showers described in the chronicles of the East, Middle East and Europe. One astronomer who took a particular interest in this was another American, Hubert Anson Newton, from Yale College. Using ancient records, he identified 13 past major Leonid displays – the first in AD 902. He showed that they tended to occur at roughly 33-year intervals, and predicted another storm for November 1866. It took place just as he had expected, on 14 November. It was well seen from Europe; from Greenwich it became obvious from about 11 pm that meteors were abundant, and after midnight the numbers increased so rapidly that it was impossible to do much except count them. The peak occurred about 1:10 am, when meteors were falling at a rate of more than 120 per minute. Many observers plotted the tracks so that a radiant could be found; using this position, together with the time of maximum and the orbital period of 32.25 years, Giovanni Schiaparelli, Urbain Le Verrier and John Couch Adams independently worked out an orbit for the particles in the Leonid stream. It was realized that this orbit was identical with that of the periodic comet Tempel–Tuttle, seen in 1866. The retrograde motion means that the comet's orbit almost intersects that of the Earth at what is called the descending node. Nowadays, the Earth is closest to this point on or about 17–18 November each year. However, we do not see a Leonid storm every year at this time.

The crucial factors in determining whether or not a major Leonid shower will be observed are (1) the number of days before or after the passage of the comet through its descending node, and (2) how close the Earth approaches the comet's orbit at this point. If the separation is too great, no major shower can occur. Good displays occur slightly ahead of, but mainly behind, the parent comet. Most of the great storms have occurred between 750 days before and 1750 days after the parent comet passes through the node.

Conditions between 1997 and 2000 were much the same as those between 1865 and 1868. There was a strong shower in 1865, and a magnificent storm in 1866 when, as seen from Greenwich, rates reached over 7000 meteors per hour over a brief period. The 1867 rates were again high, with a peak of 1500 meteors per hour seen despite strong moonlight, and there was another good shower in 1868. However, there was no major display in 1899, or in 1933, because the separation was too great. In 1966 the Leonids were back with a grand display, unfortunately missed from Britain because it occurred during daylight there; the best views were obtained from parts of North America, such as Arizona.

There was an encouraging Leonid display in 1998, but the peak of activity occurred between 16 and 18 hours earlier than had been expected. Another surprise was that activity went on for much longer than usual, and the zenithal hourly rate exceeded 200 for between six and eight hours; a rate of 100 meteors per hour was observed for almost a day. (The zenithal hourly rate is the number of meteors which would in theory be seen with the naked eye by an observer under ideal conditions, with the radiant at the zenith.) This was confirmed by radio observations, which can of course be carried out even when the sky is too bright for any meteors to be seen visually; meteor trails disturb the ionosphere, the layer from which radio waves are reflected back to Earth from ground-based transmitters. Also, the 1998 Leonids were rich in very bright fireballs, but unexpectedly poor in fainter meteors.

It has now been established that the structure of the stream of dust left behind by Comet Tempel–Tuttle is much more complex than had been previously thought. The stream does not have straightforward cylindrical structure. Instead, there are several discrete, separate arcs of dust, each released at a different return of the comet.

In some cases the Earth passes through a thin filament of the stream, resulting in a brief but intense shower. Secondly, the Earth may pass through a much broader filament, producing a shower which is less intense than in the first case but which lasts for longer. The Earth may pass through a gap between filaments, and there will be no major display. Or the Earth may pass through a broad filament first and then through the edge of a much narrower filament, resulting in a main peak of activity and a much smaller peak later on. Calculations show that the great storm of 1833 was due to dust which had been expelled from the comet just 33 years earlier, in 1800, while the 1966 storm was caused by particles released 67 years before, in 1899.

In 1998 the Earth passed through an arc-shaped cloud of dust shed by the comet in 1366 – 666 years earlier. The overall swarm of dust left behind by the comet contains particles with orbits very similar to, but not identical with, that of the comet, and as time passes the orbits of these particles will evolve away from the comet, due to planetary perturbations and other effects. The arc of dust released in 1366 had evolved so much that the Earth ploughed through it some 16 hours before the closest approach to the comet's orbit – catching many observers unawares. (England, needless to say,

▼ **'Meteor radiant'** –
the meteors are in fact
moving in parallel paths,
but seem instead to come
from a definite radiant.
(Illustration by Paul Doherty.)

▲ *Leonid meteors.*   *as streaks against*
The meteors show up   *the background stars.*

was mainly cloudy.) If you start off with a fresh young dust filament, then over several centuries it will broaden, and more of the smallest dust particles will be forced out of the filament by solar radiation pressure; eventually, some of the medium-sized particles will also be lost. The very oldest filaments will have lost most of the small particles and many of those of medium size, leaving a preponderance of relatively large particles – which will produce fireballs. This was the situation with the 1998 display.

On to 1999 – and a really good display, even if it did not rival those of 1866 or 1966. It peaked just after midnight on 18 November, and was well seen from many areas – including Scotland – though again England was mainly cloudy. On 11 August 1999 I was trying to observe the total solar eclipse – the first visible from England since 1927. I went to the central line, at Falmouth in Cornwall. During totality I sat on the sea front, making a television broadcast and holding an umbrella to shield myself from the rain. On 18 November I sat in my garden at Selsey, carrying out a television broadcast at the peak of the Leonid shower, holding up the same umbrella and protecting myself from the same kind of rain. Observationally, 1999 was not my year!

When can we expect the next really good display of Leonids? Probably in the year 2032. I will not see it, unless of course I live to the advanced age of 109, but perhaps some readers of this book will bear it in mind and remember to watch out for it!

Choosing Equipment

There is a common belief that nobody can take a serious interest in astronomy without acquiring a large and expensive telescope. This is quite wrong. A great deal of observing, and indeed some useful research can be carried out with the naked eye alone. But it is true that sooner or later – probably sooner rather than later – the newcomer to astronomy will feel the need for some optical equipment, and this is often where troubles begin. Telescopes are either good or cheap – not both; and though good second-hand telescopes can sometimes be found, they are much less common than they used to be. Moreover, care is needed. A poor-quality telescope does not always show its weaknesses until thoroughly tested.

The thing *not* to do is to go to a camera shop and buy a small, nice-looking telescope for a few tens of pounds. Unless you have at least £200 available, it is wiser not to buy a telescope at all. (For this article, I have quoted prices as they stand – more or less – at the start of 2002.) Luckily there is a good alternative: obtain binoculars. These have most of the advantages of a small telescope, and few of the disadvantages apart from the fact that they cannot yield a high magnification.

First, check on magnification and aperture; aperture is always given in millimetres. For example, a pair of 7 × 50 binoculars will have a magnification of 7, with each object-glass 50 mm in diameter. Do not be tempted to go for too high a magnification; binoculars giving a power of, say, ×20 can be obtained, but they are bound to be heavy and cumbersome, so that they will need to be mounted on a tripod. For an all-purpose pair, I would recommend a magnification of from 7 to 10 – certainly no higher than 12. A good pair of Russian 10 × 50 binoculars can be obtained for less than £100.

Remember, binoculars give a wide field of view, and this is advantageous when looking at objects such as star clusters. The Pleiades are beautiful when viewed in this way, but with a telescope it is difficult to get the whole cluster into the same field. A word of warning – never turn your binoculars anywhere near the Sun. A moment's carelessness can have tragic consequences.

▶ **One to avoid!**
A telescope with a flimsy mount, and an object-glass stopped down from 2 inches to half an inch. Totally useless!

◀ *A 3-inch refractor:* probably the smallest telescope that is of any real use. I acquired this telescope when I was aged 11 – in 1934. It cost £7!

There is only one golden rule for looking directly at the Sun through any binoculars, telescope or camera: *don't.* Unfortunately, some small telescopes are sold with dark 'sun caps'. These should never be used; consign them to the nearest dustbin.

Telescopes are of two main types: refractors and reflectors. The refractor collects its light by means of a lens termed an object-glass or objective, and in my view the minimum really useful aperture is 3 inches. Smaller telescopes will never be really satisfying, though they are of course much better than nothing at all.

One problem is that a single lens brings different wavelengths of light to a focus in different places, producing false colour. A compound lens can reduce the effect, but the cost rises steeply. An outlay of £200 should be enough to buy a useful refractor, and remember that the cost is non-recurring; neither does it seem a great deal when compared with, say, a couple of rail tickets between London and Manchester.

Reflectors, which collect their light by means of a mirror, do not have false-colour problems, because the mirror reflects all wavelengths equally. The familiar pattern is the Newtonian, where the light is collected by the main speculum and is then sent into the side of the tube via a smaller flat mirror placed at an angle of 45 degrees. Here, my view is that the minimum useful aperture is 6 inches (150 mm). There are more complex optical systems, and here the main mirror can be as small as 4 inches (100 mm); the cost is of the order of £400, but again is non-recurring, though it is true that a reflector requires more maintenance than a refractor.

Any astronomical telescope should have several eyepieces – a low power for wide-field objects such as clusters, a moderate power for general use, and a high power for specialized work. In general the maximum useful magnification is ×50 per inch of aperture; this applies to refractors and reflectors equally. Never buy a telescope which is advertised by magnification alone. I recently saw a refractor which, it was claimed, would yield a magnification of ×300. The object-glass was only 2 inches (50 mm) across, so that with any power above ×100, at most, the resulting image would be hopelessly faint.

Mounting is all-important. The old-fashioned pillar and claw is about as steady as the average blancmange, and any target object will describe a wild waltz in the heavens. A heavy tripod is suitable – and I *mean* heavy. A simple altazimuth mounting is easy to make and use, but it does have the disadvantage that it has to be moved all the time to compensate for the rotation of the sky. With an equatorial there is only one motion to be considered: east/west, because the up or down motion will look after itself. Moreover, an equatorial mounting is more or less essential if any photography is to be attempted.

The simplest mounting of all is the Dobsonian, named after the Californian ex-monk who devised it. It is truly basic, and suited only to low magnifications, but it is quite possible to mount a large reflector in this way, suited to the needs of the 'deep-sky' observer who is far more interested in clusters and nebulae than in the Moon and planets. A 6-inch (150 mm) Dobsonian costs around £300, and £400 will buy you an 8-inch (200 mm). I have even seen a 24-inch (600 mm) Dobsonian, and its great light-grasp provides superb views of stellar objects.

Computerized telescopes are now on the market; these can be used to find any object automatically. And, of course, electronic equipment is now within the range of the serious amateur.

If you want to obtain a telescope, it is only sensible to take expert advice, and luckily there are many astronomical societies around, quite apart from the national British Astronomical Association (BAA). There are also magazines which carry advertisements – but always remember to take the greatest care; it is only too easy to make a mistake.

Finally, remember that astronomy is still just about the only science in which the amateur can play a really valuable role; amateur work is warmly welcomed by professional astronomers. This has always been so, and it will be equally true as we enter the new millennium.

Millennium Astronomy

We have entered the new millennium. It began on 1 January 2001 – not 1 January 2000 (remember, there was no Year 0; in those far-off days the zero had not been invented). Our understanding of the universe has changed beyond all recognition during the past thousand years. So what was astronomical science like in AD 1000?

First, remember that astronomy was the first really well-founded science. At a time when astronomers could predict the time of a solar eclipse to within a quarter of an hour, no physician knew what caused a common fever, and no biologist could differentiate scientifically between various types of organisms. In many ways, the scientific thinking developed by astronomers would later be adopted by other sciences, and in that sense alone astronomy may be regarded as the 'mother' of modern science.

In AD 1000, the main on-going astronomical issue was the calculation of an accurate calendar. In Europe this was motivated by Christianity, because it was regarded as all-important to work out the date of Easter, and this could be done only by astronomical observation. It was, of course, known that the Earth is a sphere rather than a flat plane, if only because of the shape of its shadow during a lunar eclipse, but it was believed that the Earth lay at the centre of a universe which consisted of a series of nine transparent, crystalline spheres resting inside each other like the skins of an onion. Beyond the Earth these spheres carried, in order, the Moon, Mercury, Venus, the Sun, Mars, Jupiter and Saturn; then came the sphere containing the fixed stars, and finally the 'Prime Mover', a kind of gear which was turned by angels and which moved all the other spheres. Therefore, a calendar had to chart these movements very precisely.

The civil calendar, used in everyday life, becomes increasingly at odds with the astronomical calendar as determined by the position of the Sun. In fact, it does not keep perfect step with the heavens. The trouble is that the length of the year is not 365 days, or even 365¼ days, but 365 days, 5 hours and around 49 minutes. In AD 1000 the astronomers' task was to determine this period with great accuracy in order to prevent errors accumulating. These errors, if unchecked, could lead to Easter being celebrated at the wrong time. To calculate the true date of Easter, it was necessary to know the exact date of the 'Paschal moon' – the exact date of the full moon following the spring equinox.

If the true astronomical equinox (the date midway between the longest and shortest days, in June and December), falls on 14 March, and yet the civil calendar says that the equinox falls on 21 March, there is an immediate problem. In fact – if a full or Paschal moon falls on (say) 19 March, where do we put Easter, given the conflict between the civil and the astronomical calendars?

The first man to tackle the problem satisfactorily was the Venerable Bede, a monk from Jarrow, who lived from 673 to 735, and was England's first mathematician and astronomer. Indeed, in 700 it may be said that Jarrow was the European centre of astronomy. Certainly the calendar was a problem, and there were several different systems in use. For example, the

Greeks used 'Olympiad Cycles', based on the date of the founding of Rome. In 664 the Synod of Whitby met in Yorkshire – a major Church Council, aimed at sorting out the calendrical and other matters. It left no written proceedings, but 40 years later Bede picked up the main points which had been sent down by word of mouth, and embedded them in his written works. They included the first generalized use of 'AD', Anno Domini, as a starting-point of the calendar, even though in fact Christ was certainly born a few years before AD 1 (and not on 25 December, so that our Christmas is wrong too). Bede also sorted out the way to calculate the correct date of Easter. Centuries later, in AD 1000, Bede's system was still in use.

In the Christian world, the key to Easter was a correct solar calendar. However, the Arab calendar was essentially lunar, also for religious reasons. In Muslim countries it is important to be able to predict the time of new moon both in summer and in winter. Their calendar was not concerned only with specific days, but with the phase of the Moon.

In order to fix prayer times, they developed the astrolabe, which is an astronomical calculating machine which can be used to measure the altitudes and directions of the stars – and also to predict their movements. Astrolabes are decidedly complicated, but can be pleasingly accurate. They were, in fact, primitive computers.

▼ The statue of Tycho Brahe, at Hven in Denmark (see page 204 overleaf also). I look rather small by comparison!

Optics were not neglected in AD 1000. For example, Alhazen, a young Egyptian physician, demonstrated how the Earth's atmosphere bends or refracts light, and how this produced twilight; he also projected images by the pinhole method. Perhaps his most exciting discovery was to show how polished pieces of crystal can enlarge images. All in all, it is curious that the invention of the telescope was delayed for several centuries after Alhazen's time.

There was much that the ancients did not know, but there was also a great deal that they had found out. What are some of the 'highlights' of astronomical discovery following AD 1000?

Around 1455 Regiomontanus and his colleagues at Nürnberg generated original, accurate observations of the movements of the planets. By 1500 clocks were good enough to measure time with reasonable accuracy. In 1543 Copernicus proposed that the Sun, not the Earth, was the centre of the Solar System. From 1576–98 Tycho Brahe, in Denmark, catalogued the stars from his observatory at Hven (Uraniburg, 'Castle of the Stars') and built accurate instruments such as quadrants. Using Tycho's observations, Johannes Kepler proved that the planets do move round the Sun, in orbits that are elliptical rather than circular. By 1610 Galileo had made a telescope powerful enough to show the moons of Jupiter, the phases of Venus and the stars of the Milky Way. Isaac Newton laid down the laws of gravitation in his immortal *Principia* (1687).

During the 19th century, light was split up by spectroscopes, and astronomers could find out 'what stars are made of'. Astrophysics was born; and in the 20th century, just ended, cosmology. Albert Einstein showed that there was no single frame of time and space throughout the universe, as Newton had assumed, but that time and space are 'relative'. In 1924 Edwin Hubble showed that the dim, misty objects once called nebulae were in many cases independent galaxies, made up of thousands of millions of stars; then came the 'Big Bang' theory of the origin of the universe as we know it, dating back for at least 12,000 million years.

Yet, ironically, some of these ideas had been discussed by medieval figures such as Thomas Bradwardine, who argued that on Earth and in space the perception of time must be different in heaven and in hell. In fact, it was the astronomers of the Middle Ages who first geared our imaginations to the possibility of relative time and space.

Where will the next millennium take us? We can only wait and see.

Two of a Kind

Our Sun is a single star. True, it has a family of planets, of which the Earth is one, but its nearest stellar neighbour, Proxima Centauri, is over 4 light-years away. However, many stars – perhaps most – are not solitary wanderers; they make up what are termed binary systems.

The force of gravity pervades all our lives, giving us weight, ensuring that the Earth is spherical, and – of course – causing apples to fall off trees, *à la* Newton! It extends out into space, theoretically to the very edge of the universe (assuming that the universe really does have an edge). The force of the Earth's gravitational pull weakens with increasing distance, but at 385,000 km (239,000 miles) it is still strong enough to hold the Moon in its orbit – something which would need a steel cable 970 km (600 miles) across if gravity were not there.

Gravity also holds the Solar System together, keeping the planets in their paths round the Sun and the satellites in their orbits round their parent planets. It also holds the Sun together, against the enormous internal pressure due to the core temperature of around 15,000,000°C. And it is equally all-important in the universe as a whole.

Physicists recognize four forces. Two operate only within atomic nuclei: these are the so-called strong and weak forces. There is electromagnetic force, and, finally, gravity. Only gravity is effective over really large distances, and this leads us on to the binary star-systems.

Many double stars are within the range of small telescopes, and even with the naked eye, but not all of these are binaries; some are pure line-of-sight effects. Consider Al Giedi (Alpha Capricorni), in the constellation of the Sea-Goat. Here we have two components, separated by a distance about one-fifth the diameter of the full moon. Yet the brighter component is only 100 light-years away, while the other lies in the background at 1600 light-years; there is no real connection between the two. Yet, oddly, optical pairs of this kind are less common than binaries. Look at Albireo or Beta Cygni, in the Swan. Here we have a golden-yellow primary with a vivid blue companion; this time the two really are associated, though they are a long way apart (about 5000 times as far as the distance between the Earth and the Sun). They are moving round their common centre of gravity, but the orbital period is very long indeed.

A famous binary is Rasalgethi or Alpha Herculis; the main star is a red supergiant, the fainter component greenish (partly by contrast). The revolution period is about 3500 years. With Rutilicus or Zeta Herculis, in the same constellation, the period is a mere 34 years; the mean apparent separation is 1.7 seconds of arc, around the size of a pound coin at a range of about 2.5 km (1.5 miles). The real separation is 15 times the Earth–Sun distance, or around the distance between the Sun and Uranus.

With apparent separations much less than this, the stars are difficult to see separately, and about 0.2 of a second of arc is the limit, though there are other ways of detecting the binary nature of what seems to be a single star. We also have eclipsing binaries, such as Algol in Perseus, where the light drops when one component passes in front of the other.

A star's spectrum is made up of a rainbow band, from red to violet, crossed by dark lines, each of which is characteristic of some particular element or group of elements. These lines shift according to the star's velocity of approach or recession (the Doppler effect), so that the lines betray binary systems. Of course, many pairs are very prominent – notably Mizar or Zeta Ursae Majoris, in the Great Bear, where the companion, Alcor, is easily visible with the naked eye; telescopically, Mizar itself is seen to be double. The brighter component is again a spectroscopic binary, and so is Alcor, so that the entire system is very complex.

Binaries are very useful. Their movements make it possible to determine the star's mass – something which is much more difficult with a single star. There are also novae, all of which are binary systems. Close to each star, the gravitational field of the star is dominant; electrons, nuclei, atoms and other small particles will be firmly held. Further out in a binary system, the gravitational fields of both stars interact, and there may be transfer of material from one component to the other. The two zones of influence form a figure-of-eight shape, with a contact point between the two. When a binary system is first formed, the individual stars will be much smaller than their zones of gravitational influence, but when the larger star expands to become a red giant, it will fill its zone – and matter will 'spill over'. The material will form an accretion disk round the secondary star, and when enough mass has been accumulated there will be a nova-like outburst. When one component is a neutron star, the interactions may lead to X-ray

▼ **Coloured double stars,** as imaged by L. F. Ball, using a 3-inch refractor. Clockwise from top left, these are Alpha Herculis, 70 Ophiuchi, Alpha Piscium, Gamma Andromedae, Gamma Arietis, and Gamma Delphini.

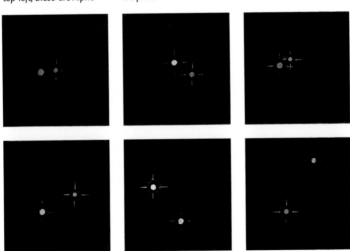

▲ **Young binary
stars,** *as viewed by the
Hubble Space Telescope*
*in near-infrared, showing
also a faint companion.
Could this be a planet?*

binaries and bursters. It is possible that the occasional flashes seen in the
sky at very short wavelengths (gamma-rays) may result from a neutron star
being ripped apart by a black hole.

Finally, the most compelling evidence for a nearby black hole (6000 light-
years away) comes from a binary system. A few degrees from Albireo there
is a blue supergiant, part of a binary system with a period of 5.6 days;
it is an intense X-ray source, and is known as Cygnus X-1. The companion
is not visible, but is almost certainly a black hole with a mass 8–10 times
that of the Sun.

All in all, binary systems are fascinating objects. It may be as well for us
that the Sun has no binary companion.

X-rays from Space

On 10 December 1999 the European Space Agency's spacecraft XMM-Newton, named in honour of the great Sir Isaac, was launched from French Guyana, aboard an Ariane 5 rocket. All went well, and its mission was to explore the X-ray universe, which is inaccessible to us on the Earth's surface simply because the incoming X-rays are blocked by the Earth's upper atmosphere.

Visual observations of the sky have been made ever since the dawn of human history, but X-ray astronomy had to await the development of rockets; it dates only from the 1960s. If you took an X-ray telescope, attached it to a camera, and then took it out to a dark site and pointed it up at the clear night sky, you would see nothing at all. Cosmic X-rays can be blocked effectively by a couple of sheets of ordinary paper.

The early rockets used to carry X-ray detectors were very primitive; for example, converted wartime V2 rockets were pressed into service, and proved to be very useful indeed. Ariane, at the Guyana base, is very

▼ *The Sun's corona in X-rays,* imaged on 21 August 1973, from the Skylab space-station. The curved black streak across the Sun is a 'coronal hole', where the density of the gas making up the corona is less than elsewhere.

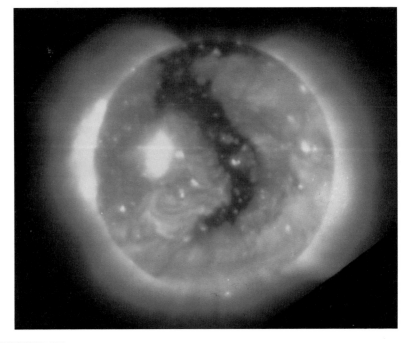

different. For example, an Ariane sent the Giotto probe on its way to Halley's Comet, and now we have Newton.

Bear in mind that X-ray astronomers do not 'produce' X-rays – they set out to examine X-rays created inside stars and galaxies, thereby 'seeing' regions that are hidden from us if viewed in ordinary light. Because of the way evolution has worked, our eyes are 'tuned' to the frequency range which extends from red through to violet; and it was Newton who first used a prism to split up 'white' light into all the colours of the rainbow. Other radiations do not affect our eyes at all. At long wavelengths, beyond red light, we have infrared and radio waves; shorter than violet we have ultraviolet, X-rays and gamma-rays.

We are used to seeing the world around us in the visible spectrum, but it would look very different if our eyes were sensitive to other parts of the electromagnetic spectrum. The same applies when we take pictures. For example, Orion is familiar to most people, but in X-ray vision it would be unfamiliar. Some stars (such as Betelgeux) would be lost completely; other objects, obscure or absent in visible light, would become prominent.

The universe can be a violent place. X-ray methods make it possible to study some of the most extreme processes. For example, in some binary star-systems gas is being sucked from one component into the other; quasars, harbouring black holes 1000 million times as massive as the Sun, produce their power by annually converting the equivalent of the entire mass of the Sun into energy. Then there are the remnants of supernovae; the hot gas, at a temperature of several millions of degrees, is best studied at X-ray wavelengths.

The Newton probe is a project of the European Space Agency. The Americans have also launched an important X-ray satellite, Chandra (named after the great Indian astrophysicist Chandrasekhar). Chandra is able to produce X-ray images five times sharper than any previous satellite has been able to do; on the other hand, Newton has the most sensitive X-ray telescope ever built. Just as with Isaac Newton's original experiment with sunlight and prism, so we need to split the energies up into the equivalent of X-ray colours. X-rays can be thought of as photons (small packets of energy). Let us take an example, and imagine that in a given time we collect 1000 X-ray photons from a distant galaxy. We want to study the origin of these X-rays, so we split up the 1000 photons into 100 X-ray colours – on average that means 10 photons per X-ray colour. This is enough to be useful. But now consider a situation where we have only 100 X-ray photons. When we split these up to 100 X-ray colours, we get only 1 photon per colour, which is inadequate. So Newton has more photon-gathering power than Chandra, but Chandra will provide the clearest pictures. The two satellites are complementary. (There is an analogy here with two top cricketers, a batsman and a bowler. Neither would be ideally suited to the other's talent, but both are excellent at what they do!)

To collect X-rays, you need a large collecting area. For optical telescopes this is straightforward enough – simply keep making larger and larger mirrors; for example, the Keck telescopes in Hawaii have 10-metre mirrors.

But X-rays do not reflect in the same way as visible light; they are absorbed in the surface of the mirror.

A simple experiment can show the problem. Take a sheet of glass, or transparent plastic, and hold it up so that the flat side is towards your eyes; you can see straight through it. Now tilt it until it is almost edge-on; when the angle has been reduced to a few degrees, the image can be seen as the light glances off the surface ('grazing incidence'). There is an analogy here with a flat stone skimming over a pond. If the angle is wrong, the stone sinks; but if the angle is small, the stone can be directed along the surface. And X-rays can in this way be brought to focus to produce an image.

Therefore, the technical challenge is to make a mirror that will be able to reflect X-rays at their grazing incidence. Because we want a focus at the centre, the mirror must be in the form of a shell – rather like a cone that has its sharp end cut off. We can increase the area of the mirror, and hence the number of X-rays it can focus, by putting a large number of these mirror shells one inside the other, like a Russian doll. Newton has 58 separate mirror shells, separated by less than 1 mm. Much of the work is British; university groups at Leicester, the Mullard Space Science Laboratory at University College London, and Birmingham have been involved. The centre where the observations will be converted from a bunch of spacecraft signals into images and spectra will be based at Leicester University.

Images have already been received; one shows the gas in the Large Cloud of Magellan, with colours indicating the temperature – the hottest regions are shown as blue, and the coolest as red; we can see the shell of gas left over after a supernova outburst. The glowing gas contains the chemical elements of which we are all made. For example, the iron in our blood was fabricated in the cores of stars which then exploded as supernovae and ejected the iron into the interstellar medium. We are, literally, stardust!

One unique feature of Newton is that it carries a small telescope which is sensitive to visible and ultraviolet light; we can make an immediate comparison with the corresponding X-ray pictures, and this often helps in understanding the processes which are producing the X-rays.

Newton is a success, but already we want to start planning for the next New Generation X-ray Observatory. This will be called XEUS (X-ray Evolving Universe Spectroscopy mission). Briefly, the problem is that we cannot launch an X-ray telescope much larger than Newton, because we lack the rocket power. The solution is to 'do it in parts'. With XEUS, the International Space Station will be used as an assembly platform and collect the bits of a giant mirror for an X-ray telescope ten times bigger than Newton. With XEUS, the mirror part, and the camera part which detects the image formed by the mirror, need not be connected to each other. In orbit everything is weightless, so that if we can keep these two parts in exactly the right places, by using tiny rocket jets, there is no need to have any connecting tube or strut. We hope that XEUS will help us to study the very beginnings of the universe, and show us the formation of the first black holes, which could be an important ingredient towards our understanding of how galaxies are born.

A Massing of Planets

In early May 2000, there was an unusual arrangement of the planets in the sky. Most of them were lined up – though all were so close to the Sun that nothing was seen with the naked eye. Earlier, during April, there had been a beautiful grouping of Jupiter, Saturn, Mars and the Moon, and by sheer chance there was a brilliant display of aurorae on 6 April – the best for more than ten years. But the actual 'massing' on 5 May was hidden by the glare of the Sun, though images taken from the SOHO spacecraft showed it well.

Obviously, the planets were not genuinely close together; we were dealing with nothing more than a line-of-sight effect. A conjunction, when two planets are in the same region, occurs quite often; a massing, involving three or more planets, does not occur nearly so often – on average, about once in 20 years.

They come about because of the relationship between the orbits of the various planets round the Sun. The planets move according to the three

▼ **Planetary massing:** an image from SOHO (the Solar and Heliospheric Observatory), taken on 15 May 2000. The 'real' distances were: Sun at 150 million km away, with Mercury about 58 million km, Venus 110 million km, Jupiter 780 million km, and Saturn 1400 million km beyond the Sun.

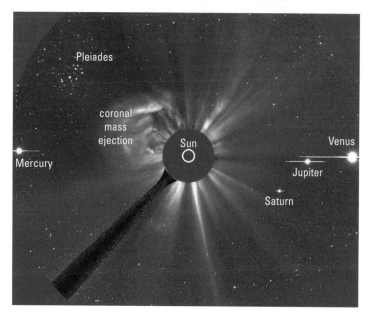

fundamental Laws of Planetary Motion laid down by Johannes Kepler in the early 17th century. The First Law states that the orbit of a planet is an ellipse, with the Sun lying at one of the foci of the ellipse, while the other focus is empty. The Second Law states that the radius vector – an imaginary line joining the centre of the planet to the centre of the Sun – sweeps out equal areas in equal times, so that the planet moves quickest when it is closest-in, near perihelion, and slowest when it is furthest out, near aphelion. But it is the Third Law which is of the greatest interest to us in connection with planetary groupings. It states that the squares of the orbital periods of any two planets are proportional to the cubes of their mean distances from the Sun, usually given in astronomical units: in fact, if P is the period and a is the distance, then $P^2 = a^3$. If we plot P^2 against a^3 on a graph, the result is a straight line.

The two giant planets are Jupiter and Saturn; Jupiter takes just under 12 years to complete one circuit, while Saturn needs 29 years. Planetary massings can potentially occur every 20 years, when Saturn, Jupiter and the Sun line up. Cast your mind back to 1 January 1940, when Jupiter and Saturn were nowhere near each other. Jupiter travels faster than Saturn, and so catches it up; they were aligned in May 1941, and in fact the more distant Uranus, which has an orbital period of 84 years, was also in line.

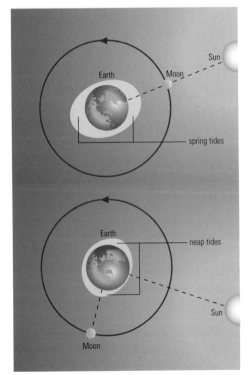

◀ **Tides:** the oceans on Earth are distorted by the gravitational effects of the Sun and Moon. High tides are at their highest, and the difference between high/low tides is greatest, when the Sun and Moon are lying in the same direction. Neap tides result when the Sun and Moon are pulling in different directions.

So too were Mercury and Venus, which of course are closer to the Sun than we are. There was a true massing of planets, though it was close to the Sun in the sky.

Run the clock forwards; from 10 May 1941 we saw Jupiter moving ahead of Saturn, while the inner planets whirled along much more quickly. By 1960 Jupiter was catching Saturn up once more, and by 4 February 1962 they were close together, as were the inner planets; on that day, all five naked-eye planets were crowded together.

Twenty years later, on 10 March 1982, another Jupiter-led alignment was greeted with predictions of dire calamities, particularly in California. Needless to say, nothing happened, and in any case the degree of alignment was by no means perfect.

This time, in May 2000, there was another massing, involving all five naked-eye planets. Astrologers became excited about it, but astronomers did not; it was interesting to watch, but it was not in the least important. An even better massing occurred in April/May 2002, when all five naked-eye planets were in the same part of the sky.

There have been some much more spectacular massings in the past. One, on 26 February 1953 BC, was recorded in China; this was the tightest known grouping of the five bright planets occurring at any time between 3000 BC and AD 5000 – a span of 8000 years. All the planets were within an arc of only 4.3 degrees, less than nine times the diameter of the full moon.

The second tightest known grouping occurred just under 900 years later, on 28 May 1059 BC, and was again recorded by the Chinese; this time the five planets were clustered within an arc of 6.5 degrees, or 13 Moon diameters. During February of 6 BC Mars, Jupiter and Saturn were seen together in the evening twilight sky, and Jupiter and Saturn passed close by each other three times during this period, making a rare Triple Conjunction; it has been suggested that this may have been the Star of Bethlehem, but all in all this seems to be most unlikely.

On 14 September, AD 1186, all five naked-eye planets were spread along in an arc of 11.6 degrees, with the Sun only a few degrees away – and there was also a solar eclipse. There was also a solar eclipse during the massing of 1962; the total eclipse was visible from the area of the Pacific.

The planetary massing of 1186 also led to one of the earliest 'End-of-the-World' scares, with predictions that the event would cause floods, earthquakes and whirlwinds. The event of 19 June 1385, when four planets (excluding Venus) and also the Sun were grouped together within an arc of 6 degrees, led to predictions of a great flood of Biblical proportions. Again, nothing happened. The most famous of the flood panics occurred in the years leading up to 19 February 1524, when the five planets and the Sun were massed within an arc of 12.4 degrees. Some people went so far as to build arks! But can there be any effects on Earth?

Tidal effects seem at first sight to be the only real possibility. We all know the ocean tides, but there are also tides in the Earth's crust. The magnitude of tidal stress on the Earth caused by the Moon, the Sun and each planet is proportional to its mass divided by the cube of its distance from the Earth, and by far the most powerful tide-raiser is the Moon, which has on average about twice the tidal effect of the Sun. Compared with these two bodies, the contributions of the planets are negligible. Even the closest to us, Venus, causes only 1/8th of the tidal stress due to the Sun at maximum.

With the Moon and the Sun, the tidal influence varies according to their varying distance from Earth. At perigee, the Moon's tidal pull is nearly 50% greater than it is at apogee. The highest spring tides occur at full moon and new moon, when the Sun, Moon and Earth are aligned (syzygy). The highest tides of all will be when full or new moon occurs at perigee, with the Earth at perihelion. In 2000, the maximum tidal pull on Earth had been declining since the start of the year. Although the tidal force of the new moon had been increasing since then, the total force was still less than it was in December 1999.

At the 1982 massing, the science writer Dr John Gribbin claimed that there would be tidal disturbances on the Sun, and that these would in turn affect the Earth, but the 'Jupiter effect' proved to be a myth. The tidal stress on the Sun caused by any planet is proportional to the planet's mass divided by the cube of its distance from the Sun. The greatest effect is due to Jupiter, followed by Venus, Mercury and then the Earth–Moon system, though there are considerable variations between perihelion and aphelion. If we calculate the total tidal force on the Sun due to all the planets combined, we find that to have the greatest possible effect the planets have to be in an almost straight line, though not necessarily all on the same side of the Sun. Over the past 400 years, the greatest peak occurred on 14 November 1703; the line was almost perfect, with Mercury almost at perihelion. Other peaks occurred in 1775, 1846 and during the massing of May 1941; as usual, the effects on Earth were nil. The maximum tidal force in May 2000 was less than on any of these previous occasions, so that there was no cause for alarm. At the start of the month the planets were spread along an arc of about 27 degrees; the new moon joined the group on 4 May. The massing grew steadily tighter; the combined tidal influence on the Sun was greatest on 9 May, but was not particularly high, because the grouping of planets was not particularly close. On 17 May the five planets lay within an arc of just under 20 degrees. Naked-eye viewers had to wait until the end of May, when Jupiter and Saturn reappeared in the dawn sky.

Things should be better on 8 September 2040, when there will be a lovely grouping of all five naked-eye planets, plus the crescent moon. It takes place some way to the east of the Sun, so that observers will have a superb view of it in the twilight sky that evening.

We hope that the sky will be clear. And I look forward very much to seeing this massing of planets – provided, of course, that I live to the age of 117!

Moon in Focus

The Moon is our nearest neighbour in space. It is our faithful companion, and always stays together with us as we travel round the Sun. It is also the only world which we have so far been able to reach. Cast your mind back to July 1969, when Neil Armstrong made his 'one small step' on to the Sea of Tranquillity: 'One small step for a man, one giant leap for mankind.' The gap between the two worlds had at last been bridged.

But, of course, the Sea of Tranquillity is not a sea. There is no water on the Moon, and no air either; the lunar atmosphere is so thin that for all practical purposes we can ignore it. The Moon's weak gravitational pull means that it has been unable to hold on to any atmosphere it may once have had.

The Moon is a mountainous world; its surface is dominated by craters, which are due to meteoritic impacts. Some are impressive – such as Copernicus, 90 km (56 miles) in diameter, with terraced walls and a massive central mountain group. The craters are old; not much has happened on the Moon for at least 1000 million years. The dinosaurs would have seen the

▼ **Lunar craters:** from the top of the image (south) the large plains are Petavius (with rill), Vendelinus (broken) and Langrenus.

Moon just as we do. But imagine the scene when those craters were being formed! The Moon is quiet now, but it must have been a wild place then.

Look at the Moon with the naked eye, or binoculars, and you will see the craters, mountains, waterless 'seas' and other features. On the disk, they seem to remain almost in the same positions, because the Moon always keeps the same face turned towards us. It goes round the Earth in 27⅓ days, and spins round in exactly the same time, so that from Earth we never see 'the back of the Moon'. There is no mystery about this. The Earth and the Moon are of about the same age – 4600 million years – and tidal friction over the years has been responsible for 'locking' one side of the Moon to face the Earth. Only in 1959 did we get the first pictures of the far side of the Moon, sent back by the Russian spacecraft Lunik 3. The pictures are blurred by modern standards, but were a real breakthrough for their time. The Russians had used my charts of the Moon's libration areas, and promised to send me the pictures as soon as they came in; they did so, and they arrived during a

▼ **Lunar eclipse,** *photographed on 29 November 1993, by the late Don Trombino.*

The photograph was taken using Ektachrom 200, exposure 10 seconds, 915 mm fl, at f/6.

Sky at Night live programme, so that I was able to show them for the first time. That was a great moment!

Since then, of course, we have obtained detailed maps of the entire Moon from various spacecraft. Details do not alter, but there are occasional local glows and obscurations which have been known as TLP, or Transient Lunar Phenomena (a term for which I believe I was originally responsible). Their reality was questioned by many astronomers, but positive confirmation has now been obtained; the eminent French observer Audouin Dollfus has observed and recorded activity inside the great walled plain Langrenus, due to material lifted off the lunar surface by gas seeping out from below. Of course, the activity is very mild indeed, but it does show that the Moon is not completely inert.

Lunar photography is a fascinating pastime. The Moon is easy to find, and is large and bright; there are various aspects which do not need expensive equipment. Even automatic cameras can produce reasonable results. What is needed is a standard SLR, a standard lens or a zoom with a relatively fast aperture of around f/2.8, a tripod, and ideally a cable release.

What about phase? It is impossible to see a truly new moon, as the Sun is behind it illuminating the far side, and only the dark side of the Moon is turned towards us. The only time to see a new moon is during a solar eclipse. Normally, the first sighting will not come until the Moon is at least 24 hours old, though occasionally it has been glimpsed much earlier than this. You need to be at the right longitude for evening twilight to occur around 12 hours after the new moon, on a day when the Moon and Sun are well separated – and of course you need clear skies and good seeing; you must also know exactly where to look. Photographing the newest of Moons can be quite a challenge. If you are using manual control, bracket a series of exposures.

Background? While there is a tendency to wait until the sky is completely dark, a picture with a colourful twilight sky can be aesthetically beautiful. If planets are around – as in May 2000 – take care over exposures; to get good images of planets, the Moon will inevitably be overexposed.

Earthshine pictures are pleasing, but to get the best images you really need a long lens or telescope with a focal length of at least 500 mm. Usually such lenses will be slow, and longer exposures will be needed even with films of ISO 400, 800 or faster. With exposures of several seconds or more, you really need a clock drive to compensate for the rotation of the Earth.

There is little colour on the Moon, and black-and-white film is ideal, but today this is not easy to obtain or to process. So using colour (and in particular colour negative film, which is more forgiving) may be essential. The results are tolerable, but one needs to be aware that different colour films have different colour balances and processing can sometimes go astray.

CCDs, video cameras and other advanced equipment now have important roles to play. Subsequent digital manipulation can help greatly. Occultations of stars and planets by the Moon are of great interest to many amateurs, but imaging them can be difficult, because the leading or trailing edge of a sunlit Moon limb will be so much brighter than a planet such as Saturn.

▲ **The Moon,** as   Cassini spacecraft in 1999
viewed by the passing   on its journey to Saturn.

To take high-quality pictures you need an excellent telescope, tracking at the lunar rate, with a good film or digital camera. You need good weather, no cloud, and the minimum of atmospheric turbulence. Nor is that all. Different times of the year are best for certain phases of the Moon. Spring is the best time for the crescent waxing moon, because it is high in the sky and therefore shining through the shallowest possible depth of the Earth's atmosphere; autumn is best for the waning crescent moon, and so on. Then there is the question of phase. If you want as much detail as possible, take your pictures during the lunar morning or evening, not at full moon – when there are no shadows.

Lunar eclipses can be dramatic, but photographically they are little different from the areas already discussed. As the Earth's umbra moves across the disk, the partial phases can be imaged as though taking shots of the normal Moon, and the fully eclipsed Moon should receive an exposure approximating to that given for Earthshine. Finally, the Moon is a marvellous subject upon which to learn photography and the Moon is a fascinating world. Before long we will go back there, and during the 21st century I am sure that we will have a Lunar Base, acting as a scientific laboratory, observation point and medical centre – and it will be truly international. Many of you now reading this book may go there. The Moon awaits us, and offers us a challenge which we must not ignore.

The Caldwell Catalogue

In 1781, the year in which William Herschel discovered Uranus, the French astronomer Charles Messier published a catalogue of over 100 star-clusters and nebulae. There were objects of all kinds; open clusters such as the Pleiades and Praesepe, globular clusters, spirals such as the Great Nebula in Andromeda, gaseous nebulae such as the Sword of Orion, and even one supernova remnant, the Crab Nebula in Taurus. Messier gave them numbers; thus the Pleiades are listed as M45, the Andromeda Spiral as M31, the Orion Nebula as M42 and the Crab, fittingly, as M1. Since then everybody has used Messier's list, and there are countless Messier clubs and Messier books.

Yet, ironically, Messier was not in the least interested in clusters or nebulae. He was a comet-hunter, and he was constantly misled by dim, misty patches that looked like comets, but were not. Eventually he lost patience, and decided to list them as 'objects to avoid'. The final touch of irony is that today very few people remember his comet discoveries!

▼ **The Eskimo Nebula (NGC 2392),** *as imaged by the Hubble Space Telescope in 2000. This* *planetary nebula is about 5000 light-years away from Earth, in the constellation of Gemini.*

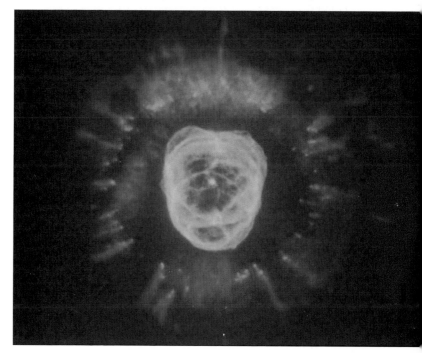

The catalogue was defective in two ways. First, Messier lived in France for the whole of his life, and never saw any objects that were too far south in the sky to rise above the French horizon. Secondly, he omitted objects that could not possibly be mistaken for comets, such as the Hyades in Taurus and the Sword-Handle in Perseus. Of course, later catalogues were much more exhaustive, notably the NGC or New General Catalogue drawn up by J. L. E. Dreyer in the 1880s, but the Messier list remained popular – and still does.

One evening, in 1995, I was in my observatory making some routine observations of the Moon. When I had finished, I turned my 15-inch reflector to the double cluster in Perseus, known as the Sword-Handle, and 669/884 in the New General Catalogue. It is a glorious sight; there are two rich open clusters in the same telescopic field, genuinely associated and about 7000 light-years away from us. I then looked at the North America Nebula in Cygnus, whose outline really does conjure up the impression of the American continent; it is NGC 7000, but not in Messier. In my study on the following morning, an idea came to me. Why not compile a new list of bright nebular objects, leaving out any contained in Messier, and making sure that all were accessible to modest telescopes? It sounded rather fun, so I set to work. By the end of the morning I had my list. The final Messier

▼ **NGC 5139 Omega Centauri (C80) –** *imaged at the La Silla* *Observatory in Chile (European Southern Observatory).*

catalogue contained 109 entries; so did mine, but there was one major difference in arrangement. Messier's objects were spread haphazardly around the sky. I worked in declination, from north to south, so that my first object was an open cluster in Cepheus (declination +85° 20′) and my last a planetary nebula in Chamaeleon (−80° 52′). This seemed to me to be pleasingly systematic.

What to call the catalogue? Moore begins with M – but so does Messier. However, a solution was to hand. My actual surname is a hyphenated one, Caldwell-Moore, which I have to use on official documents (as, for instance, in the RAF during my spell in the Forces, from 1940–5, when I was flying with Bomber Command). So I used C. The Cepheus cluster became C1, and the Chamaeleon planetary became C109.

Over the years I had actually observed all the C objects, and had notes in my observing books of most of them. I did my best to make sure that there were none beyond the range of a 6-inch telescope, though it is true that a few are severe tests for such an aperture, and there was a degree of confusion with C100, which was my fault. Initially, the catalogue was compiled for my own amusement, but on impulse I sent it over to *Sky & Telescope*, the world's leading astronomical monthly magazine. I thought no more about it – until I was utterly taken by surprise. *Sky & Telescope* liked it. They publicized it, and it was the lead article in their issue for December 1995. Letters poured in. It 'caught on', and observers everywhere started to use it. Books came out, of which the first was *Observing the Caldwell Objects*, written by David Ratledge and published in Britain by Springer Verlag. In an amazingly short time the catalogue had been tacitly accepted, and became an integral part of the literature. I admit that I was taken aback, because the reception given to it was 99.9% favourable – I had only a couple of letters from people who were piqued because they hadn't thought of the idea themselves!

The arrangement in order of declination means that it is well nigh impossible to observe all the Caldwell objects in one night, as has often been done with Messier's 109. For example, the latitude of my observatory at Selsey, in Sussex, is (in round figures) +51 degrees. This means that declination −39 degrees is on my southern horizon, and any object south of that is inaccessible; in practice, of course, it would not be possible to go right down to the theoretical limit. In the Caldwell list I should be able to see C67, in Fornax (declination −30 degrees), but I have never seen down as far as C68, in Corona Australis (declination −37 degrees). The only hope of seeing all the Caldwell objects in one run would be to go to the equator, but I very much doubt whether anyone will be able to do so!

I had to make some immediate decisions. I included the Hyades, as C41, and also the Coal Sack in the Southern Cross, as C99. My main mistake was with C100. I meant it to represent the Lambda Centauri cluster, but in the event it corresponds to a rather sparse open cluster, Collinder 249. Luckily, binoculars will show it, and by now the catalogue is so widely used that there seems little point in making an alteration. My original choice, IC 2944 round Lambda Centauri, is much fainter, and below what I call the 'Caldwell limit'.

For the *Sky at Night* programme, I selected a few of my favourite Caldwell objects. This was my list:

C6, the Cat's Eye Nebula in Draco (NGC 6543)
This is a lovely planetary nebula with an integrated magnitude of just below 8, not far from the second-magnitude star Gamma Draconis.

C14, the Sword-Handle in Perseus (NGC 869/884)
Two open clusters, with 200 and 150 stars respectively. There is nothing else in the sky quite like them. Easily visible with the naked eye, between Perseus and Cassiopeia. The best views are obtained with binoculars, or very low powers; both clusters are rich in young O- and B-type stars.

C20, the North America Nebula in Cygnus (NGC 7000)
A bright nebula, about 2 degrees wide, not far from Deneb.

C23, an edge-on spiral galaxy in Andromeda (NGC 891)
It is 31 million light-years away, and is between 3 and 4 degrees east of Gamma Andromeda. You need a large telescope to see the dark dust-lane which crosses it.

C39, the Eskimo Nebula in Gemini (NGC 2392)
A planetary nebula, sometimes called the Clown Face Nebula. It is about 2.3 degrees east-south-east of Delta Geminorum. In size it is about equal to the disk of Jupiter, but the integrated magnitude is below 8, so that it does tend to be somewhat elusive.

C44, a barred spiral galaxy in Pegasus (NGC 7479)
Probably the northern hemisphere's best barred spiral, but it is a long way off – about 100 million light-years. Despite its apparent dimness it is not hard to find, about 3 degrees south of Markab (Alpha Pegasi) in the Square of Pegasus.

C55, the Saturn Nebula in Aquarius (NGC 7009)
The nickname was given to it by Lord Rosse, in 1845, when he observed it with his great 72-inch reflector at Birr Castle in Ireland. It is not a difficult object to locate, but at least a 12-inch telescope is needed to show the Saturn-like extensions. One of the best of all planetary nebulae.

C65, the Sculptor galaxy (NGC 253)
This has been called the southern hemisphere's answer to the northern Andromeda Spiral, M31. C65 is half a degree long; it lies just over 7 degrees south of the bright star Diphda (Beta Ceti). It is easy to find, even though from Britain it is always rather low down.

C77, the Centaurus radio galaxy Centaurus A (NGC 5128)
We are now too far south for British observers, but C77 is truly magnificent,

with its famous dark band. It is thought to result from the merger of a large elliptical galaxy and a smaller, dusty spiral around 1000 million years ago. It is a strong radio emitter, and may have a central black hole. It is only about 4 degrees from the giant globular.

C80, Omega Centauri (NGC 5139)

Much the largest and brightest of all the globulars, 17,000 light-years away. Even with the naked eye it is unmistakable, and Flamsteed gave it a Greek letter.

C94, Kappa Crucis; the Jewel Box cluster in the Southern Cross (NGC 4755)

About 1 degree south-east of Beta Crucis. Most of its leaders are bluish, but there is one prominent red supergiant. William Herschel called it 'a superb piece of fancy jewellery'.

C103, the Tarantula Nebula in the Large Cloud of Magellan (NGC 2070)

In Dorado; a member of the Cloud – 169,000 light-years away. The structure is intricate. If C103 lay as close to us as M42, the Sword of Orion, it would cast shadows.

C106, 47 Tucanae (NGC 104)

To complete my 'Top 12', I must include 47 Tucanae, which as a globular is second only to Omega Centauri; in fact, telescopically, it is the more impressive of the two because it can be included in one telescopic field, whereas Omega is too large. It contains at least a million stars, and is around 15,000 light-years away. It is almost silhouetted against the Small Cloud of Magellan, but of course the two are not connected; the Cloud is at least 180 million light-years away. It is interesting to note that the surface brightness of 47 Tucanae far surpasses that of the Cloud.

Well – those are some of the Caldwell objects. I hope that many people will enjoy tracking them down; I still find it rather amusing that the list was drawn up, more or less for fun, by an observer of the Moon!

The Language of Astronomy

Astronomy has its own language. Over the past 45 years, in *The Sky at Night* we have used many terms, and while some of these will be familiar to most people, there are others which are not. So, for the first time, we propose to go back to 'square one' and say something about astronomical terminology.

First, the *Solar System*. As the name implies, this is the system dominated by the Sun, which is an ordinary star – it appears so much brighter than the rest only because it is so much closer to us. Its distance is a mere 150 million km (93 million miles), or 1 *astronomical unit* (a.u.); the nearest star beyond the Sun – a faint red star named Proxima Centauri – is 25,000 times as remote.

Round the Sun move the nine *planets*, which have no light of their own, and shine only by reflecting the rays of the Sun. In order of distance they are Mercury, Venus, the Earth, Mars, Jupiter, Saturn, Uranus, Neptune and Pluto. Between the paths of Mars and Jupiter move thousands of dwarf worlds known as minor planets or *asteroids*. So far over 20,000 have had their paths or *orbits* worked out, and around 50,000 have been observed. There are also *comets*, the most erratic members of the Solar System. A comet has been described as a dirty iceball; it is made up of an icy head or nucleus, never more than a few kilometres across, which begins to evaporate when the comet nears the Sun, producing a dusty head and tails of both gas and dust. Most comets move in highly elliptical orbits, and only one bright comet –

▼ **The Earth's seasons** occur because the Earth's axis is tilted relative to its plane of orbit. The side *that is inclined towards the Sun enjoys longer days and thus experiences the months of summer.*

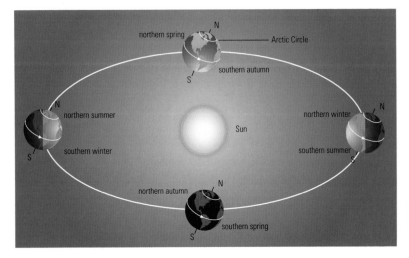

Halley's – is seen regularly; it returns every 76 years, and was last on view in 1986. Smaller comets are very common. Because they are millions of kilometres away, they do not seem to shift quickly against the starry background. If you see an object showing perceptible motion, it cannot be a comet.

As a comet moves, it leaves a dusty trail behind it. If one of these pieces of dust flashes into the Earth's upper air, moving at anything up to 72 km/s (45 miles/s), it is heated by friction against the air-particles, and burns away in the luminous streak which we call a *meteor* or shooting-star. The actual object is too small to be observed; what we see are the luminous effects that it produces during its headlong plunge. Meteors burn out at around 65 km (40 miles) above the ground. Larger bodies may land intact, and are then called *meteorites*; but a meteorite has no connection with a meteor, or with comets. Meteorites come from the asteroid zone. Occasionally they may produce *impact craters*, such as the famous crater in Arizona. Luckily, major impacts are rare – though it is possible that a large impactor hit the Earth 65 million years ago, changing the entire climate and leading to the extinction of the dinosaurs.

Most of the planets have *satellites* moving round then. We have one – our familiar Moon – but Uranus has as many as 30.

The Earth's *sidereal period*, or year, is the time taken to go once round the Sun: one year, or 365.25 days. Other planets have different sidereal periods, from 88 days (Mercury) up to nearly 248 years (Pluto). We can, of course, give their distances from the Sun in astronomical units (for example, 0.39 a.u. for Mercury), though most people prefer to use kilometres or miles.

It is usually said that the Moon moves round the Earth at a mean distance of 385,000 km (239,000 miles), in a period of 27.3 days. This statement needs qualifying. Two bodies in orbit move round their common centre of mass. If the masses of the two bodies are equal, the centre of mass is halfway between them; but the Earth is 81 times as massive as the Moon, so that the centre of mass, or *barycentre*, is displaced. However, the barycentre lies inside the Earth's globe, so that the simple statement that 'the Moon goes round the Earth' is good enough for most purposes.

The Moon's movement round the Earth is responsible for its *phases*, or apparent changes of shape from new to full. When the Moon is between the Earth and the Sun, its dark side faces us, and normally we cannot see it; this is the true new moon. If the alignment is exact, the Moon temporarily hides the Sun, and we have a *solar eclipse*. After new, the Moon moves along in its orbit, showing up as a crescent, half (*First Quarter*), between half and full (*gibbous*), full, and then gibbous, half (*Last Quarter*), crescent and back to new. During the crescent phase, the non-sunlit side is often to be seen shining faintly, because it is being illuminated by light reflected from the Earth; this is the *Earthshine*.

The two planets closer to the Sun than the Earth are Mercury and Venus, termed the *inferior planets*. Like the Moon, they show phases from new to full. When an inferior planet is between the Sun and the Earth, it is said to be at *inferior conjunction*, and is new. If the alignment is exact, the planet is seen silhouetted against the Sun; this is a *transit*. The orbits of the planets are tilted or inclined to that of the Earth, and so transits do not happen often. The last transit of Mercury was in 1999; the last transit of Venus was as long ago as 1882, though there will be another in 2004. Obviously, both planets can pass on the far side of the Sun, at *superior conjunction*.

The planets beyond the orbit of the Earth can never pass through inferior conjunction, but do come to superior conjunction. If the Earth, Sun and planet are lined up, with the Earth in the mid position, the planet is at *opposition*; this is the best time to observe it, because it will be above the horizon all through the hours of darkness. Away from opposition, Mars shows a definite gibbous phase, but with the more distant planets the phase is inappreciable.

Consider Mars, which has a sidereal period of 687 Earth days (equal to 668 Mars days or *sols*, because Mars has a slower rotation period than the Earth: 24h 37m). Mars was at opposition on 24 April 1999. One year later, the Earth had been right round the Sun and had arrived back at the same position, but Mars, travelling more slowly in a larger path, had not had time to do so; its mean distance from the Sun is 228 million km (141.5 million miles). The Earth had to 'catch Mars up', and did so on 21 June 2001, when there was another opposition. The interval between successive oppositions is known as the *synodic period*: 779 days for Mars.

Around the time of opposition a planet seems to stop, and then for a while move against the stars in an east-to-west direction instead of the normal west-to-east. This is purely an effect of the Earth 'passing' the planet. This temporary reverse motion in the sky is called *retrograding*. Against the starry background, the planet performs a slow 'loop'. The more distant planets have shorter synodic periods, because it takes less time for the Earth to catch them up; thus Jupiter came to opposition on 23 October 1999, and again on 28 November 2000.

The orbits of the planets are not perfectly circular, as was once thought; they are elliptical. Thus the Earth is 147 million km (91½ million miles) from the Sun at its closest (*perihelion*) and 152 million km (94½ million miles) out at its furthest (*aphelion*) These terms apply to a body orbiting the Sun; for the Moon, which orbits the Earth, the corresponding terms are *perigee* and *apogee*. At perigee the Moon is 356,000 km (221,000 miles) from us; at apogee, 406,000 km (252,000 miles).

Curiously, our British winter occurs in December, when the Earth is at its closest to the Sun. The *seasons* are due not to changing distance, but to the tilt or inclination of the axis of rotation. Like all the planets, the Earth's axis points northwards to a point in the sky called the *north celestial pole*, marked fairly closely by the bright star Polaris. The axis is inclined to the perpendicular to the orbital plane by 23.5 degrees. In northern winter, the Earth's northern hemisphere is tilted away from the Sun; in June the northern hemisphere is tilted sunwards. Of course, the reverse applies in the southern hemisphere of the Earth. Of the other planets, Mars has an axial inclination almost the same as ours (24 degrees); Jupiter and Mercury are almost 'upright'. Venus has an inclination of 178 degrees, and so seems to rotate 'backwards', while Uranus has an inclination of 98 degrees, more than a right angle. The Uranian seasons are indeed peculiar. Why these planets have unusual inclinations remains a mystery.

Now let us look further afield.

Look at a time exposure of the stars at night, and you will see that the stars are drawn out into streaks, because of the Earth's rotation. Polaris seems to remain almost motionless, with the entire sky moving round it (in the northern hemisphere of the Earth, that is to say; there is no bright star near the south celestial pole).

In the sky we need equivalents for latitude and longitude on the surface of the Earth. On Earth, your *latitude* is your angular distance north or south of the equator; my home at Selsey, in Sussex, is at latitude 52°N. *Longitude* is your angular distance east or west of the Greenwich meridian, which is an

▼ **The celestial sphere** – a useful means for describing the positions of astronomical bodies. The celestial poles are defined by the projection of the Earth's axis on to the celestial sphere; the north pole is marked closely by Polaris in Ursa Major, but there is no equivalent bright south pole star.

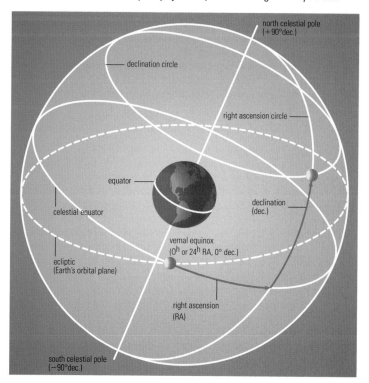

imaginary line on Earth passing through both the poles and Greenwich Observatory in Outer London. (Greenwich was chosen in 1884, by international agreement. The only nation to object was France!)

The sky equivalent of latitude is easy. The celestial equator is the projection of the Earth's equator on to the *celestial sphere*, an imaginary sphere whose centre is coincident with the centre of the Earth. The *declination* of a body is simply its angular distance north or south of the celestial equator – for instance, 7 degrees 25 minutes for Betelgeux, the bright orange-red star in Orion. Note that on the Earth, the point directly above your head is the *zenith*, while the point directly below your feet is the *nadir*.

The celestial equivalent of longitude is more difficult. We have to begin by selecting our 'Greenwich', and luckily we can find one. Because the Earth goes round the Sun in a period of one year, the Sun seems to go right round the sky in one year, passing through the constellations of the *Zodiac*; the apparent path of the Sun against the stars is termed the *ecliptic*. (Of course, the Sun and the stars cannot be seen at the same time, but it is easy to work out just where the Sun will be at any particular moment.) The ecliptic is tilted to the celestial equator at an angle of 23½ degrees, and the Sun crosses the equator twice a year – in March, with the Sun moving from south to north (spring or *vernal equinox*), and in September, with the Sun moving from north to south (*autumnal equinox*). The points during the year when the Sun reaches the most northerly or southerly points of the ecliptic are termed the *solstices*, and these mark midsummer and midwinter.

The March equinox used to lie in the constellation of Aries, the Ram, and was called the *First Point of Aries*. This is our celestial Greenwich, and the angular distance of a body east or west of this point is the *Right Ascension*, or RA. However, RA is measured in a different way to terrestrial longitude. As the Earth spins, a body rises, reaches its highest point in the sky (*culmination*) and then begins to set. The First Point of Aries culminates once every 24 hours. The RA of an object is simply the time difference between the culmination of the First Point of Aries and the culmination of the body. Thus, Betelgeux culminates 5 hours 55 minutes after the First Point of Aries has done so – and this means that the RA of Betelgeux is 5h 55m.

The RA and declinations of the stars do not change much; the stars are so far away from us that their individual or proper motions are inappreciable – the constellations we see today are to all intents and purposes the same that would have been seen by King Canute or Julius Caesar. But the bodies of the Solar System are much closer to us, and their RA and declination values are changing all the time. This is why the planets seem to wander around from one Zodiacal constellation to another.

There is another complication. The First Point of Aries is no longer in Aries; it has shifted since ancient times, and is now in the adjacent constellation of Pisces, the Fishes. This is because of *precession*.

Over a long timescale, the Earth's rotation is not as steady as it might be thought. If you look at a gyroscope, and imagine that the top represents the pole, you can see that when it is running down it starts to wobble, or precess, in a circle. The Earth acts in the same way, though of course slowly; it takes

25,800 years for the axis to make a full circle. Precession changes the tilt of the Earth, and so changes the position of the First Point of Aries by 50 arc seconds per year. The position of the celestial pole also changes. When the Pyramids were being built, the north pole star was Thuban, in the constellation of Draco (the Dragon); in 12,000 years' time, *Sky at Night* viewers will look forward to a sky rotating around the brilliant blue Vega, in Lyra.

Meanwhile, Polaris holds the place of honour. From Selsey it appears 52 degrees above the horizon (because the latitude of Selsey is 52°N). Thus, 90 minus 52 equals 38; so any star north of declination +38 degrees will never set – it will be *circumpolar* – and any star south of declination −38 degrees will never rise. From the Earth's North Pole, the celestial pole marked so closely by Polaris will be overhead; all stars north of the celestial equator will be circumpolar, and those south of the celestial equator will never be seen. Exactly the opposite would apply to an observer at the Earth's South Pole.

Remember that the Sun is a very ordinary star. At a range of 150 million km (93 million miles) it is very close to us on the astronomical scale, and the stars are much more remote. We have to deal with distances so vast that ordinary units, such as kilometres or miles, become clumsy, just as it would be cumbersome to measure the distance between London and Manchester in millimetres or inches. So we use the speed of light to provide us with a better unit. Light travels at 300,000 km/s (186,000 miles/s), so in a year it covers rather less than 10 million million km (6 million million miles). This is termed a *light-year*. The nearest star beyond the Sun, a faint red one called Proxima Centauri, is just over 4 light-years away, equivalent to 38 million million km (24 million million miles). The Pole Star is 680 light-years away – over 6000 million million km (4000 million million miles). And with our most powerful telescopes we cannot see star-systems well over 10,000 million light-years away.

In recent times, professional astronomers at least have moved away from the light-year to a unit called the *parsec*, approximately 3.26 light-years. This involves another term – *parallax*.

Shut one eye, hold up a finger, and align it with some more distant object, such as a picture on the wall. Now, without moving, use the other eye. The alignment will no longer be exact, because your eyes are not in the same place. Knowing the distance between your eyes, and also the amount of the angular shift or parallax, it is easy to work out the distance between your finger and your eyes. In the same way, observing a star from opposite sides of the Earth's orbit – say in December and then in June – will reveal a parallax shift of a relatively nearby star against the background of more distant stars. This was first done in 1838 by the German astronomer F. W. Bessel, who measured the distance of the dim star 61 Cygni, around 11 light-years from us.

A star at a distance of 3.26 light-years would show an annual parallax shift of 1 *second of arc*. In each degree there are 60 minutes of arc, and in each minute of arc there are 60 seconds; so 1 arc second is 1/3600th of a degree, just as a normal second is 1/3600th of an hour of time. More distant objects have distances given in *kiloparsecs* (1000 parsecs) or *megaparsecs* (1 million parsecs).

One problem about trigonometrical parallax is that for a star more than 300 or 400 light-years away, the shifts are so small that they are swamped by unavoidable errors in observation. We have to use less direct methods, involving the magnitudes of the stars.

A star's *apparent magnitude* is a measure of its brightness as seen from Earth. The scale works in the same way as a golfer's handicap; the lower the magnitude, the brighter the star. Thus Aldebaran (magnitude 1) is brighter than Polaris (magnitude 2), and so on. Stars below about magnitude 6 cannot normally be seen with the naked eye; telescopes can now reach down to magnitude +30. Sirius, the brightest star in the sky, is of magnitude −1.5, and on the same scale the Sun's magnitude is about −27.

It is interesting to find that the apparent magnitude of a star can be estimated to around 0.1 with the naked eye alone. Most stars shine more or less steadily, but some are variable; thus, in the Square of Pegasus, prominent in the autumn sky during evenings, one star (Scheat or Beta Pegasi) varies between magnitude 2.3 and 2.7. Sometimes it is slightly brighter than Alpha Pegasi or Markab (2.5), sometimes slightly fainter. The variations are not very regular, but the mean *period*, or interval between one maximum and the next, is 38 days.

A star may look bright either because it is relatively close to us, or because it is really very luminous, or a combination of both factors. The *absolute magnitude* of a star is the apparent magnitude which it would have if it were seen from a standard distance of 10 parsecs (32.6 light-years). From that range Sirius would be of magnitude 1.4; it looks so bright because it is close (a mere 28.6 light-years). But Deneb, in Cygnus – one member of the unofficial Summer Triangle – has an apparent magnitude of 1.25, but an absolute magnitude of −7. If seen from our standard distance, it would look more brilliant than Venus does to us, and would cast strong shadows. Its distance is 1400 light-years, so that we now see it as it used to be in the days of the Roman Occupation! The Sun's absolute magnitude is +4.8.

Delta Cephei, in the far north of the sky is a variable star, but behaves very differently from Beta Pegasi. It is very regular, and ranges between magnitudes 3½ and 4½ in a period of 5.3 days. There are many variables of the same type; they are called *Cepheids*, and they are very useful indeed, because the way in which they behave tells us how luminous they really are. The longer the period, the more luminous the star, and once the power of the star is known, its distance can be worked out. Cepheids are 'standard candles' in space, and they are thousands of times more luminous than the Sun, so that they can be seen out to very great distances.

Some stars are members of pairs. When two stars are genuinely associated, and move round their common centre of gravity, we have a *binary* system; sometimes the two members of the pair are so close that they almost touch, while in other binaries the separation may be many thousands of millions of kilometres. The revolution periods range from a few hours up to tens of thousands of years.

In some binaries, one member of the pair is a very small, old, very dense star called a *white dwarf*. It may be that the white dwarf pulls material away from its companion; eventually, the situation becomes unstable and there is an explosion, so that the white dwarf flares up to many times its normal brilliancy before fading back to obscurity. This produces a *nova* or new star – a misleading term, because a nova is not a new star at all. Naked-eye novae are not very uncommon, and they can become very brilliant for a few days, weeks or even months. A nova seen in the constellation of Aquila in 1918 temporarily outshone every star in the sky apart from Sirius, but it has now become an excessively faint telescopic object.

In some cases the outburst may be much more violent, and the white dwarf literally blows itself to pieces, so that it never returns to its old state. This is a Type I *supernova*. At peak power, the luminosity may be over 1000 million times that of the Sun. The maximum power is always about the same, so that these supernovae can be used as 'standard candles' in the same way as Cepheids, though they are so much more luminous that they can be seen over much greater distances. There are also Type II supernovae, which are different; a supernova of this kind does not involve a white dwarf, but is due to the collapse and subsequent explosion of a star much more massive than the Sun. In our Galaxy, the last naked-eye supernova was seen as long ago as 1604, though many have been detected in external star-systems.

▼ **Binary stars:** the two components of a binary system move in elliptical orbits around their common centre of gravity (G) but do not travel at the same rate. In diagram (2) they are moving slowly and are far apart; in (6) they are moving more quickly and are closer together.

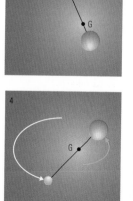

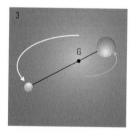
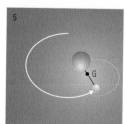
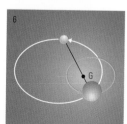

The collapse of a giant star in a Type II supernova outburst is so cataclysmic that nothing can stop it. The star becomes smaller and smaller and denser and denser; eventually it pulls so strongly that not even light can escape from it. The old star is now surrounded by a 'forbidden zone', cut off from the rest of the universe. It has created a *black hole*.

Obviously, black holes are not easy to detect, since they emit no radiation at all, and we can locate them only by their gravitational effects on visible objects. One case is that of Cygnus X-1. The main component of the binary pair is a giant star. Associated with it is a companion which seems certainly to be a black hole. Material is being pulled from the giant star; before it is sucked into

the black hole, to vanish for ever, it is intensely heated, and gives off X-rays which we can detect – hence the name: Cygnus X-1. There is every reason to believe that black holes are very common in the universe, and lurk in the cores of quasars and active galaxies. A *quasar* is a small, energetic core of a galaxy.

Our star-system, containing about 100,000 million stars, is termed the *Galaxy* – often referred to as the Milky Way, though this term is properly restricted to the luminous band seen crossing the night sky. The Galaxy is a flattened system, shaped rather like two fried eggs clapped together back to back; the Sun is around 28,000 light-years from the centre of the system, which is 100,000 light-years across. The centre bulges out; when we look

◄ **The Andromeda Galaxy (M31),** photographed by Jason Ware. This is the nearest major galaxy to our own Milky Way Galaxy.

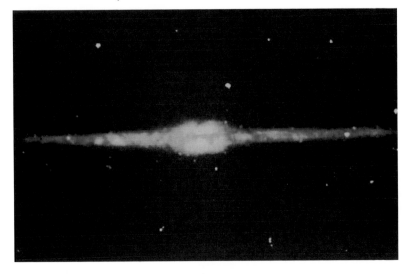

▲ *The shape of our Milky Way Galaxy,*   *as imaged by the COBE satellite in 1990.*

along the main plane of the system, we see many stars in the same line of sight, and it is this which produces the Milky Way effect. The whole Galaxy is rotating round its centre; the Sun takes 225 million years to complete one orbit – a term usually called the *cosmic year*. One cosmic year ago, even the dinosaurs had not yet appeared.

The Galaxy contains groups of stars; there are *open clusters*, such as the Pleiades or Seven Sisters, which have no particular shape. Around the edge of the Galaxy are *globular clusters* – vast symmetrical systems, containing in cases many millions of stars. All are remote, and only three are clearly visible with the naked eye: the Hercules cluster in the northern hemisphere of the sky, and Omega Centauri and 47 Tucanae in the southern.

The Galaxy contains clouds of dust and gas known as *nebulae*; these are stellar nurseries, inside which new stars are being formed. Around 5000 million years ago, our Sun was formed inside such a nebula. There are various nebulae visible with the naked eye, notably the Great Nebula in Orion's Sword, and telescopically they are very numerous indeed.

Other patches in the sky are obviously made up of stars. Some are spiral in form, and were once called spiral nebulae; others are elliptical, spherical or irregular. They are in fact outer galaxies, some of them much larger and more populous than ours. The Andromeda Spiral, visible with the naked eye, is 2.2 million light-years away; its distance was first measured, in 1923, by the American astronomer Edwin Hubble, who detected Cepheid variables inside it. The Andromeda Spiral is one of the nearest of the galaxies; most are many millions of light-years away, and the most distant objects so far detected are at least 12,000 million light-years from us.

Hubble also made another discovery of vital importance. He proved that the universe is expanding.

Pass a beam of light through a prism (or a grating, which has the same effect), and the beam will be split up into its constituent wavelengths or colours. When a spectroscope is aimed at a gas lamp, such as a sodium streetlight, a series of bright lines against a dark background will be seen; this is an *emission spectrum*. If one particular chemical element is viewed, no matter under what conditions, these bright lines will always appear in the same pattern, and at the same wavelengths.

Things become slightly more complicated when we look at objects such as the Sun. Instead of bright emission lines, we now see dark lines against a bright rainbow background; this is an *absorption spectrum*. The effect is due to the reabsorption of light emitted by the outer layers of the solar surface, but the principle is the same. Each pattern of lines corresponds to a particular element or group of elements, and can therefore be identified by comparison with laboratory data.

In the 19th century Norman Lockyer, a British astronomer, discovered a set of lines in the solar spectrum that could not be identified with any known substance. He realized that he had found a new element, and named it helium (Greek *helios*, the Sun). It was a further 20 years before helium was identified on the Earth.

In examining the spectra of the galaxies, Hubble realized that they were shifted from their 'laboratory' position. (The effect had been previously noted by V. M. Slipher, at the Lowell Observatory in Arizona, but it was Hubble who made the critical breakthrough.) In most of the spectra of the galaxies, the lines were shifted over to the red or long-wavelength end of the spectral band. Only in a few cases were the shifts to the blue or short-wave end; it is now known that these cases applied to the members of our *Local Group* of galaxies.

The effect is due to the *Doppler* shift, best illustrated by a simple analogy. We are all familiar with the sound made by the horn to a passing ambulance or police car. As the vehicle moves away, the pitch of the horn drops, indicating a change in wavelength; fewer sound-waves per second reach your ear than they would do if the source of the sound were stationary. The same principle applies to light-waves; a red shift indicates a velocity of recession. Therefore, all the galaxies with red shifts in their spectra – that is to say, all the galaxies beyond our Local Group – are moving away; and the further away they are, the faster they are receding. The entire universe is expanding.

The constant of proportionality between distance and red shift is termed the *Hubble Constant*. If you measure the red shift in the spectrum of a galaxy, multiplying this by the Hubble Constant converts the value to a distance. Attempting to find the exact value of the Hubble Constant, which will give us the expansion rate and hence an idea of the age of the universe, has been one of the major undertakings of astronomy for the past 50 years.

These are just some of the terms used in all astronomical research. They are easy to remember – and there is a strange attraction in the language of astronomy.

Wimps and Machos

Look up into a clear sky on a moonless night, and you can see thousands of stars. Through our largest telescopes we can see thousands of millions of galaxies, each containing thousands of millions of stars, out to a distance of over 10,000 million light-years. But is this the whole story? Is luminous matter even the main content of the universe? In recent years, there has been growing evidence that there may also be a great deal of dark matter, and that the visible stars and galaxies may be no more than a tiny fraction of the universe.

The first evidence comes from the ways in which the spiral galaxies rotate. The Sun is a member of the Milky Way galaxy, which contains around 100,000 million stars together with clouds of gas and dust. Seen edgewise-on, it would look like a flattened disk, with the main concentration of stars in a central bulge. The rest of the stars and gas-clouds are more thinly spread out through the disk, which is around 100,000 light-years in diameter. The Sun is about 28,000 light-years from the centre. Seen face-on,

▼ **MACHOs (massive compact halo objects).** In this image, the MACHO is a nearby red dwarf star *(arrowed). However, most of these objects are invisible. (Courtesy ESA/ ESO/MACHO Project Team.)*

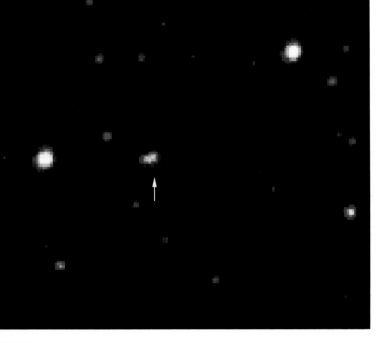

the Galaxy would resemble a huge Catherine wheel, with young, brilliant stars and luminous gas-clouds arranged in a pattern of spiral arms. Many other galaxies are similarly spiral. Most of the light they emit, and most of the stars they contain, are concentrated in their central bulges.

If a galaxy consisted only of visible material – that is to say, stars and gas-clouds – then, because most of the visible matter is concentrated in the central bulge, the rotation should be of the same type as that of our Solar System. The objects closer to the centre should move more quickly than those further out. But this does not happen. When we measure the speeds of stars and gas-clouds at different distances from the centre of our Galaxy, we find that the situation is quite different. Working outwards from the centre, the rotation speed increases at first, as we move out towards the edge of the bulge, but beyond – in other spirals, as well as ours – the rotation speed remains fairly constant, or even shows a slight increase. Therefore, the main mass cannot be concentrated in the central bulge. There must be a great deal of mass in the outer regions, providing enough gravitational pull to keep the outer stars rotating as fast, or faster, than those closer in. The galaxies must contain huge haloes of dark matter, which does not give out detectable amounts of light or any other radiation (for example, X-rays or radio waves). The visible material is embedded in this invisible halo, which may have five or ten times the mass of the visible stars and gas-clouds.

Also, when we look at groups and clusters of galaxies, such as the Virgo cluster, we find that the speeds at which individual member galaxies are milling around are such that the whole cluster would disperse. They have not done so, and something is 'glueing' them together; again, a vast mass of dark matter seems to be the logical cause. There could be ten times or even 50 times as much dark matter as luminous matter; in general, the more populous the cluster, the greater the proportion of dark matter to luminous matter.

What can the dark matter be? One suggestion is that it is due to stars so faint that with our present techniques we cannot detect them. They might be old white dwarfs, brown dwarfs, neutron stars or simply ultra-faint red dwarfs. Brown dwarfs are not believed to be common; they are stars of so low mass that they never became hot enough to trigger off nuclear reactions inside them. There also seem to be 'free-floating planets', around ten times as massive as Jupiter. Yet their masses are so low that their total contribution to the overall mass of the Galaxy is to all intents and purposes negligible.

Next, there could be dark bodies in the halo of the Galaxy which are known collectively as MACHOs – an acronym for Massive Astrophysical Compact Halo Objects. In recent years astronomers in Australia, America and France have been carrying out searches for MACHOs by looking for evidence of a phenomenon known as gravitational lensing.

As Einstein showed, rays of light are deflected, usually by very small amounts, when they pass close to massive bodies. If a massive body lies between the Earth and a background star, its gravitational field can act like a lens, producing a magnified image of the background object. Because the gravitational lens concentrates together the light-rays from the background object, the object itself appears brighter than it would normally do.

Therefore, when a MACHO in the halo of our Galaxy passes in front of a background star, the star's light increases, and then decreases again in a very distinctive way. In particular, the brightness increases and decreases in the same way for all colours, because gravity affects all wavelengths equally.

The main problem is that for any effects to be detectable, the alignment between the source, the lens and the observer has to be very precise. This means that millions of stars must be monitored continuously in order to have any realistic chance of detecting any events during an observing programme lasting for several years. Since 1995 the MACHO programme has monitored about 20 million stars, concentrating on the Large Magellanic Cloud, a system 169,000 light-years away. Between 13 and 17 events have been found, about five times as many as would have been statistically expected on the basis of the known number of ordinary stars in the outer regions of our Galaxy. One of these MACHOs is thought to be a black hole, about six times as massive as the Sun.

Most of the reported events last for from 34 to 230 days, indicating that the MACHOs responsible for them must be around six-tenths the mass of the Sun. These masses fit in better with white dwarfs than with brown dwarfs. Yet from the data obtained so far, we have to admit that MACHOs are unlikely to account for more than 10–20% of the total mass of the Galaxy, and certainly not more than half the mass of the Galaxy's dark matter halo.

MACHOs are objects composed of ordinary matter, made up of particles such as protons and neutrons – the basic building blocks of atoms, stars and ourselves, known collectively as baryons. Therefore, ordinary matter is termed baryonic matter. Many cosmologists believe that a large fraction of the dark matter content of our Galaxy, and of the universe as a whole, is made up of completely different particles which hardly ever interact with ordinary matter.

The first non-baryonic candidates were bizarre particles called neutrinos. According to the standard model of modern particle physics, a neutrino has no electrical charge and has zero mass, so that a motionless neutrino would weigh nothing at all. However, it has also been suggested that neutrinos do have a certain amount of mass. Because the Big Bang is believed to have generated vast numbers of neutrinos, there should be more than 100 million neutrinos in every cubic metre of space, averaged over the whole universe. If the mass of a neutrino were more than about one ten-thousandth of the mass of an electron, the total mass of this sea of neutrinos would be enough to account for the dark matter content of our Galaxy.

Recent results, notably from the underground Super-Kamiokande detector in Japan, support the idea that neutrinos do have mass. The Super-K detector consists of a 40-metre drum, containing 50,000 tons of pure water surrounded by 13,000 photomultiplier tubes designed to detect the flash of light produced on those very rare occasions when a neutrino interacts with the water. The detector has to be underground to shield it from cosmic rays, which would otherwise produce spurious results.

The Super-K data imply that the masses of neutrinos are likely to be very small – perhaps less than a millionth the mass of an electron. If so, although

▲ **The Super-Kamiokande neutrino detector, Japan,** located underground to shield it from cosmic rays that would affect the data.

the total mass due to neutrinos would be great, it would not be nearly enough to account for the overall dark matter content of the Galaxy, or indeed the universe as a whole.

The most favoured dark matter candidates are particles called WIMPS – Weakly Interacting Massive Particles. Like neutrinos, WIMPs – if they exist – would hardly ever interact with ordinary matter, but unlike neutrinos they would be expected to have considerable mass, from 10 to 100 times that of a proton.

The existence of WIMPs has been predicted by recent theories which try to account for the fundamental particles and forces of nature. In particular, the theory of supersymmetry predicts the existence of a whole range of WIMPs, with exotic-sounding names such as photinos and neutralinos. If they do exist, they are likely to be plentiful enough for their combined masses to account for most or all of the dark matter content of the universe. But do they really exist at all?

If so, then millions of WIMPs must be passing through our bodies every second of time. Only very rarely will a WIMP interact with an atomic nucleus, but when this happens the effects are appreciable, because a WIMP is much heavier than a typical atomic nucleus, and is moving at over 800,000 km/h (over 500,000 mph). It and the atomic nucleus recoil in the manner of two colliding snooker balls.

A recoil could be detected in one of several ways: by measuring the tiny amount of heat produced by the event; by detecting the electrical charge that is liberated when a WIMP ionizes the atom; or by detecting the flash of light released when the impacted nucleus recoils. Obviously the most sensitive equipment is needed, deep underground, and the detectors have to be surrounded by jackets of water to guard against the effects of cosmic rays and natural radioactivity in the Earth's rocks. Even so, spurious results are bound to far outweigh genuine ones.

Early in 2000 the Italian Dark Matter group, DAMA, announced the discovery of evidence in favour of WIMPs. The argument runs as follows. If our Galaxy is embedded in a halo of WIMPs (the dark matter halo), then the Solar System must be moving through this back ground of WIMPs at a rate of about 220 km/s (137 miles/s), the orbital velocity of the Sun around the galactic centre. In addition, the Earth travels round the Sun at about 30 km/s (18½ miles/s). Therefore, for half the year, when the Earth is heading in approximately the same direction as the Sun's motion, the speed of the Earth relative to the WIMPs is greater than the speed of the Sun, while for the other half of the year it is less. When the Earth is moving at its fastest relative to the WIMPs (in June), it ought to encounter more WIMPS than when it is moving at its slowest (in December). The DAMA team claims that over a four-year period, the event rate in their data shows a variation of about 1%.

However, an American group, the Stanford-based Cryogenic Dark Matter Search (CDMS) disputes these findings. By the beginning of 2000 they had detected 13 recoil events, but were fairly certain that they were caused by stray background neutrinos rather than WIMPs. They also argued that if the DAMA results were correct, the CDMS detector should have recorded far more recoils than it actually did. So far as the reality of WIMPs is concerned, the jury is still out, and the problem of the nature of the dark matter remains to be solved.

We know that the universe is expanding; every group of galaxies is racing away from every other group. Dark matter may have a profound influence upon the way in which the universe is evolving – and its ultimate fate.

The universe is believed to have originated in a Big Bang, from 13 to 15 thousand million years ago; space, time and matter came into existence simultaneously, and the universe has been expanding ever since. Whether or not this expansion will continue indefinitely depends upon the average density of matter in space (or, to be more precise, the mean density of matter and energy, because energy, too, makes a contribution to the overall density of the universe). We would expect gravity to be slowing down the rate of expansion, but if the mean density is too low, the expansion will slow to a steady value and then go on for ever. If the mean density is high enough, gravity will eventually win the battle; at some time in the distant future, the universe will cease to expand and will then collapse. If the mean density has just the right value – termed the critical density – then the universe will just, but only just, be able to expand for ever. The rate of expansion will approach zero, but will never reach it. A universe which continues to expand for ever at a finite rate is said to be 'open'; a universe which eventually collapses is 'closed', and a universe at the critical density is said to be 'flat'. The term 'flat' here refers to the curvature of space. According to Einstein's General Theory of Relativity, the presence of matter and energy distorts space. If there is enough matter and energy to make a closed universe, space will be positively curved – wrapped round on itself rather like the surface of a sphere – and rays of light travelling through space will follow curved paths. If the universe is 'sitting on the fence', it will be flat in the sense that the overall curvature is zero, and rays of light will indeed follow straight lines. In fact, the curvature of space is determined by the mean density. The ratio of the actual mean density of matter and energy to the critical density is called Omega (denoted by the Greek letter omega, Ω). If Omega is greater than 1 (actual density greater than critical), the universe is closed. If Omega is less than 1, the universe is open – and if Omega is exactly equal to 1, the universe is flat.

A flat universe would be a special case, and we must try to account for it. A popular variant of the standard Big Bang model is the 'inflationary theory'. This assumes that very early in its history, about 10^{-35} seconds after the beginning of time, the universe went through a brief but dramatic phase of accelerating expansion, which blew it up to such a size that the curvature became flat. If you imagine the very early universe to be like a tiny sphere, then in a tiny fraction of a second inflation expanded it to become so large that all hint of curvature disappeared.

The inflationary model has been very successful in tackling some problems inherent in the Big Bang picture, and in predicting the ways in which large-scale structures appeared in the universe, but it does require that Omega should be virtually equal to 1.

If luminous matter were the only constituent of the universe, we have to agree that there cannot be nearly enough of it to make Omega equal to 1. In fact, the mean density gives only about half of 1% of the critical density. If the universe is flat, as the inflationary theory requires, then the mean density has to be over 100 times greater than the density contributed by visible matter. So is there enough dark matter to make up the shortfall?

It seems that baryonic matter – including baryonic dark matter – cannot account for more than about 5% of the critical density. The Big Bang theory is very successful in showing how the relative proportions of the lightest elements – hydrogen, helium, deuterium (heavy hydrogen) and lithium – in the universe of today were determined by nuclear reactions in the first few minutes after the Creation. But if the density of baryons exceeded more than about 5% of the critical density, then the proportions of helium-3, deuterium and lithium in the universe today would be far less than they actually are.

We must also consider studies of the cosmic microwave background – a faint background of cool radiation, spread across the whole of the sky, which is left over from the time, around 300,000 years into the history of the universe, when the temperature everywhere had fallen to 3000 degrees, and for the first time space became transparent to radiation. The radiation released at that time has been diluted, stretched and cooled by the expansion of space, and is now no more than a dim glow at centimetre and millimetre wavelengths. Images of the whole sky obtained in 1992 by COBE (the Cosmic Background Explorer satellite) show slightly hotter and cooler areas of the background radiation.

Detailed studies of the background radiation have recently been carried out by two balloon-borne experiments, MAXIMA (which flew over Texas) and BOOMERANG (which flew over the Antarctic ice-cap). The BOOMERANG result shows hundreds of complex structures in the very early universe, corresponding to tiny temperature variations – around 100-millionth of a degree – in the background radiation. If space were positively curved, the structures would be larger than they actually are; if space were negatively curved, they would have been smaller. The observed results fit in very well with the 'flat' universe: Omega = 1.

The size and distribution of these features is also consistent with a universe with a mean density of ordinary (baryonic) matter which is only from 5–10% of the critical density. This also agrees with what we learn from the relative abundance of the lightest elements. The results also indicate that cold dark matter (WIMPs) makes up only about 30% of the critical density. If Omega really is equal to 1, the shortfall in density needs to be made up by something else.

Because energy, as well as mass, contributes to the curving of space, some cosmologists are now considering the possibility that in addition to luminous matter, dark baryonic matter and dark non-baryonic matter (WIMPs), the universe also contains a mysterious commodity known as dark energy, which makes up the remainder of the mean density. If so, we have luminous matter contributing 0.5%, neutrinos 0.3%, dark baryonic matter 5%, dark non-baryonic matter (WIMPs) 30%, and dark energy 65%. But what dark energy may be – if it exists at all – is anybody's guess. The simplest idea is that it is the cosmological constant, a hypothetical property of space introduced by Einstein around 80 years ago and subsequently rejected by him as 'his greatest blunder'. The cosmological constant was a property of space which caused it to stretch, producing a form of cosmical repulsion which opposed conventional gravity and tended to accelerate groups of galaxies away from each other. Because it was a form of energy, it would contribute to the total mass-energy of the universe and the overall curvature of space.

Recent observations of supernovae in very remote galaxies have led to the suggestion that the universe is expanding at an accelerating rate, rather than slowing down. It is claimed that these distant supernovae are significantly fainter than they would be if the expansion were slowing down. In an accelerating universe, distant objects will appear fainter than expected because the accelerating expansion of space actually stretches space, and the supernovae appear fainter because their light then has to travel further to reach us. An accelerating universe fits in with the possibility of a cosmological constant, and that, in turn, is one possible candidate for the alleged dark energy content of the universe. But it must be stressed that these observations are no more than preliminary, and it would be unwise to place too much faith in them.

All in all, we have to concede that it is too early to say definitely whether or not dark matter is a real or major factor in the universe. What does seem certain is that we still have a great deal to learn!

▼ **The BOOMERANG balloon,** seen here just before launch with Mount Erebus in the background, completed its circumnavigation of the South Pole in January 1999. It provided the most detailed map of the cosmic background temperature ever obtained.

Other Earths?

Are there planets moving round stars other than the Sun? This is a question which we have been asking for a very long time. There seems no reason why not. Our Sun is one of 100,000 million stars in our Galaxy alone, and we can see many millions of other galaxies; moreover, the Sun is a very ordinary star – there is nothing at all special about it. The problem has always been one of sheer distance. Even the nearest star beyond the Sun is over four light-years away; a planet has no light of its own, and is small compared with a normal star, so that it will be very difficult to make out.

A star forms from the collapse of a giant cloud of gas and dust, and there ought to be some material left over which will form a disk of matter circling the star. Planets may be expected to form out of this accretion disk, again in a completely natural way as material clumps together. If this is correct, then planets should be common in the Galaxy – and in other galaxies, too.

The first breakthrough came in 1983, when IRAS – Europe's Infrared Astronomical Satellite – went up, and detected clouds of cool material round stars such as Vega. Visually Vega is quite normal (it is a hot blue star), but IRAS found what was called a 'huge infrared excess', indicating possible planet-forming material. Another star of the same type was the southern Beta Pictoris, and here the disk has actually been seen, both with Earth-based telescopes in Chile and with the Hubble Space Telescope. Moreover, the HST image showed 'ripples' that could well be due to unseen planets. But what was needed was real proof.

There is always the astrometric or 'wobble' technique. A massive planet orbiting a lightweight star will make the star shift slightly to and fro, and this can be monitored by means of the Doppler effect; the spectral lines move according to whether the light-source is approaching or receding. In 1995 the Swiss astronomers Mayor and Queloz were able to measure these shifts in the star 51 Pegasi, and give the first real proof of an extra-solar planet.

Curiously, the planet of 51 Pegasi was very massive – comparable with Jupiter, the most massive planet in our Solar System – and was very close to the star; in fact, closer than Mercury is to our Sun. Other cases followed, mainly of much the same type, though one star, Upsilon Andromedae, seems to have three planets – a real solar system. Of course, the method tells us only a little about the planet: its size and mass, its orbital period, and so on. Much depends upon the angle from which we are viewing.

There are other techniques, too. The Americans have used the 'transit' method. If a planet is lined up against its parent star, it can block out a little of the star's light; this was detected by D. Charbonneau and T. Brown for the star HD 209458, and confirmation was obtained by Rachel Street with the James Gregory telescope at the University of St Andrews, Scotland.

Alan Penny's team is now using the Isaac Newton Telescope on La Palma to look at thousands of stars in the open cluster NGC 7789, to see if any of them have planets with suitably-aligned orbits. Another student, Yiannis Tsapras, is using the Kapteyn telescope, also on La Palma, to search by the 'microlensing' method; we are also trying to obtain funds for a set of

Size of Pluto's Orbit

▲ *Beta Pictoris,*   *Hubble Space Telescope*
as imaged by the   *in January 1996.*

robotic telescopes (ROBONET), to extend the microlensing technique sufficiently to detect Earth-sized planets. There will, we hope, be six robotic telescopes at different locations, so that the target stars can be kept under constant observation.

A visual sighting of an extra-solar planet would, of course, be decisive, and in December 1999 it was thought that this had been achieved by a team of British astronomers using the William Herschel Telescope on La Palma. The star concerned was Tau Boötis, in the constellation of the Herdsman, not far from the brilliant Arcturus. It is 55 light-years away, so that we now see it as it used to be at the end of World War II; it is 3½ times as luminous as the Sun, as well as being rather hotter, and the wobble technique had found it to be attended by a planet almost four times as massive as Jupiter, moving round the star in an almost circular orbit at a distance of 74 million km (46 million miles). The orbital period was known to be 3.3.

The Tau Boötis planet seemed to be promising, and the British team set out to identify its reflected spectrum. Over 12 nights at La Palma, they took several thousand spectra of Tau Boötis. Detecting the Doppler shift in the spectrum of the star's light as it swings to and fro because of the presence of the planet is an established technique, but there is also the faint light of the planet to be considered. This is simply light reflected from the star, so that the spectrum will be the same – but very much dimmer. As the planet moves round the star, its spectrum too will show the telltale shifts in the lines, but these shifts will be greater than those of the star, because of the planet's greater orbital speed. When the planet is coming towards us, the star will be receding, and vice versa. So when the star's lines are moving one way, those due to the planet will be moving in the opposite direction. The planet's lines will shift back and forth amid the light from the star. This is exactly what was found – even though the light of the planet was about 20,000 times fainter than that of the star.

It all seemed pleasingly definite. But . . . when the team went back to La Palma, their results were completely negative. They realized that they had been deceived by a random pattern of light. It was a tremendous disappointment, but the method is perfectly sound in principle, and eventually it ought to give valid results.

Meanwhile, other plans are being made. The Hubble Space Telescope is not ideal for planet-hunting, and neither is its proposed successor, the NGST (New Generation Space Telescope), scheduled for completion within the next ten years. As Alan Penny, one of the main participants, commented on the programme, the HST and NGST are ideal for finding searchlights in space, but so not good at finding glow-worms close to searchlights. However, the Hubble telescope did make a survey of many stars

▼ *Four protoplanetary disks,* as imaged by the Hubble Space Telescope. They are located around young stars in the Orion Nebula, some 1500 light-years away. Each image is the equivalent of 30 times the diameter of our own Solar System.

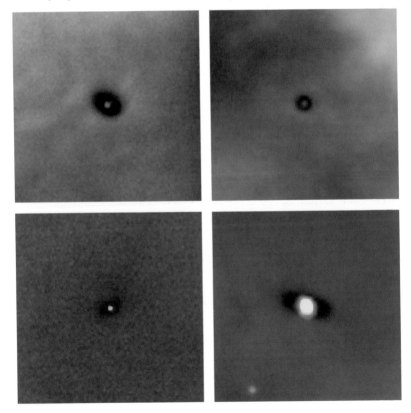

in the globular cluster 47 Tucanae, hoping to record some 'transit' phenomena. The results were negative, and it may be that stars in globular clusters are not suitable candidates for planetary systems. Hubble was more successful with stars nearer to us, and several transit phenomena have been reliably recorded.

All the extra-solar planets so far detected are 'hot Jupiters', but space research methods may allow us to track down planets similar in size to the Earth, and moving round what is termed the habitable zone of their parent star – that is to say, the region which is neither too hot nor too cold for Earth-type life to exist. In our Solar System, Venus is on the inner edge of the habitable zone, Earth in the middle of it, and Mars right at the outer limit.

The first space mission to be launched for a deliberate search for an Earth-type planet may well be Corot, initiated by the French Space Agency. It will carry a 12-inch telescope with the latest electronic equipment, and will monitor selected stars to detect transit events. Small though the Corot telescope may be, it will have the advantage of being specialized. It will be followed by the Eddington mission – named after the great English astronomer, Sir Arthur Eddington – carrying a telescope half the size of Hubble's. But perhaps the most promising mission is Darwin, a combined ESA/NASA venture. This involves sending six small infrared telescopes into the outer part of the Solar System, away from most of the interplanetary dust. The telescopes will probably be mounted on separate spacecraft, and will work together as an interferometer; the search will concentrate upon 300 solar-type stars within 50 light-years of us. If planets are found, we will want to know what they are like, and the way to do this is by spectroscopy. Darwin may be able to identify chemical substances in the planets; if, for example, carbon dioxide and oxygen are identified, we may be at least reasonably confident that there is life.

Of course, this is all very speculative – and even more so is the planned Planet Imager mission for the 2020s, aiming to take actual pictures of these other Earths. It is an exciting prospect – and it is strange now to realize that less than ten years ago we had no definite proof of the existence of any planets apart from those in our own Solar System.

Next Stop – Saturn!

On 15 October 1997, an important space mission was launched from Cape Canaveral. It was sent on its way to the ringed planet Saturn, and it was named Cassini, after the Italian astronomer who discovered four of Saturn's satellites, and also the main division in the ring system. It carried a much smaller probe, named in honour of Christiaan Huygens, the Dutch astronomer who discovered Titan, the largest of Saturn's satellites, in 1655. Cassini was scheduled to orbit Saturn, sending back data, while Huygens would be separated and brought down gently on to the surface of Titan.

Cassini is a heavy probe – too heavy to be sent directly from Earth to Saturn. It had to go by a circuitous route, using the gravity-assist technique and making swings past Venus (April 1998), Venus again (June 1999), Earth (August 1999) and Jupiter (December 2000), before starting the final leg of its journey, and reaching Saturn in November 2004. It is certainly complicated, but with our present techniques there is no alternative.

On 1 July 2004, Cassini will be put into an orbit round Saturn, only 20,000 km (12,000 miles) above the cloud-tops. On 6 November the spacecraft will be manoeuvred into an impact trajectory with Titan, and on 8 November the Huygens lander will be released. Cassini itself will be deflected away from the collision course, leaving Huygens to land on Titan,

▼ The Cassini probe – *interplanetary trajectory*
a diagram showing its *to rendezvous with Saturn.*

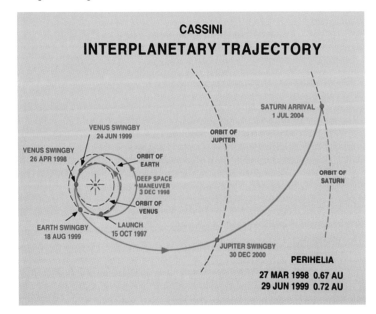

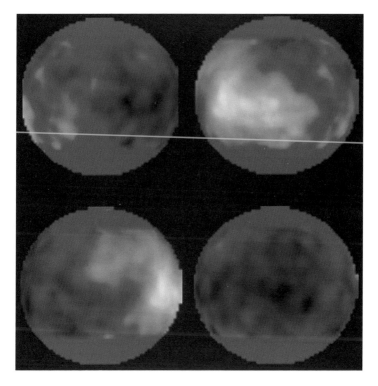

▲ *The surface of* *Titan,* *imaged by the* *Hubble Space Telescope.*

The nature of the *dark areas is as* *yet unknown.*

18.4 degrees north of the satellite's equator. But what will it find – and why is Titan regarded as so important?

It is a large world, with a diameter of 5150 km (3200 miles) – slightly greater than that of the planet Mercury – and moves round Saturn at a mean distance of 1.2 million km (760,000 miles) in a period of almost 16 days. Any small telescope will show it. What singles it out is that it is the only planetary satellite with a dense atmosphere. Information sent back by the two Voyager probes in 1980 and 1981 showed that the atmosphere is much denser than ours, and consists largely of nitrogen, which of course makes up 78% of the air we breathe. Most of the rest of the atmosphere is made up of methane (marsh gas), and this, together with the very low temperature, seems to rule out life of the kind we know, though of course it is impossible to be sure.

When the Voyagers bypassed Titan, all they could image was the top of a layer of what might be termed orange smog. No surface details could be made out, and at that time we had no real idea of what might lie below the clouds. Since then, excellent images have been obtained with the Hubble

Space Telescope and with the Keck I telescope on Mauna Kea in Hawaii, showing a mottled appearance and large areas that are dark at infrared wavelengths. It was suggested that there might be seas there – not of water, but of a chemical substance, such as ethane or methane. The surface temperature is close to what is called the triple point of methane, which may exist as a solid, liquid or gas; on Earth we are near the triple point of H_2O, so that we can have water, water vapour and ice.

Huygens has to be slowed down before dashing into Titan's upper air. A heat-shield will be deployed, and then a series of three parachutes, which will reduce the speed to a manageable level. The probe will take 2½ hours to drop to the surface, and during this time it will send back data about the atmospheric composition and temperature, as well as looking for lightning (there is even a microphone to listen to any sounds of thunder!). Radar measurements will map the surface features. Then will come the landing. The probe may come down on an icy surface, on a rocky landscape, or splash down in a chemical ocean. We hope that the on-board camera will provide at least a few glimpses of this strange place.

How long will the spacecraft be able to transmit? It may be damaged on landing; it may quickly freeze; its power may fail; it could come down at an extreme angle, preventing its radio link from functioning. If it splashes into a sea, it could be swamped by waves. But even if all goes well, the effective operating time on the surface has been given as three minutes, and it cannot possibly be more than half an hour. All data will be relayed via the Cassini orbiter, and after 30 minutes at the very most Cassini will pass out of range. Before it is again suitably positioned, Huygens will be dead.

Just half an hour's transmission seems strange after a journey lasting more than seven years, but of course Cassini's work is not done; it will continue to orbit Saturn, sending back data about the planet itself and the numerous satellites. It should be able to transmit until the summer of 2008.

It is an ambitious programme. At the moment (April 2002) all is going well, and we may hope that when Huygens completes its hazardous descent we will at last be able to find out what Titan is really like.

Mission to Eros

On 12 February 2001 the NEAR-Shoemaker spacecraft made a controlled landing on an asteroid, 433 Eros. This was the first time that anything of the sort had been attempted, and its success was all the more remarkable because the landing had not been part of the original plan!

To recapitulate: the asteroids are midget worlds, most of which keep to the main belt between the orbits of Mars and Jupiter – where no large planet could form, because of the overpowering pull of Jupiter itself. Only one asteroid (Ceres) is as much as 800 km (500 miles) in diameter, and only one (Vesta) is ever visible with the naked eye. Collisions between small asteroids must be frequent, and lead to some bizarre shapes, as with Kleopatra, which looks remarkably like a dog's bone. From Earth, the asteroids look like stars, though spacecraft and the Hubble Space Telescope have been able to show surface details upon some of them.

Some small asteroids swing away from the main swarm, and may pass close to Earth. The first asteroid known to come within the orbit of Mars was No. 433, Eros, discovered in 1898 by Witt, from Berlin. (To be precise, asteroid 132, Aethra – discovered as long ago as 1873 – has a perihelion distance very slightly less than the aphelion distance of Mars, but Aethra is not usually classed as a Mars-crosser.) Eros was the first asteroid to be given a masculine name, after the God of Love. It passed within 24 million km (15 million miles) of us in 1931, when it was carefully imaged, because it provided a method of measuring the length of the astronomical unit, or

▼ **Map of Eros:** the features have been given appropriate names!

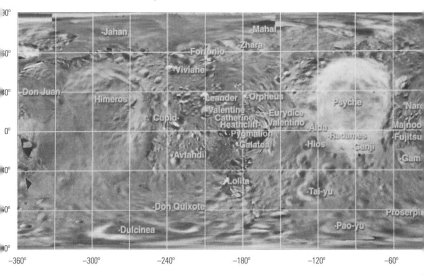

Earth–Sun distance. The method is now obsolete, and the last close pass, in 1975, was regarded as less important from this point of view.

Asteroids such as Eros, whose orbits cross that of Mars but not that of the Earth, are said to be of the Amor type. Many are now known, but Eros is one of the larger members of the group. It is sausage-shaped, 34 km (21 miles) long, 13 km (8 miles) wide and 13 km (8 miles) thick, though its whole shape is irregular, and it is certainly a fragment of a larger body which was broken up by collision. Its gravitational pull is feeble; if you weigh 90 kg (200 lbs) on Earth, you would weigh no more than 57 g (2 oz) on Eros, and the escape velocity is a mere 35 km/h (22 mph).

Plans were made to send a spacecraft to Eros, and enter a closed orbit round the asteroid – something never previously attempted. The probe was originally called NEAR (Near Earth Asteroid Rendezvous), but was then named in honour of Gene Shoemaker, the famous American planetary geologist – a great friend of mine – who, sadly, had been killed in a car accident in 1997. The spacecraft was about the size of a family car, but carried very sophisticated equipment. Note that it cost much less than a nuclear submarine . . . .

On 17 February 1996 it was launched, by a Delta-2 rocket, from Cape Canaveral, and sent on its way. By 23 December 1998 it was approaching Eros, but on-board problems meant that the attempt to enter closed orbit had to be postponed. After another trip round the Sun, Eros orbit was finally achieved on 14 February 2001 – appropriately, St Valentine's Day; the distance from Earth was then about 258 million km (160 million miles), further away than the Sun.

The initial closed orbit was some 322 km (200 miles) from Eros, and excellent pictures were received, showing an irregular, cratered surface. There were many boulders, which in view of the weak gravity was rather unexpected. And as the orbit was modified, and NEAR was brought closer to Eros, the pictures became better and better; by 17 April the range had been reduced to 50 km (31 miles). One very important fact was established. Some asteroids are to all intents and purposes loose rubble piles – such as the curious, black 253 Mathilde, which had already been imaged by NEAR during the flight towards Eros (on Mathilde, the main surface features have been named after coal-mines!). But Eros turned out to be much more substantial, with a density about the same as that of the crust of the Earth; the composition was similar to those of the meteoroids known as chondrites. And Eros is very old indeed – one of the most ancient rocks in the Solar System. It is what is termed an S-type asteroid. These asteroids are common in the main belt; prominent members of the class are 3 Juno (the third asteroid to be found, in 1804) and 5 Astra (found in 1845).

By mid-July the pictures showed features down to a resolution of less than 6 metres (20 ft). There was a dark surface regolith, which also covered some of the crater floors. A map was drawn up; a particularly prominent crater was christened Psyche, while the largest feature, 13 km (8 miles) wide, was called Himeros, after an attendant of the god. By late October, NEAR had swooped

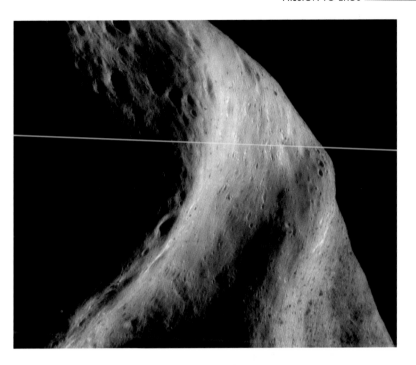

▲ Asteroid Eros, *visited by NASA's* NEAR-Shoemaker probe *in February 2000.*

to less than 6 km (4 miles) from Eros, showing littered boulders and rocks no more than 1.5 metres (5 ft) across.

Much had been learned, and this was important. The danger of the Earth being hit by a wandering asteroid may be slight, but it is not nil, so that the more we know about asteroids the better. But by the end of 2000, NEAR was coming close to the end of its orbital career and a daring decision was taken – try to make a controlled landing on Eros' surface!

Nothing of the sort had been in the original plan, and the chances of success were remote, but there was nothing to lose. So early on 12 February the descent manoeuvre began. The target area was close to Himeros at the boundary between two distinct types of terrain.

To everybody's surprise, all went well. From its 35-km (22-mile) orbit NEAR swooped down, sending back images of rocks as small as a man's hand, and came to rest on the surface, apparently undamaged and still able to transmit.

It is there now – and there it will remain, though of course we have lost touch with it. I wonder whether it will ever be collected and taken to a museum? I hope so, and in any case it has its place in history. This was surely one of the most remarkable and most unexpected space triumphs to date.

Index